BESTOWER OF LIGHT

Published by Khaniqahi Nimatullahi Publications
U.K.: 41 Chepstow Place, London W2 4TS
U.S.A.: 306 West 11th Street, New York, N.Y. 10014

Library of Congress Cataloging-in-Publication Data

Rothschild, Jeffrey, 1950–
Bestower of light: a portrait of Dr. Javad Nurbakhsh, master of the Nimatullahi Sufi order/Jeffrey Rothschild
p. cm.
Includes bibliographical references
ISBN 0-933546-98-X (hb: alk. paper)
1. Nurbakhsh, Javad. 2. Sufis–Biography
3. Khanaqah-i Nimat Allahi   I. Title.

BP80.N882R68 1999   98-37912
297.4'092–dc21   CIP

Printed in the United States of America

Typeset in Caslon
Designed by James Killough

JEFFREY ROTHSCHILD

BESTOWER
of LIGHT

A Portrait of Dr. Javad Nurbakhsh,
Master of the Nimatullahi Sufi Order

KHANIQAHI NIMATULLAHI PUBLICATIONS
LONDON   NEW YORK

One Who Knows God

Whoever knows God will be freed
    from concern for what is other than Him.

Whoever becomes afflicted by Him
    knows that His pain is the cure.

Worship of self is not the worship of God:
    this truth is our creed.

Be non-existent so you can truly be,
    for Absolute Being is God alone.

When the drop no longer sees itself, it becomes the Ocean;
    the former is *fana*, the latter *baqa*.

No disputes arise among the sober-like drunkards *(rendan)*;
    whoever becomes such a one will be pure.

The Bestower of Light* to all creation is One,
    though a thousand mirrors there may be.

—DR. JAVAD NURBAKHSH

* *The meaning of Nurbakhsh in Persian is "bestower of light."*

ACKNOWLEDGMENTS

Although the writing of any book is in large part a solitary process carried out in isolation, there are almost always certain other individuals who are essential to that process. In the present case, there are a number of such people who I would like to thank.

I must begin by expressing my gratitude and indebtedness to Dr. Nurbakhsh himself. Had he not given me his blessing to undertake this work, I would never even have attempted to write it. And had he not been willing to sit for the many hours of interviews the book required, I would never have been able to succeed. His assistance was, quite simply, indispensable.

Among the other people I would like to thank are Alireza Nurbakhsh, the editor of the journal *Sufi*, for overseeing the entire process of writing and publishing this work; Sima Johnston who acted as the translator during all my interviews with Dr. Nurbakhsh (except for the final one), a task she performed so effectively that it often seemed as if I was talking directly to the master; Paul Weber who helped me both prepare the questions for these interviews and also edit this book; and Llewellyn Smith, who read various earlier versions of the manuscript and offered invaluable suggestions for its improvement.

I must also acknowledge my great debt to Ali A. Mazhari, who wrote a biography of Dr. Nurbakhsh in Persian a number of years ago (published by Khanaqahi-Nimatullahi Publications in London) on which much of the present work is based. Without Mr. Mazhari's previous research and intimate familiarity with Dr. Nurbakhsh's early life, I doubt that I could have succeeded in my task.

Finally, I need to add one last acknowledgment. As I was about to leave Dr. Nurbakhsh's sitting room after completing my final interview with him, he called me back and dictated the following dedication, which he asked me to place in the book, a request that I now gladly fulfill:

I owe a large part of the success I have had in my sufi life to my wife,

Parveneh Daneshvar (the daughter of Dr. Abdullah Daneshvar), who has assisted me in every possible way and who has always worked toward the perfect upbringing of our children. It is, therefore, important that I express my deepest gratitude to her.

TABLE OF CONTENTS

INTRODUCTION

THE BOOK you are about to read is not meant to be a scholarly, objective biography of Javad Nurbakhsh. As a disciple of Dr. Nurbakhsh for the past twenty years, I could not have written such a book. What I have attempted rather is to dramatically portray certain key events in Dr. Nurbakhsh's life as a way of providing readers with an introduction to the man himself. Whatever imaginative details I have added to this account, I have nevertheless striven to be as faithful as possible to the overall events themselves—all of which, to the best of my knowledge, occurred as described. Moreover, all of the quotations cited in the book from letters or documents have been taken verbatim from the originals.

A second thing this book is not meant to be is a comprehensive account of Dr. Nurbakhsh's whole life. I have ended it, as you will see if you read what follows, with Dr. Nurbakhsh becoming master of the Nimatullahi Order when he was just twenty-six years old. My decision to focus upon this period was motivated by the possibility that much of the material about Dr. Nurbakhsh's early life might be lost if not set down soon (which is certainly not the case with the later years of his life). Most of the people depicted in this book are now dead, and many of the sources for the material used are no longer available. By writing this book, I hoped to preserve as much of this information as possible before the passage of time either erased or exaggerated it.

As a result of this decision, however, I was unable to describe the many accomplishments achieved by Dr. Nurbakhsh in his years as master. For example, at the time he assumed responsibility for the Nimatullahi Order, only three khanaqahs existed—in Tehran, Kermanshah, and Mashad. Over the next two decades, though, Dr. Nurbakhsh would oversee the construction of approximately seventy Nimatullahi khanaqahs throughout Iran, in every major city as well as many small towns, and the number of darvishes in the Order would grow from a few hundred to many thousands.

Assisting the master in the construction of these khanaqahs was a disciple he had initiated shortly after becoming master: Mashallah Niktab. Mr. Niktab was a man in his forties who had been searching for a spiritual guide for twenty years when he learned of Dr. Nurbakhsh and sought him out in Bam where he was then living. After a four hour conversation with the master, Mr. Niktab was initiated into the Order and from that point on devoted his entire life to it. The first task assigned to him by Dr. Nurbakhsh was to travel to Kerman and rebuild the khanaqah of Shaikh Kamal al-Din Nurbakhsh, one of the master's distant ancestors, thereby fulfilling a promise that the master had made as a young man (as will be described later in this book). Subsequently, he was responsible for directing the building of virtually all of the Nimatullahi khanaqahs in Iran. As Dr. Nurbakhsh put it during one of our interviews, "All the troubles and hardships involved in the building of these khanaqahs were borne by Mr. Niktab."

During this same twenty year period, the master also devoted himself to the development of Khanaqahi-Nimatullahi Publications (*Entesharat-e Khanagah Nemato'llahi*) in Tehran, which previously had issued only a limited number of books. Under his supervision, over a hundred works on Sufism were published in Persian by the Order (most of them edited or written by Dr. Nurbakhsh himself), including various writings of Shah Nimatullah, which until then had existed only in manuscript form.

As part of his development of Khanaqahi-Nimatullahi Publications, Dr. Nurbakhsh greatly expanded the library housed in the Tehran khanaqah, collecting and preserving the original manuscripts of numerous treatises on Sufism and collections of sufi poetry written by renowned Persian and Arab sufis of the past, together with various historical documents and letters relating to Sufism. This library was housed in one of the buildings of a large complex that Dr. Nurbakhsh constructed over a number of years on the site of the original Tehran khanaqah.

Even with all his many responsibilities to the Order, Dr. Nurbakhsh still did not neglect his life in the outside world. Psychiatry had been his favorite subject in medical school, and after the death of his master, Munes 'Ali Shah, he decided to enroll again in Tehran University to specialize in this area, at the same time obtaining a position as a psychiatric assistant at Ruzbeh Hospital in Tehran to gain practical experience.

Upon completing his specialization in psychiatry at the University, he was offered and subsequently accepted a position as an assistant professor of Psychiatry in the medical school. In those days, to become a full professor, one had to pursue advanced studies at a Western university. To determine who would qualify for such studies, a special exam was given on which Dr. Nurbakhsh received the top-ranking score. As a result, he was offered a full scholarship by the French Consulate in Iran to continue his psychiatric studies at the University of Paris, where he obtained an *Assistant Etranger* diploma.

While in Paris, Dr. Nurbakhsh established friendships with some of the leading Western scholars of Sufism at that time, most notably Professor Henry Corbin who invited Dr. Nurbakhsh to deliver a speech on Sufism at the Sorbonne in 1963. This speech was to provide one of the first introductions to the living practice of Sufism for those in the West. (The text of this speech was later published as the introductory essay in Dr. Nurbakhsh's first English book, *In the Tavern of Ruin: Seven Essays on Sufism*.) Four years later, Dr. Nurbakhsh would deliver a second speech describing the nature of Sufism at a major conference on the unity of religion at the American University in Beirut (the text of which was published as the introductory essay in his second English book, *In the Paradise of the Sufis*).

Upon his return to Iran after the conclusion of his studies in France, Dr. Nurbakhsh was promoted to the position of associate professor at Tehran University and after a few years to a full professorship in the faculty of Psychiatry, eventually becoming Chair of the Department of Psychiatry. Moreover, having resumed his work at Ruzbeh Hospital, he was eventually appointed director of that hospital as well.

During his tenure as director, he oversaw the construction of additional units to the hospital and greatly expanded its facilities, for example supervising the building of a modern conference hall which was later selected as the site for an international conference on psychiatry. In addition to serving as president of the Society of Psychiatrists in Iran, he wrote and edited numerous works on psychiatry, most of which were published in Persian by Tehran University though some in Western scientific journals such as the *Journal of Psychological Health* and the *Journal of General Medicine*. During this time, he also maintained a private psychiatric practice in a clinic that he established adjacent to the Tehran khanaqah, where he treated patients who couldn't afford to pay for psychiatric care.

Perhaps Dr. Nurbakhsh's most significant accomplishment of all, however, was the role he played in bringing Persian Sufism to the rest of the world, especially the West. Not since the fifteenth century, when the Nimatullahi Order relocated to the Deccan in India for three hundred years, had the Order gone beyond the borders of Iran. Early in the 1970's, though, a number of young Americans were introduced to Dr. Nurbakhsh in Iran and felt so strongly drawn to him that they asked for permission to be initiated into the Order, a request that Dr. Nurbakhsh eventually granted. The initiation of these American darvishes led the master to establish the first Nimatullahi khanaqah in the West in a large house in the heart of London in 1974 and then to make his first trip to America in 1975 during which he traveled across the country by car, initiating both Americans and Iranians in various cities.

The following year, the master decided in view of the growing number of disciples in America to send Mr. Niktab (who by then had become shaikh of the Shiraz khanaqah) to the United States as his representative, with instructions to explore the possibility of establishing a khanaqah there. After investigating various sites, Mr. Niktab received permission to set up the first American khanaqah in San Francisco. This khanaqah was followed a year later by the opening of a khanaqah in New York City in a building that previously had been used as a parking facility but was transformed into a Persian style khanaqah.

In the years that followed, Dr. Nurbakhsh established khanaqahs throughout the United States—in Washington D.C, Boston, Los Angeles, Santa Cruz, Seattle, Chicago, Santa Fe, and San Diego. With the initiation of disciples from various places around the world, he also began to open khanaqahs on other continents in various countries, including Australia, Africa (in the Ivory Coast and Benin), Canada (in Montreal and Toronto), France (in Paris and Lyon), Germany, Spain, Sweden, and the Netherlands, as well as a second English khanaqah in Manchester.

With the expansion of the Order into the West, Dr. Nurbakhsh felt that it was necessary to have his most essential works on Sufism translated into English and collected together for a Western audience. To this end, he arranged for the founding of an English-language division of Khanaqahi-Nimatullahi Publications in America and England. The first book in English, *In the Tavern of Ruin: Seven Essays on Sufism*, was issued by Khanaqahi-Nimatullahi Publications in 1978 and collected a series of introductory essays by Dr. Nurbakhsh on the basic elements of Sufism and the sufi path. The following year, a second collection of essays describing the essential spiritual practices of the Nimatullahi Order was published, entitled *In the Paradise of the Sufis*. Since then, over thirty-five books by Dr. Nurbakhsh have been issued in English by Khanaqahi-Nimatullahi Publications, a number of which have been translated into French, German, Spanish, Italian, Russian, and Dutch.

The steady growth of interest in Sufism, in both Iran and the West, eventually led Dr. Nurbakhsh to come up with the idea of creating an international center for the study of Sufism in all its aspects—historical, literary, artistic, theoretical, and practical. Wishing to devote all his time and energy to the establishment of such a center, he retired in 1977 from his positions as the Chairperson of the Department of Psychiatry at Tehran University and the Director of Ruzbeh Hospital. Shortly thereafter, he purchased a large area of land in the mountains overlooking Karaj (a small city roughly thirty miles west of Tehran) with the intention of constructing a complex of buildings to house the center. However, due to the revolution in Iran that took place shortly afterwards with its attendant political upheavals, Dr. Nurbakhsh was unable to carry out this plan and subsequently departed from Iran, having concluded that he could better accomplish this work in the West.

For ten years after leaving Iran, Dr. Nurbakhsh lived in the khanaqah in London, continuing to establish khanaqahs and to write sufi works.

Then, as the last decade of the twentieth century began, he purchased a tract of farm land north of London in the county of Oxfordshire, known locally as the Old Windmill. It was here that he finally began work again on creating the Nimatullahi Research Center, which was the name he had given to the international center for the study of Sufism that he had first envisioned some two decades earlier.

The heart of the Nimatullahi Research Center is an extensive library collecting books, manuscripts, articles, and papers in all languages about every facet of Sufism—its history (from the classical period to contemporary times), literature (both poetry and prose), music, art, philosophy, theoretical underpinnings, and especially its practice. As part of the Nimatullahi Research Center, Dr. Nurbakhsh founded the journal *Sufi* in 1989 under the editorial direction of his eldest son, Alireza Nurbakhsh, a quarterly devoted to the study of mysticism in all its various aspects, irrespective of religious denomination. Since its inception, the journal has published almost forty issues with articles, stories, and poetry by such well-known scholars and authors as Annemarie Schimmel, Seyyed Hossein Nasr, William Chittick, Herbert Mason, Carl Ernst, Huston Smith, Robert Bly, and P.L. Travers.

The initial projects undertaken by the Center involved the organization of three international conferences on Sufism, at each of which Dr. Nurbakhsh was the keynote speaker. The first, which took place over three days in December of 1990 in London, was jointly sponsored with the School of Oriental and African Studies at the University of London. Entitled "The Legacy of Medieval Persian Sufism", the conference assembled many of the foremost specialists in the field of sufi studies from Great Britain, France, Germany, Holland, Switzerland, and the United States. (A complete listing of the speakers and the titles of their papers can be found in the report on the conference published in *Sufi: A Journal of Sufism*, Issue 8.) The second conference, which also lasted three days, took place in May of 1992 in Washington D.C, jointly sponsored with George Washington University. This conference was devoted to an examination of Persian Sufism from its origins to the time of Rumi and again featured many of the foremost sufi scholars from three continents.

(See Issue 13 of *Sufi: A Journal of Sufism* for a complete listing of the speakers and the titles of their papers.) The third conference, which took place in 1997, dealt with the late classical period of Sufism and was convened in conjunction once again with the School of Oriental and African Studies at the University of London.

Dr. Nurbakhsh has resided at the Old Windmill, overseeing and directing the activities of the Nimatullahi Research Center, since shortly after its purchase. It was there that the interview with which this book ends took place. My hope is that this interview, in conjunction with the following account of Dr. Nurbakhsh's early life, will succeed in conveying a clear portrait of the man of God who has been the master of the Nimatullahi Order for almost half a century.

1.

ATTRACTION TO GOD

1626 A.D.

Night had already begun to fall by the time Shah Abbas, ruler of all Persia, arrived with his entourage in the district of Baghain near the city of Kerman. Kerman was their ultimate destination, but since it was too late to enter the city, the Shah issued orders for a camp to be made. With a small party of officers, he then set out to explore the surrounding area.

After riding a few miles, they came upon a small building in the distance which, though clearly not a mosque, nevertheless seemed to them to be some sort of religious center. His curiosity piqued, Shah Abbas set off for the building, waving for his men to follow. When they reached the house and knocked on the door, they were greeted warmly by a darvish clad in a brown woolen cloak. Shah Abbas dismounted from his horse and approached the man.

"Greetings, friend. We are but humble travelers on our way to Kerman, strangers to this area with no place to stay tonight. We wondered if perhaps you might be able to help us."

"I would be honored by your presence, whoever you may be," the man replied, bowing. "Feel free to stay here as long as you need."

"And who is it that would provide such hospitality to total strangers? What place is this?"

"God is the provider of all things. But in answer to your questions, my name is Shaikh Kamal al-Din Nurbakhsh, and this is a house of God, a refuge for all who come here—whatever the reason."

Without asking their names or anything else about them, the Shaikh showed the men inside and saw to it that they were fed and made comfortable for the night.

As soon as the Shaikh had retired to his room, leaving the men alone, Shah Abbas turned to one of his officers.

"Do you see how this man welcomes us without so much as inquiring who we are or what our religion is? Though ignorant of who I really am, he nevertheless treats us as if we were kings. This man is a true Muslim."

Gesturing to the officer to follow, the Shah went to a desk in a corner of the room. There, he sat and wrote a declaration bestowing upon the Shaikh all the property surrounding the area for miles to be used for the upkeep of the khanaqah. After sealing the document, he handed it to the officer.

"Here, take this declaration and place it under the sheepskin of the Shaikh sometime during the night. Such kindness deserves to be repaid with kindness. Say nothing to him, though, for if you do he will surely refuse this gift."

1926 A.D.

Hasan Nurbakhsh hurried along the dusty streets of Kerman, his wearied legs buoyed up by the news that had just been conveyed to him: his son Asdollah and daughter-in-law Khanom Bibi had been blessed with the birth of a healthy boy, their first child and his first grandchild!

As he wove his way through the stalls of the bazaar on his way to see the child, he happened to notice an acquaintance who had a shop there selling rugs.

"Tell me," he shouted out, "what day is today? I mean, what's the date?"

"The date? December 10th, I think. Why?"

"Because I'm a grandfather today!"

He fixed the date in his mind—surely a day of great blessing, he told himself.

From the day he was born, Javad had been his grandfather's favorite. Entranced by the boy's radiant eyes and smile, he had spent hours sitting beside the baby's crib. But as Javad grew older, even his grandfather found he could no longer answer the boy's many questions about the world and life, about how things worked and why things were the way they were. Although obviously not an objective judge, he had no doubt whatsoever that his grandson possessed an intelligence and insight into people and things that was way beyond his years, even remarkable. Of course, Javad also had a mischievous side that went along with his curiosity, a mischieviousness that often drove his grandfather and parents to distraction. What it would all come to in the end, only God knew. But he was sure the boy would turn out to be something special—however difficult his inquisitive nature admittedly made him now.

Khanom Bibi had just finished preparing the kabob when Asdollah came into the kitchen and sat at the table. She could tell from his expression that something was on his mind, but she knew from experience it was better to be patient and wait: whatever it was, he would bring it up himself when he was ready.

After a few minutes had passed in silence, Asdollah asked her to sit and have some tea with him.

With the tea poured, he looked over at his wife and spoke. "I think it's time for Javad to begin studying the *Koran*."

Even though the study of the *Koran* was a normal part of most young people's education, Khanom was still taken aback by his suggestion since Javad was so young. "There's plenty of time," she replied. "He *is* only five years old."

"I know, but he's already reading. And something tells me it's time for him to start...even if he only finishes a small portion of it."

Khanom knew better than to argue with her husband once his mind was made up about something and reluctantly agreed.

Over the next nine months, to the surprise of his parents and the religious authority teaching him, Javad managed to read through much more of the *Koran* than any of them would have thought possible. He was then placed with a group of older children who were studying the works of Hafez, the greatest of Persian poets. Although the instructor who taught the class didn't appreciate Javad's constant challenging questions, he nevertheless chose to overlook this difficulty in light of the boy's obvious knowledge and ability.

"Excuse me, sir. But one of the sixth grade teachers is here to talk to you."

The secretary to the Principal of the Shahab Elementary School stood hesitantly in the doorway of the office with a folder in her hand.

"Yes, yes, come in. What's the problem?" the principal asked.

"It's about Javad Nurbakhsh."

"Again?" he asked with a sigh.

She walked over and placed the folder on his desk.

"It's his folder. I thought you might want to see it."

"Thank you. Give me a few minutes and then send his teacher in."

The secretary nodded and then left the room. Once she'd closed the door, the principal picked up the file and flipped through it, although he already knew from past experience what was there. Javad had been enrolled in the school since he was six years old. For three years in a row, he

Javad Nurbakhsh at 18 years old

Mr. Morshedi, shaikh of Kerman, who initiated Dr. Nurbakhsh into the Order

had been the top-ranked student in his class, demonstrating a remarkable intelligence and memory. At the end of that third year, based upon his own recommendation as principal, Javad's father had hired a private tutor to instruct the boy over the summer in the fourth-year curriculum. He'd made the recommendation because he'd recognized the boy's ability and hadn't wished to see him become bored, to turn into a troublemaker. Even knowing all this, he was still stunned when Javad had taken the exams given at the beginning of the year and passed with such high grades that he skipped not only the fourth grade but the fifth as well, going directly into the sixth grade that September.

As the principal looked through the folder, he noted the numerous times that Javad's teachers had come to him to complain. The boy was constantly challenging them, asking such complex questions that they found it hard to accept that someone his age could possibly raise them.

The principal sighed again. Javad was surely having a hard enough time already being so much younger and smaller than all the other sixth year students. He didn't need to have things made any harder for him.

The next year, seventh grade, had been the start of high school for Javad, there being no junior high schools in Iran as there are in America.

High school constituted a new beginning for Javad in more than just an academic sense. He discovered, for the first time, that he possessed a literary talent which he now began to develop, composing poetry that was well-received by his teachers. Yet to most of them, he still remained an enigma, a disturbing combination of academic ability and unsuitable behavior.

A few, however, recognized his true potential. As one of them wrote: "Nurbakhsh's body is incapable of containing his untamed, wild spirit—which is why he can never remain still. Even after skipping a number of grades and finding a place among the older students, he remains unsatisfied and continues to seek something else. Whatever that something may be, he will never find satisfaction or calm in his life until he attains it."

"Javad, are you still up?"

Asdollah knew that his son didn't like to be disturbed at night when he was studying, but during the day there never seemed to be time to talk.

"I've been thinking," he went on after pulling over a chair and sitting. "This is your last year in high school, and the time has come for you to begin considering what to do with your life. It's time for you to pick a career, to start preparing for the future."

Javad lowered his head in thought, saying nothing.

His father went on to explain that he had spent a good deal of time considering the matter and had decided that a position either in a bank or as a civil servant would provide Javad with the steady income and stability necessary for a happy life.

Javad had always done his best to obey and please his father. But he had no desire to work in a bank or be a civil servant. Throughout high school, his dream had always been to attend Tehran University once he'd graduated. He knew his father wouldn't be happy with the idea, so he'd kept quiet about it. Now he had no choice: he had to say something.

After hearing his son out, Asdollah remained silent for a long time before speaking.

"I think you're making a big mistake. And what makes you think you'd be admitted into the University, even with your grades? You know how few people from around the country are accepted each year."

Javad granted that this was so. But he explained how he planned to spend the entire summer studying for the University's entrance exams. Since he already had a strong grounding in literature, his plan was to concentrate on the natural sciences so he could qualify for a high school diploma in both areas. That way, he told his father, he would have a choice whether to study law or medicine at the University, the two areas in which he was interested.

Asdollah was stunned when he heard this and thought his son had gone crazy.

"Are you telling me you expect not only to be accepted into the University but to qualify to study either law *or* medicine?"

Javad nodded and explained that he wasn't sure yet which one he wanted to major in. Then he reminded his father that since he wasn't eighteen, the lawful age for employment at the time, he couldn't get a job even if he wanted to.

Asdollah knew that his son was right, unfortunately.

"We'll just have to see what happens. If you do pass the entrance exams, then we'll discuss the matter again more seriously."

As it turned out, circumstances didn't allow Javad to take the entrance exams for Tehran University that Fall, forcing him to wait until the following year. This meant, however, that he was now free to delve even further into the exploration of literature he'd begun in high school.

Javad's father, of course, had other plans. Throughout the year, he kept arranging for job offers to be made to his son by relatives and friends, hoping that he would find one to his liking. But since Javad had already made up his mind to attend the University no matter what, much to his father's chagrin, he turned down each of these offers.

Freed for the first time to pursue his own direction, Javad began to explore the works of the great Persian sufi poets, an interest that had been stimulated by his earlier study of Hafez. Before long, he became completely absorbed in his study of Sufism. It was as if a whole new universe had opened up before him. His discovery of Rumi's *Mathnawi* had an especially powerful effect upon him, acting as a kind of catalyst leading him deeper and deeper into his pursuit of spiritual Truth. So absorbed did he become in his reading of these classical sufi texts that he soon found himself thinking constantly about visiting the khanaqah of Shaikh Kamal al-Din Nurbakhsh, one of his distant ancestors who had been a well-known sufi of his time. While growing up, he had often heard his grandfather and father talk, usually late at night, about their ancestor and the khanaqah he'd founded in Kerman three centuries earlier, marveling at the spiritual life to which he had devoted himself. Finally, growing tired of just day-dreaming, Javad decided one day to approach his father to ask for permission to visit the khanaqah.

Though surprised by his son's request, Javad's father saw no reason why the boy shouldn't be allowed to make such a trip. It did take him a while, however, to remember the exact location of the khanaqah in Kerman and how to get there.

Javad squinted up in the bright sunlight trying to make out the name of the street onto which he'd just turned. The khanaqah of Shaikh Kamal al-Din had been built in what was now known as the old district of Kerman, and it had taken him a lot longer than he'd expected to make his way through the winding, crowded streets of the city. A number of times he'd been forced to stop and ask for directions. To his dismay, almost no one seemed to know anything about the khanaqah.

When he turned the corner of the street on which the khanaqah was located, he immediately understood why. Where once a center of hospitality and spirituality had flourished, there now stood only some ruins, strewn with garbage. Javad wandered through the rubble picturing what it must have been like three hundred years earlier. A strange disturbance came over him, stirring his heart.

Standing there amid the ruins of the khanaqah, he vowed that after finishing his education and finding a job, he would somehow renovate the ruins and revive the khanaqah to honor the memory of Shaikh Kamal al-Din Nurbakhsh.

A dramatic change had overcome Javad since his return from the khanaqah of his ancestor, a strangeness he didn't understand, whose cause eluded him however much he sought to find it. All he knew was that some kind of turbulence, beyond his control, had arisen within him. Where before he had enjoyed the company of others, now he preferred to remain alone as much as possible. The only contentment he found was in solitude. For hours each day, he would sit at home by himself meditating on life and God: nothing else seemed to matter to him anymore.

Bestower of Light

Although Javad's parents and family had noticed the change in his behavior, it was one of his father's close friends who first understood what was happening. The man had known the family for years and been a darvish of the Nimatullahi Sufi Order even longer. For weeks, he had been watching the boy, observing his strange actions. He had hesitated to say anything until he was sure, but now he knew there was no other possible explanation: he clearly recognized the signs of one attracted to God.

A few days later, after visiting with the family, he took Javad aside.

"I hope you will not be offended," he told him, "but I have seen certain changes in you. And I think you might find it helpful to talk to a friend of mine, Mr. Morshedi. He is a follower of the sufi path, a shaikh of the Nimatullahi Order here in Kerman. You can tell him that I was the one who recommended you go see him."

Javad wasn't sure if this Mr. Morshedi could do anything for him, but he respected his father's friend and decided he had nothing to lose by meeting with the shaikh.

Seyyed Morshedi sat at the desk in his bedroom barely able to hold the pen steady in his hand so great was the excitement and joy in his heart. But he had to let his darvish brother in Kermanshah know about the boy he had initiated earlier that evening.

As carefully as he could, he slowly drew the pen across the paper and wrote a single sentence: "Tonight, a young student named Javad Nurbakhsh Kermani stepped into the circle of the dwellers of the heart: no longer will anyone be able to complain now that there exists a shortage of water."

After a moment's reflection, he carefully added a line in Arabic to the letter, a quote from Sura 21, Verse 30 of the *Koran*, "...and from water We made all things living."

Then he signed his name.

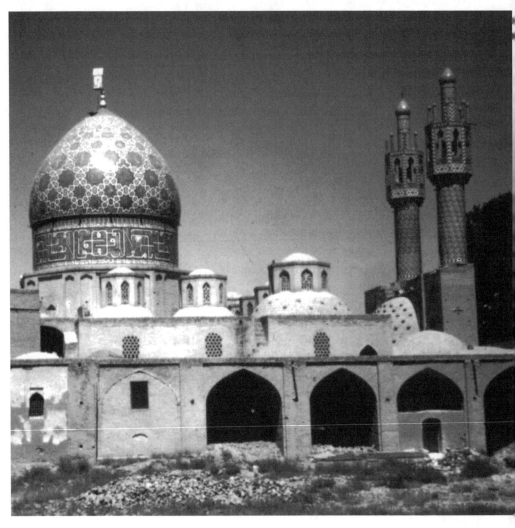

Tomb of Shah Nimatullah (Mahan, Kerman)

2.

THE PATH

ALARMED BY the drastic change in her son's nature, the cause of which remained a total mystery to her, Javad's mother was growing increasingly anxious with each day. Before, he had just seemed preoccupied and distracted, but now she was sure something serious was going on.

And it worried her.

Over the past few weeks, his eyes, once bright with happiness, had grown bloodshot, even taken on a wild appearance, and dark circles had appeared beneath them. It was obvious to her that he wasn't sleeping much.

Eventually, these fears led her to begin sneaking up to his room at night to check on him. Each time she looked, however, she found the lights off and, seeing nothing, assumed with relief that he'd finally gone to bed. Yet in the morning, he always looked as tired as before. She just couldn't understand it.

Then one night, noticing a light burning in his room, she had peeked through the curtains and found him sitting on the floor, knees pressed to his chest, in a state of meditation. So that, she suddenly realized, was what he'd been doing all those nights. He had just forgotten to put out the light that night.

Shaken by her discovery, Javad's mother returned to the bedroom to tell her husband what she'd found. She also told him about the boy's refusal to eat much of anything any more or see his friends, of how he had been staying alone in his room for hours on end, using his studies as what was clearly just a pretext.

In the morning, his father went to the friend who had originally sent Javad to the shaikh and informed him about the things his wife had seen. He then asked whether his son's strange actions resulted from certain instructions the shaikh had given him or rather from practices he'd undertaken on his own.

The friend was clearly uncomfortable with the news Javad's father had brought. After a long pause, he seemed to come to some kind of decision. Leaning forward in his chair, he apologized and told Asdollah that he hadn't been completely forthright with him.

"You know that I own some property outside the city. Because of this, I have to go there almost every day to take care of business. A few times on my way, I happened to see Javad's bicycle parked at the foot of one of the mountains.

"My curiosity finally got the better of me, and one afternoon I climbed the mountain looking for him. High atop it, I found him all alone, crying, clearly upset about something.

"The day after, if you remember, I told you that your son must have fallen in love and that you had to do something about it."

"I remember. And then I asked Javad about it and he denied having fallen in love, telling me he didn't know what I was talking about."

"When you told me that and said you believed him, I knew from what I'd seen that if he wasn't in love, then he must have been experiencing a spiritual kind of pain. And so, with your permission, I suggested to him that he might want to meet with the shaikh of the Nimatullahi

Order here in Kerman, Mr. Morshedi."

Asdollah nodded. "And so?"

"Well, after their meeting, Javad started visiting with the shaikh often. Soon, he began to experience certain spiritual states, states so intense that they have affected not only me but the shaikh as well. When I continued to see his bicycle by the mountain, I went to talk to him and discovered that he had been going there every day, like Moses to Mount Sinai, with a burning in his heart, crying for hours, not understanding the pain he was experiencing.

"That is why, without telling you, I approached the shaikh to let him know what I'd seen and ask if he thought perhaps Javad should be initiated. Upon hearing about your son, he seemed delighted and told me he'd known since their first meeting that Javad would soon be initiated.

"Then a week ago, I was on my way to visit the shaikh when I happened to run into Javad. I asked if he wanted to come with me, and he gladly agreed. Just before we reached Mr. Morshedi's house, we stopped at the public baths where I always go to perform my ablutions before visiting the shaikh. I suggested that Javad might also want to perform the ablutions, and he did so. Then we went straight to Mr. Morshedi's house.

"After we greeted the shaikh, I went to sit, but he indicated that he wanted to be left alone with Javad. So I departed and went home.

"The next day I heard that your son had been initiated at that very meeting. Since his initiation had taken place without the traditional sufi ceremonies and without even a *pir-e dalil* to guide him to the shaikh's room, I became extremely curious about what had happened. When I saw Javad the following day and asked him about it, he said that after I left, the shaikh had asked him, 'Does your heart want to step upon the path to God, to the Truth, and find the only true remedy for your pain?' Javad told me he'd immediately said yes, and the shaikh—as if knowing he'd already done the ablutions and been prepared—instructed him to kneel and initiated him into the path, bestowing a *zekr* upon him."

When he heard this, Javad's father began to repeat the words "Mount Sinai" over and over again.

"It's strange," he finally said to his friend. "Javad himself once asked me about that very mountain where you found him. He wanted to know its name. Having no idea, I replied jokingly, 'All mountains are Mount Sinai and the creation of God.' I didn't know how right I was."

Javad's father fell silent for a while and prepared his pipe. He then turned back to his friend.

"I know this is all for the best, but please tell Javad how much he is worrying his mother. If you think it necessary, go to your shaikh and ask him to be more careful about Javad's states."

The friend gladly agreed, promising to carry out Asdollah's wishes.

Not being aware of any of this, Javad, of course, just continued to go about his business, traveling to the mountain each day, each day becoming more and more absorbed in his search for the Truth and less and less interested in the everyday world.

It was dawn of one of the coldest days of winter. Javad's father, preparing for the morning prayers, was breaking the ice in the pool outside his house in order to perform his ablutions. Just as he was about to wash, he noticed Javad running towards him in an extremely distraught state. His eyes were all bloodshot and had taken on a wild appearance. After staring intently at his father for a few moments, he burst out in an angry voice, accusing his father of providing him with some kind of unlawful sustenance. There was no other explanation, he told his father, because no matter what he did the veil still remained.

Shocked at his son's bizarre outburst, Javad's father went to chastise him, but seeing the fire burning in his eyes decided to remain silent for the time being. In a calm yet firm voice, he instructed his son to return to his room immediately and get some rest, which to his relief Javad did. Then, without a word to his wife, he set out for the city.

Mr. Morshedi was just finishing some paperwork when he heard the knock on the door. After blowing out the candle on his desk, he went to see who could be there so early in the morning. Finding Javad's father at the door, he welcomed him into the house and took him to the living room where they sat opposite each other. Asdollah politely refused Shaikh Morshedi's offer of tea and then, doing his best to restrain his emotions, explained why he was there.

"When my son first became distraught, we thought that he had fallen in love. But we soon learned this was not the case. In accordance with a friend's recommendation, we then agreed to let him come to you, hoping he might even follow in his ancestor's footsteps and devote himself to spirituality. Yet now, it has gone too far. He seems to have approached the very threshold of madness, and I am afraid that he risks throwing his whole life away. I have come here to beg you to do something about the situation. If this goes on much longer, his mother will surely die of grief."

Javad's father then informed the shaikh about his son's strange behavior after being initiated, especially about the incident that had just taken place at home and how the boy had screamed at him so crazily. He finished by again begging Mr. Morshedi to do something.

As the shaikh sat there listening to the words of Javad's father, his heart filled with joy, and he grew more and more elated. With tears in his eyes, he told Asdollah not to worry and assured him his son would be fine, indicating that as a sufi the boy would one day bring great honor to his family.

Asdollah shook the shaikh's hand and in total disbelief left the house. Rather than return home where he might have to confront his son again, and wishing to avoid the questions his wife would surely ask about where he'd been, he decided to go instead to his shop in the bazaar. Maybe work would take his mind off his worries about his son.

That afternoon, Mr. Morshedi called up one of the darvishes and asked him to bring Javad Nurbakhsh to his house. The darvish, however, had no luck finding Javad and reluctantly went to the shaikh to let him know. Concerned about the boy's absence, Mr. Morshedi decided to go himself to the mountain about which Javad's father had spoken. From what he'd said, there was a good chance the boy could be found there.

Accompanied by the darvish, Mr. Morshedi set out for the mountain. Once they reached their destination, he asked the darvish to return home. Then, with great effort, he began to climb the mountain alone.

When Javad looked down and saw the shaikh climbing the mountain by himself, he was shocked and rushed to help him.

Mr. Morshedi embraced Javad and insisted that they return to the exact place where Javad had been going each day to do his meditation, saying that he wanted to sit at that spot with him. Once there, the two of them sat in silence for quite some time until the shaikh finally raised his head and spoke.

"I am aware of the burning in your heart and that you no longer know the difference between day and night. So you are not at fault for this. But you should know that you have disturbed your parents, and this is not the way of a sufi. A sufi has only respect for his parents and would never do anything to harm or disturb them.

"The reason the veil has not been removed for you has nothing to do with any improper sustenance provided by your father. If you want to know the truth, it is because you have upset your mother and frightened her. Your father is a patient man, but he too has been upset, especially by your words this morning. So upset that he no longer knows what to do.

"You should be aware that the state you are now experiencing is the state of 'seeking.' This is a very exalted state. And in the short time since your initiation, you have traveled a long way, so far in fact that it amazes me. But you must not expect all the veils to be removed so quickly. A seeker is like a fisherman: he must sit by the water for long periods, casting his line hundreds of times, over and over again, if he wishes to catch anything, and even then he may sometimes go home empty-handed.

"Be calm rather than hasty, for this path cannot be traveled except with great patience, more patience than most possess. Rest assured, though, that you have been blessed with certain sure signs of progress. As long as you persevere and your faith remains unwavering, His grace will become your constant companion and, God willing, you will eventually traverse the rest of the path."

The shaikh remained silent for a few moments before going on.

"Soon you will be going to Tehran to attend the University. There, you will have the opportunity to enjoy the companionship of our beloved master. For now, though, you must strive to remain calm and patient since without these qualities you will never be able to continue your journey to the end. Even more importantly, you must make sure not to cause your parents any further anxiety. Remember, for them these matters are incomprehensible, and therefore they are understandably and rightfully horrified by your strange state. Thus, you must reassure them and be more careful not to disturb them."

Ashamed to have caused his parents such pain and humbled by the shaikh's words, Javad remained silent. The shaikh finally nodded, and together they climbed down the mountain.

Asdollah was sweeping out his shop when he saw Javad weaving his way through the bazaar, his bike by his side. He feared another outburst from his son, especially one in public, but to his surprise Javad greeted him with a warm smile and then embraced him. He went on to apologize for the way he had been acting and told his father not to worry, that it would never happen again.

Overjoyed to see Javad in such a relaxed, talkative mood as if he had finally returned to himself, Asdollah invited his son to sit next to him, then took out his pipe and began to fill it. He didn't know what had caused Javad's change of state, whether Mr. Morshedi had already spoken to him, but he didn't care: he was elated to see it. In his happiness, he asked his son about his plans for the University, and this time he raised no objection, saying nothing to dissuade him or convince him he should get a job.

Javad, for his part, was equally elated to hear this implicit endorsement of his plan to go to Tehran. After explaining to his father that he had some errands to run and borrowing some money, he asked for permission to return home.

On the way, he decided to stop and visit his uncle whom he hadn't seen in quite some time. His uncle was surprised to see Javad there since he'd heard from his sister that he was spending almost all his time involved in ascetic practices and meditation, and not seeing anyone. But like Asdollah, he was delighted to find Javad in such a changed, happy state.

Once Javad satisfied himself that he'd reassured his uncle, he said good-bye and, after stopping to buy some halwah, returned home to make amends with the rest of his family as well, telling them with a smile that he hoped the sweets he'd bought them would relieve whatever bitterness he might have caused.

Each day since his meeting with the shaikh, Javad had been going to his father's shop in the bazaar. They would sit together and pass the time talking about various matters, both insignificant and important. One day, the subject arose of their ancestor, Shaikh Kamal al-Din Nurbakhsh, and the khanaqah he had founded. It gave Javad a chance to raise an issue that had been bothering him since his visit there.

How, he wanted to know, had the khanaqah of Shaikh Kamal al-Din been allowed to fall apart, to turn into no more than a garbage dump? Why hadn't anyone taken care of it all those years?

Javad's father explained to his son how none of the descendants of the shaikh had wanted to spend the income from the property bestowed by Shah Abbas on the khanaqah's upkeep, most of them being poor and needing it themselves. Gradually, he went on, everyone in the family had sold their shares in the land such that only a few shops in the market-place remained as a source of income for the khanaqah, shops that unfortunately made little money.

"In fact," he concluded, "it's been many years since our family has been in charge of these shops. They belong to a different line of descendants of the shaikh, a line that has refused generation after generation to spend so much as one rial on the khanaqah's upkeep."

Seeing the sadness in his father's eyes, Javad let him know about the promise he'd made to himself to one day restore the khanaqah, a promise he once more swore to keep.

As Asdollah thought back on his earlier worries about his son, he chuckled to himself and thanked God that his concern had been for nothing.

Javad Nurbakhsh at 22 years old with his master, Munes Ali Shah

3.

MEETING THE MASTER

IT HAD taken Javad three days by bus to make the six hundred mile journey to Tehran. The roads were old and unpaved, and they had been forced to stop for two nights, one in Yazd and another in Esfahan.

For a while before he left, Javad had been afraid his father wasn't going to let him attend the University after all. But his mother had been insistent on his going and had prevailed upon her husband, putting aside all the necessary items for her son's journey so that no objection could be raised when the time came. She had even prepared his suitcase at her sister's and performed the traditional blessing for one who was about to travel that was common in Iran at the time.

The bus finally arrived on the third day at one of the squares in the south of Tehran, the old area of the city that had yet to be modernized. Exhausted from the journey yet exhilarated by his arrival in the capital, Javad went directly to see a friend to whom he had written earlier about his plan to attend the University. With his friend's help, he rented a room in one of the older houses in the southern part of the city and set about preparing for the University's entrance exams. In those days, a general entrance exam wasn't given since there weren't that many qualified applicants; rather, every faculty had its own exam, on the basis of which they then accepted students.

As he had planned, Javad registered for the exams for both law and medicine, passed both, and was accepted by the Department of Law and the Department of Medicine. After a little further investigation, however, he was able to make an easy decision. Since a degree in medicine would take him the longest to complete, this would give him as many years as possible with the master.

Once he'd made his decision, he took out a sheet of paper to write to his family. He knew his father hadn't really believed he would be accepted into medical school. But he also knew his father would be delighted to have been proven wrong.

Javad stood in front of the door of the Tehran khanaqah and stared up at the blue tiles on the wall that depicted the symbol of the Nimatullahi Order—an empty begging bowl signifying the sufi's reliance on nothing except for God, below two crossed axes, one of which indicated the cutting away of the sufi's attachment to this world and the other the cutting away of the sufi's attachment to the next world; between the two axes hung a strand of beads symbolizing the sufi's constant remembrance of God.

With the letter in hand that Mr. Morshedi had written to introduce and recommend him to Dhor-Riyasatayn, the master of the Order, Javad knocked on the door. After giving the letter to the doorkeeper, he was shown into the sitting room of Munes Ali Shah, which was the sufi name bestowed upon him by the previous master of the Order as was the custom.

The master motioned for Javad to sit. He took the letter and read through it quickly. Then, without saying anything to Javad, he called in one of the darvishes who lived in the khanaqah.

"I want you to help this young man in his efforts to find a place to live and pass the entrance exam for medical school. Do whatever you can to assist him."

Javad had sat in silence up to this point, but now he asked for permission to speak. Respectfully, he informed the master that he had no need of such help, having already gotten an apartment and enrolled in the medical school. He then apologized for not having come to the khanaqah sooner to pay his respects to the master, but explained that he had first wanted to take care of all his business so as not to cause anyone trouble. His only wish now, he said, was to be able to serve the master.

For a long time, the master stared at Javad as he sat there with his eyes lowered. Then he finally spoke.

"We meet here on Thursday and Sunday nights," he told him. "Each Thursday, we serve a simple dinner. On those nights, it would be better for you to eat here with the other darvishes."

Still looking down, Javad nodded, certain that he had done the right thing by coming to Tehran.

For months, Javad had been regularly attending the khanaqah on the meeting nights, sitting each time by the door where the darvishes left their shoes. Though only a dozen or so darvishes attended the meetings, most of them older men, he always strove to be courteous and respectful to everyone there, no matter who they were. During the meetings, the darvishes would do their *namaz* (Islamic prayers), then sit and pray or recite Koranic verses. Occasionally, someone would sing passages from Rumi's *Mathnawi*, but no musical instruments were permitted (as they later would be once Javad became master).

One night that winter after the meeting, there was a heavy snowfall and the temperature dropped very low. Having no way of getting home and not knowing anyone, Javad decided to spend the night in the khanaqah so that the next morning he could just go directly to school.

Once all the other darvishes had gone home, he returned to the entrance room where he always sat during the meetings and began to medi-tate. When midnight came, though, the heater shut off, having run out of fuel, and the building, already cold from being so run-down, grew even colder.

Freezing now, Javad searched for some way of warming himself but couldn't find any fuel or even a blanket. The only solution, he finally decided, was to wrap himself in one of the khanaqah's rugs until he became warm. After locating a suitable rug, he lay down on the floor, took a corner of the old rug, and started rolling in it until his whole body became covered. A little while later, having once again grown warm, he finally managed to fall asleep.

Less than an hour later, though, he awoke suddenly. Not only was he covered with dust and dirt, but to his horror he discovered that his body had become infested with hundreds of tiny insects which had made their home in the old rug.

Unsuccessful in his efforts to remove the bugs from himself, Javad had no choice but to take off all of his clothes, even if it was the khanaqah. Trying to ignore how cold it had gotten, he reluctantly removed his outer garments and then sat in a corner to meditate in an effort to forget himself.

At dawn, when Munes Ali Shah went outside to do his ablutions for the morning prayer, he was startled to hear a deep, steady breathing coming from inside the khanaqah. Realizing that somebody was in the tea-room, he approached the door and was dumbfounded to see a young man clutching his knees, meditating, wearing only a pair of shorts. Who, he wondered, could be sitting alone like that in such cold weather without any heat, doing his *zekr* at this hour of the morning? After drying his hands, he entered the building to find out.

As soon as he saw the master, Javad jumped to his feet and quickly wrapped himself in his bug-ridden clothes.

"What possible explanation could there be for this state of yours?" the master asked incredulously.

Javad explained more or less everything to the master and apologized for having stayed overnight in the khanaqah without permission.

"It doesn't matter," the master let him know with kindness. "No harm has been done. Except perhaps to your body," he added with just a hint of a smile. "Go get some clean clothes and then come to my room. We can have some breakfast together." The master looked forward to learning more about this strange young darvish from Kerman.

After they had finished breakfast, the master told Javad to come early the next meeting night so that they could talk more. At that meeting, the master called in one of the elder darvishes who was in charge of the khanaqah library. He introduced Javad to the man and then let him know that he wanted Javad to be given the keys to the library and the front door of the khanaqah. From now on, he told the darvish, Javad was to be responsible for the library and could come and go in the khanaqah whenever he wished, to study or work in the library. "If necessary," the master added with a grin, "he can stay overnight in the library. But make sure the heater always has more than enough fuel." Then he instructed the darvish to take Javad to the library and show him where everything was.

Javad followed the elder darvish to the library. He was astonished to find that the man was not only undisturbed at having to relinquish all his responsibilities to such a young, new darvish, but that he even went out of his way to treat Javad with great kindness, letting him know that he was always available if needed and that if any problems or questions arose Javad should consult with him without hesitation.

Over the next few months, Javad's entire life became dedicated to the path and service to others. Every day, after attending classes at the University, he would go directly to the khanaqah and remain there until late at night, returning to his rented room only after all the other darvishes had gone home. While at the khanaqah, he constantly did his best to provide whatever service he could, for example indexing all the books in the library which had never been done before.

Throughout this period, the master displayed great affection for this young darvish from Kerman who worked so hard and with such sincerity and dedication. At every opportunity, he would call Javad to his room to discuss various matters with him, especially those of a spiritual nature, bestowing his constant attention upon him. He also began to encourage him to pursue the study of Arabic so as to become better acquainted with Arabic literature and thereby have access to all the essential sufi texts, not just those in Persian. As added encouragement, he even volunteered to teach the boy himself. The master soon grew impressed with Javad's memory and the ease with which he was able to learn, finding that he could memorize complicated theoretical sufi texts easily, often after reading or hearing them only once.

Since Javad was now spending most of his time in the khanaqah when not attending medical school, Munes Ali Shah suggested that he move from his rented room and come to live there. Javad immediately gave up his room and moved his few belongings to the khanaqah, welcoming the opportunity to be closer to the master and better able to attend to the needs of the other darvishes.

Soon after moving into the khanaqah, Javad was given the responsibility for taking care of the dinners given each Thursday night. To accomplish this, he had to leave the University as early as possible on those nights, purchase all the necessary groceries for the dinner, and then make sure everything was prepared and ready for the meeting. After the dinner, he would clear the *sofreh* (the tablecloth on which the darvishes ate), wash all the dishes, and put everything away so there would be nothing to disturb the master the next morning.

Javad's devotion to Munes Ali Shah and Munes Ali Shah's constant attention and kindness to him gradually became obvious to everyone in the khanaqah. Unfortunately, the master's bestowal of so much responsibility on this young darvish, so new to the khanaqah, and his obvious affection for him, were resented by a number of the older darvishes who found the situation intolerable and set out at every opportunity to create a rift between the two of them. Though these efforts were all doomed to fail ultimately, they were to create some difficult times for Javad.

4.

SHAIKH OF THE TEHRAN KHANAQAH

ALTHOUGH NOT a wealthy man, Javad's father had managed to put aside enough money each month to send to his son so that he was able to live a fairly comfortable, if simple, life while attending medical school. The only problem was getting him the money.

The communications system in Iran at the time was still quite primitive, especially when it came to the transferring of money, and the only safe, relatively fast, way to send funds was by telegraph. For almost three years, therefore, Asdollah had been going each month to the telegraph office to pay for the transfer of money to his son. A postman would then bring Javad a telegram announcing the arrival of the money, and he would go to the local bank to receive it.

One morning, as Asdollah was on his way to the telegraph office to send that month's money, he happened to run into a friend who owned a rug shop in the bazaar near his own shop.

"If I might make a suggestion," the friend asked after learning of Asdollah's situation, "I think I may have a solution to your difficulties."

Munes Ali Shah had been calling for Javad for hours, but he hadn't returned to the khanaqah all day and no one seemed to know where he was or when he would return. Finally, one of the darvishes who was a close friend of Javad went to the master and let him know that he was probably in the north of Tehran taking care of some personal business. What kind of business, the master wanted to know. The darvish replied that he was tutoring students to earn extra money. Why, the master asked, would he possibly need more money since his father was already sending him money each month?

The darvish hesitated to say anything, but the master made it clear that he wanted an answer. Having no choice, Javad's friend admitted that within a few days of receiving the money from his father each month, Javad had usually spent most of it on the other darvishes in the khanaqah since he felt that they needed it far more than he did. As a result, he had no money to live on the rest of the month and had to earn it some other way, which he did by tutoring students in his free time.

"But surely he can't need much money for himself, living in the khanaqah," the master asked.

The darvish became even more hesitant at this point, but again the master pressed him for an answer.

"It has to do with the khanaqah treasury," the darvish reluctantly admitted.

Months earlier, the master had given Javad responsibility for all of the financial affairs of the Tehran khanaqah. Whatever money the master received from the darvishes and others was placed in the khanaqah treasury with the understanding that Javad would use these funds to pay for the khanaqah's expenses and those of the master.

"What about the treasury?" the master asked.

The darvish went on to explain that Javad was always giving money to those darvishes who lacked any income and to various needy people that he met. Since he had no money of his own, having already given that away, he would use whatever funds were available in the khanaqah treasury. At the same time, he also felt obligated to replace whatever money he took, so he ended up having to work twice as hard at his tutoring, traveling all over the city in search of students.

When Javad finally returned to the khanaqah that night, the master called him to his room. After confirming the truth of what the darvish had told him, he let Javad know that he didn't want him working so hard, overextending himself so much, and then he encouraged him to be more careful about the expenditure of money, especially that of the khanaqah. In response, Javad agreed to set up a separate account for the khanaqah funds, which he promised to spend solely in accordance with the master's wishes. When it came to his own money, however, he admitted to the master that he couldn't bring himself to make the same promise.

With resignation, the master accepted this compromise, glad to have resolved the problem. He then opened his desk and took out an envelope.

"This letter came today from your father," he told Javad, handing him the envelope.

Javad opened it and quickly read through the letter. When he was done, he looked up and let the master know that his father had come up with a way of getting him money without having to send it by telegraph each month. He had arranged through a close friend to have a high quality Kermani rug sent to Javad in Tehran. He could then sell the rug, which was worth a substantial amount of money, and use the funds to pay for his expenses throughout the year.

As soon as Munes heard this, he instructed Javad to turn the rug over after it arrived to a certain darvish who was in the rug business and would be able to sell it for a good price. The next day, Munes called in the darvish and instructed him to sell the rug but not to give Javad the whole amount in one lump sum. Rather, he was to dole it out to him in monthly installments so that he wouldn't end up using all of it right away.

The darvish indicated that he understood, and Munes put the whole matter out of his mind—until the rug arrived.

Javad had been working all afternoon in the library, as he usually did once his classes were over, when the master entered the room to discuss some business. Javad put aside the papers on which he was working, and the two of them began to talk. In the middle of their discussion, though, the master suddenly fell silent and started looking around the room. He knew that the rug from Javad's father had arrived the day before, but to his dismay he couldn't see it anywhere.

"Where have you put the rug your father sent?" he asked.

Javad remained silent for a moment and then explained that he had met a person in great need that morning who was suffering under the heavy weight of some personal problems. In an effort to lessen the man's sorrows and difficulties, he had given him the rug.

The master could not believe what he was hearing.

"Who was this man?" he demanded to know after regaining his composure. Upon learning that the person was neither a darvish nor a close friend, he began to shout at Javad, telling him he must be crazy giving away a year's money and that for his own good he might have to be put away in a hospital for the insane until he could learn to control such irresponsible behavior. Having no idea what to say, Javad just remained silent.

Totally ignoring the business he had come to discuss, the master turned away and abruptly left the library.

That night, Javad couldn't sleep and decided to go downstairs to meditate in a corner of the tea-room. Just before dawn, Munes went outside to the pool in the garden, as he did every morning, to do his ablutions for prayers. Inside the tea-room, Javad heard the master cough and jumped up to go to him. But before he could get outside, Munes appeared in the doorway. With gentleness, the master let him know that he had done nothing wrong, assuring him that such a selfless act, rather than being blameworthy, deserved only to be praised. Then he embraced his disciple and went to perform the morning prayers.

Unable to contain his joy, Javad started dancing uncontrollably round and round the room.

For almost an hour, Javad had sat in an antechamber of the Finance Ministry waiting for his meeting with one of the Ministry's highest officials. A darvish at the khanaqah had asked for his help in resolving a particularly complicated problem, and he knew that the man he was waiting to meet with could be of great assistance.

Once he was shown into the official's chambers, it didn't take long to conclude his business satisfactorily, and he left to return to the khanaqah. Even though the official's discussion with Javad had lasted but a short time and been limited almost entirely to business, by the end of their meeting, the official began to experience a strange change of state, so strange that he found he could no longer concentrate on his work or function as usual and had to leave the office.

The official aimlessly wandered the streets of Tehran, up wide boulevards, down small alleyways, seeking to understand the state that had overcome him, a state like nothing he had ever experienced before. He was sure this state had to be connected somehow to the young man, the sufi, who had come to see him. But he had no idea what exactly had happened or why. It certainly had nothing to do with their conversation itself which had been quite business-like and mundane. He was at a total loss to explain it.

In the morning, the official called up the khanaqah and arranged to meet with Javad again the next day, this time at the khanaqah. The two of them spent over an hour talking at this meeting. Before leaving, the official asked if it would be possible to come to the khanaqah to visit with him again. Javad agreed and over the next few weeks the official met with him almost every day. During one of these visits, the official finally decided to ask for permission to be initiated into the Order. Javad told him that he would have to discuss the matter first with the master, Dhor-Riyasatayn. If the master agreed, he would take the man to him to be initiated as soon as he could.

The official shook his head upon hearing this and explained that he had no interest in being initiated by the master. If Javad's only concern was involving him in some kind of ceremonial act in which his heart had no share, he would just go and they could forget the whole thing. He finished by declaring that Javad was the person he'd been searching for all his life and that he would accept being initiated only by him.

Both men fell silent after this, and a little while later the official left without either of them saying anything further.

Javad had no idea what to do: the official's request had put him in a difficult position. Although he had responsibility by this time for virtually all of the affairs of the khanaqah, he had never initiated anyone or even considered it before since the master had always been there to perform initiations. Unsure what to do, he stayed up all night, meditating in his room.

Just before dawn, when the master came outside to perform his prayers, Javad went to him and explained about the situation with the Ministry official. The master stood in silence with his head lowered for a long time after Javad had finished. Then he looked up, smiled, and let Javad know that he had been blessed to find such a devoted individual, so detached from external concerns.

"You should be extremely grateful," he went on, "for such people are rare in this world, and he will surely be a sincere disciple and loyal friend." He finished by granting Javad permission to initiate the man whenever he felt it appropriate.

This high-ranking official, whose name was Hasan Kobari, was initiated into the Order by Javad that same week. Not long after, Mr. Kobari resigned his government post, giving up all the power and prestige that went with it, so he would be free to devote himself wholeheartedly to the path and khanaqah. And just as Munes Ali Shah had predicted, Mr. Kobari ended up becoming Javad's loyal friend and most devoted disciple, an honored position he would maintain until his death in 1978.

Among the many darvishes Javad had befriended since coming to Tehran were a number of *qalandars*—wandering darvishes with no home and few, if any, possessions—most of whom were not even members of the Nimatullahi Order. These darvishes came to him when they were in need or trouble because they knew that no matter what their difficulty he would always be willing to befriend them in whatever way he could, without ever questioning their motives or passing judgment on them.

One of these *qalandars*, a man who Javad had helped a number of times in the past, was named Haji Mohammad Jafar Kermani. It came as no surprise to Javad, therefore, when he was awoken one night by the sound of someone knocking on the khanaqah door and found Haji Mohammad there in an extremely agitated state.

Javad welcomed the *qalandar*, despite the late hour, and took him to his room. Once there, Haji Mohammad calmed down enough to explain his problem. After hearing him out, Javad instructed his friend to spend the night in his room and not to worry. Then, ignoring how late it was, he left to attend to the matter.

A few hours later, Javad returned to the khanaqah and let Haji Mohammad know that by God's grace his problem had been resolved and everything would be all right. They then sat together on the floor and shared a simple breakfast of tea, bread, and cheese.

Just as Javad was about to pour Haji Mohammad a second glass of tea, the master happened to stop by to consult with him about some urgent business. Upon seeing the *qalandar* there, however, the master immediately excused himself and left. To him, *qalandars* were people who had no sense of responsibility, who only imposed upon others without any thought of the trouble they were causing. He felt strongly that all darvishes should have an occupation and be of service to the society in which they lived, so to him *qalandars* had no place in the khanaqah. On more than one occasion, Munes had expressed his displeasure about Javad's practice of letting such darvishes into the khanaqah. But Javad considered Haji Mohammad an honorable man and couldn't bring himself to refuse his friend.

Knowing that the master had left only because of Haji Mohammad's presence, Javad excused himself and went to the master's room to see what he wanted. There, the master informed him that the printer of the books published by the khanaqah had called to say that he was on his way to deliver their most recent publication, a collection of Munes' poetry. Since they owed the printer 500 *tomans*, he instructed Javad to go to the bank and withdraw the money from the khanaqah's account.

There was only one trouble. Javad knew that less than 50 *tomans* were left in the account. However much he wanted to avoid disappointing the master, he had no choice but to tell him the truth. After letting Munes know about the shortage of funds, he admitted that he didn't think he could raise that much money on such short notice. Since nothing remained to be said or done, Javad excused himself and returned to his guest.

Haji Mohammad sensed something was wrong the moment Javad stepped into the room. What had happened, he wanted to know. Javad assured his friend that the situation had nothing to do with him and that there was nothing he could do to help. Haji Mohammad was insistent, though, saying he wished to share in his friend's problem, whatever it was—especially since Javad had been so helpful in taking care of his problem earlier.

Javad finally relented and let his friend know about the book and the khanaqah's lack of funds. With this, Haji Mohammad lowered his head in meditation. Then, after a few minutes, to Javad's astonishment, he suddenly burst out laughing.

Javad stared at his guest and wondered if he had lost his mind. Without saying anything, Haji Mohammad proceeded to remove his tattered coat and turn it inside out. Without the slightest hesitation, he tore open the lining and pulled out a small package which he handed to Javad.

"This packet contains over 500 *tomans*, money I've saved over all these years to pay for my burial, so I wouldn't be a burden to anyone. But now I realize this is in no way proper for a darvish, for it shows a lack of trust in God. This money has bothered me for a number of years now and finally I see why. You'd be doing me a great service by accepting it now as a gift."

Javad objected strenuously, saying that he couldn't possibly take the money, but Haji Mohammad would not be dissuaded.

"Truly, I will be relieved to get rid of this money. Please give the *tomans* to your master to pay the printer for the books. When the time comes, God will take care of my burial. Besides, what true *qalandar* would ever have such money?" he added with a smile.

Javad was profoundly affected by Haji Mohammad's offer, by his willingness to give up everything he had, all his worldly wealth, for the sake of something that wasn't even his concern. He tried once more to refuse the money, but he knew that Haji Mohammad had already made his decision and would not change his mind.

After excusing himself again, Javad went back to the master's room. He apologized for disturbing the master and then without saying anything further handed him the package with the money.

Upon opening it, Munes was stunned.

"Where did this come from? How could you have managed to get all this money so quickly?"

Javad let the master know that the *tomans*, all of them, were the life savings of Haji Mohammad, his guest.

Munes said nothing for a long time. Then he asked Javad to bring Haji Mohammad to his room so he could thank him personally.

His heart gladdened, Javad returned to his room to tell Haji Mohammad what the master had said. To his surprise, however, when Haji Mohammad heard, he just shook his head slowly back and forth.

"No, I will not talk to your master until after I have been initiated into the Order."

Javad nodded and said he would go to the master immediately to ask if he would initiate Haji Mohammad. If the master agreed, he went on, he would prepare and bring his friend for initiation himself.

"No, you don't understand," the *qalandar* objected. "For many years, I have wandered far from the place where I was born, searching for the Truth. I have been to many cities and sat with many shaikhs and masters. By none of them, though, did I ever wish to be initiated. And now," he went on after a pause, "I do not wish to be initiated by your master either.

"The only way I will be able to visit with your master," he concluded, "is if you, yourself, agree to initiate me. I wasn't going to tell you this, but I had a vision about you in my dreams a few nights ago. Your actions last night in selflessly helping me to solve my problem only reaffirmed my faith in you. This is why I will be initiated solely by you."

Though Javad had received authorization from the master to initiate Mr. Kobari, he had no idea how the master would react to this second request. Perhaps his granting of permission had been only for that one time. He finally decided that for Haji Mohammad's sake he had to find out.

The master listened to Javad's request and then nodded. "Your friend is absolutely right. You were the one to receive him at the khanaqah; you were the one to take care of his difficulty. Thus, you should be the one to initiate him." Munes then instructed Javad to bring his *qalandar* friend back there afterwards so they could all dine together.

Haji Mohammad was overjoyed when Javad returned to the room and let him know the master's decision, and together the two of them set out for the public baths to perform the required ablutions for the initiation ceremony. Later, back at the khanaqah, Javad would initiate his companion onto the path, a path that he faithfully followed until his death some years later.

Since only a *shaikh al-mashayekh*, a shaikh of all shaikhs, has authority to initiate seekers in a khanaqah where the master is present, Munes Ali Shah's authorization of Javad to perform these two initiations was a clear indication of the position that he now held in the Order in the master's eyes.

"I'm sorry to disturb you so late, Javad, but I think you better come to the master's room. He's having some trouble."

Javad could tell from the look on the face of the darvish standing in the doorway that it was something serious. Munes had been suffering from prostate trouble for some time and Javad suspected that it was acting up.

Sure enough, when he got to the master's room, Javad discovered that Munes had been unable to urinate for a dangerously long time. He knew this meant there had to be some kind of blockage which was potentially life-threatening. Without delay, he began to call every doctor he or the few other darvishes there could think of, but being so late at night, none of the doctors they were able to reach would agree to come to the khanaqah.

Javad returned to the master's room and examined him again. He became convinced from this examination that the situation needed to be attended to immediately. Though only in his fourth year of medical school, he saw no other choice: he would have to do the procedure himself. Without hesitation, he set out for a hospital near the khanaqah where he was well-known to borrow the necessary instruments. At the hospital, he managed to gather together what he needed and after disinfecting everything returned to the khanaqah.

Back in the master's room, Javad explained that he had to insert a shunt to release the blocked urine, and Munes agreed. He then performed the procedure, which he managed to complete without any complications. A small amount of blood had been spilled during the procedure, but Javad knew this was normal and didn't worry about it.

The next morning, a number of the elder darvishes, who considered themselves the advanced on the path, arrived at the khanaqah, having heard that something had happened to the master the previous night. They immediately went to Munes' room where he recounted the story, mentioning that he had shed some blood.

Most of these darvishes had grown so jealous of this young Kermani darvish who had become so close to the master and been given so much authority that they were ready to seize any opportunity to make trouble for him. Seeing such an opportunity now, they began to suggest to Munes that Javad must have cut some kind of hole in him and might even have been trying to kill him.

Munes, still not feeling well, lay in his bed and said nothing. The darvishes, seeing he was tired, left to let him rest. Outside, they began talking among themselves, and decided that they should get a real doctor to come check the master to find out what had been done. They would learn the truth, they swore, and perhaps with any luck be rid of this young darvish who'd been such a thorn in their sides.

When the doctor arrived at the khanaqah, he was met by the group of elder darvishes who let him know what had happened the previous night, including their suspicions about Javad. Then they summoned Javad so he would be with them when they took the doctor to see the master.

The doctor examined Munes carefully. At the end of his examination, he rose, slowly removed his glasses, and stared at the darvishes.

"What kind of sufis are you?" he finally asked them with disbelief. "If it weren't for this young man helping your master last night, he might well have died. You should be thanking him, not accusing him of trying to do harm to your master."

Munes Ali Shah just stared at the darvishes without saying anything.

Shortly after this, though, he began to refer playfully to Javad as "Dr. Nurbakhsh," a practice everyone in the khanaqah soon took up.

5.

FORTY-DAY RETREAT

DR. NURBAKHSH'S final year of medical school, his most important one academically, was soon to begin. A few weeks before registration, he was working in the khanaqah library as usual when one of the darvishes came in to let him know the master wished to see him right away. After locking up the library, he walked downstairs and quickly made his way to the master's room.

"I am on my way to the Kermanshah khanaqah to take care of some business," the master informed him, "and I have decided to honor your request to perform a *cheleh*. But the proper place for this *cheleh* is Kermanshah, not Tehran. We leave in the morning. Can you be ready?"

For months, Dr. Nurbakhsh had been preparing for this *cheleh*, a forty-day retreat during which one remained completely isolated from the world, eating and drinking as little as possible, focusing as fully as possible on God at every moment. *Chelehs* had been a traditional part of the Nimatullahi Order for centuries, and Munes Ali Shah had performed a number of such retreats himself under the guidance of Wafa Ali Shah, his father and the master of the Order at the time.

However, when Dr. Nurbakhsh had first approached the master with the intention of undergoing a *cheleh*, to his surprise the master had been hesitant to agree.

"Your everyday life," the master had objected, "consists entirely of service to humanity, which is what truly matters on the path. Being responsible for all the affairs of the Tehran khanaqah, both material and spiritual, while still maintaining your medical studies, far surpasses the difficulty of any retreat. I know of no one but you who would be capable of bearing so much responsibility."

The master had ended by telling Dr. Nurbakhsh he would consider his request but that he had to wait for the right time.

And now, it seemed, that time had come.

Dr. Nurbakhsh nodded in response to Munes' question and replied that he was ready to leave immediately if this was what the master wished. That the registration period for his final year of medical school was soon approaching didn't concern him at all.

The master assured him with a smile that the following day would be soon enough.

Upon their arrival in Kermanshah, Dr. Nurbakhsh went to the master and informed him that he planned to perform the *cheleh* while observing the strictest rules and manners, the same ones that had been prescribed in the 14th century by Shah Nimatullah himself. The master suggested that something a little less severe might be better suited to a first *cheleh*, but Dr. Nurbakhsh was adamant and showed the master how he had organized step by step what would be involved.

After hearing Dr. Nurbakhsh out, Munes objected that he couldn't possibly authorize such a *cheleh* because he himself had never received these instructions from his own master, adding that he didn't know what would happen. To be blunt, he admitted, he feared that Dr. Nurbakhsh

Dr. Nurbakhsh on a trip to Kermanshah following the death of Munes Ali Shah

Dr. Nurbakhsh, master of the Nimatullahi Order, at 31 years old

might even go completely mad if he carried out such a *cheleh*, especially fasting each day the way he planned, and would end up wandering in the desert for the rest of his life.

Dr. Nurbakhsh assured the master that he could handle such an arduous *cheleh* and volunteered to take all responsibility for it himself. Munes then suggested that he might at least eat some meat when he broke his fast each day, but Dr. Nurbakhsh insisted that he would eat only a little bread or rice, sometimes with a few vegetables.

With great reluctance, but well aware of Dr. Nurbakhsh's resolve, Munes Ali Shah relented and agreed.

For forty days, Dr. Nurbakhsh maintained his retreat according to the strict rules laid out centuries earlier by Shah Nimatullah, secluded for the most part in a room less than six feet by six feet in size. News of Dr. Nurbakhsh's austere retreat had spread quickly among the darvishes throughout Kermanshah, even to those of other Orders. On the next to the last day of the *cheleh*, a darvish from the Ahl-e Haq Order arrived at the khanaqah in Kermanshah. The darvish had come on behalf of his master to invite Dr. Nurbakhsh to a special ceremony at which a vocal *zekr* would be performed, the culmination of a traditional three day fast performed annually by the darvishes of that Order.

The following day, Munes Ali Shah arranged for a celebration at the Kermanshah khanaqah in honor of Dr. Nurbakhsh's completion of the *cheleh*, a celebration to which virtually all of the Nimatullahi darvishes in Kermanshah came. The day after, Dr. Nurbakhsh set out for the town of Sahna where the Ahl-e Haq darvishes were holding their *sama* ceremony. As it turned out, he was the only person outside of the Ahl-e Haq Order ever to have been invited to this ceremony, and since that time the Nimatullahi and Ahl-e Haq Orders have always maintained a close relationship.

Two months passed before Munes Ali Shah finally decided to leave

JEFFREY ROTHSCHILD

Kermanshah and return to the Tehran khanaqah. By that time, of course, the registration period for medical school had long since passed. When Dr. Nurbakhsh approached University officials about registering for his final year of medical school, he was informed that due to his failure to register on time he had no choice but to wait until the following year to complete his degree—providing, that is, he had an adequate reason for missing registration.

Dr. Nurbakhsh accepted this decision calmly, knowing that whatever happens on the path is for the good of the traveler, and returned to the khanaqah determined to use this extra year to continue his study of classical sufi works. A few days later, the master noticed that instead of attending the University each day, Dr. Nurbakhsh was staying in the khanaqah library all day. That evening, he called Dr. Nurbakhsh to his room and asked why he was no longer going to the University. Confronted by such a direct question, Dr. Nurbakhsh had to tell the master what had happened.

The only reason he'd chosen to get a medical degree in the first place, he explained, was because it took a year more than any other degree and would allow him to serve the master for the longest time. But through God's grace that period had been extended yet another year since he'd been unable to register on time for his final year of medical school, having been in the master's service in Kermanshah. He concluded by letting the master know what the University officials had said about reapplying the following year and how they would then decide whether to readmit him.

The master gazed at his disciple without saying anything. Then he stood and left the room. Outside, he paused and, shaking his head in wonderment, turned to the small group of darvishes who stood there awaiting him.

"This young Kermani shaikh is very different from the other darvishes," he told them. "In but a short time, he has become as ripe as aged wine. Those of you who are truly serious about the path would do well to pay heed to him, to try to emulate him as much as possible."

As it turned out, Dr. Nurbakhsh was indeed granted permission to reenter medical school at the start of the next school year and successfully completed his final year without any further difficulty. That summer, seven years after arriving in Tehran, he was at last awarded his medical degree from the University, in the words of Munes Ali Shah simultaneously completing "not only the worldly but the spiritual university as well."

As Dr. Nurbakhsh would later explain in a speech delivered at the Sorbonne University:

> One can liken the journey within the *haqiqat*, within the Truth, to training in a divine university—known in Sufism as the 'tavern of ruin'. In this true center for higher education, there are no professors, one's only guide being Absolute Love. Here one's only teacher is Love, one's books are Love, and one's entire being is Love. Before a perfect being enters this university, he or she can be defined. However, upon entering the Truth, one is indefinable, beyond the realm of mere words. As Rumi has said, 'Footprints but come to the Ocean's shore: therein no trace remains.'
>
> (*In the Tavern of Ruin: Seven Essays on Sufism*, p.11)

The usual practice of the Nimatullahi Order had always been *zekr* of the heart, or silent *zekr*. Every so often, though, a ceremony would be held in the khanaqah during which the darvishes would perform a vocal *zekr*. One night, after such a ceremony, Dr. Nurbakhsh happened to be sitting in his room with Mr. Kobari when one of the elder darvishes who especially resented this "upstart" young shaikh began to pray out loud. At the end of his prayers, the darvish then beseeched God to please make it possible for Javad Nurbakhsh to die while still young. In response, a few of the other elder darvishes, the same ones who for years had been trying to no avail to create a rift between Dr. Nurbakhsh and the master, uttered "amen."

Off in his room, Dr. Nurbakhsh heard this and looked up. "Amen," he uttered, echoing the other darvishes. Shocked, Mr. Kobari turned to him and said, "Don't you know they're talking about you, wishing for your death?"

Dr. Nurbakhsh nodded but explained that since these were prayers in the khanaqah, delivered after a vocal *zekr*, the least he could do as shaikh was bless the prayers and say "amen" as well. And with this, he burst out laughing.

6.

RETURN TO KERMAN

SHIRAZ HAD been the center of the Nimatullahi Order for decades in the eighteenth century. It was also the home of the great Persian sufi poet Hafez, and the city where Munes Ali Shah had grown up—a city of beautiful gardens, aqua-blue fountains, and numerous holy tombs and shrines.

Shortly after Dr. Nurbakhsh's graduation from medical school, the master decided to return to Shiraz for a visit. Though he didn't take Dr. Nurbakhsh with him, a few weeks after his departure, he sent a telegram to the Tehran khanaqah summoning him to Shiraz. Upon receiving the telegram, Dr. Nurbakhsh packed a bag and had one of the darvishes drive him to the bus station. Once the darvish made sure Dr. Nurbakhsh had safely boarded the bus, he telephoned the master at the Shiraz khanaqah to let him know that the shaikh was on his way.

The master then ordered a number of darvishes to go later to the outskirts of the city to meet the bus and welcome the shaikh of the Tehran khanqah. Though none of them knew Dr. Nurbakhsh personally, they had all heard a great deal about him from the master and other darvishes, and they were anxious to meet the shaikh who had performed such an impressive feat as his forty-day retreat.

The darvishes had been waiting for over an hour when they finally saw the dust of the bus in the distance. Stepping out onto the road, they signaled for the driver to stop. With apologies, they explained the situation to the driver who agreed to let them on the bus to look for their companion. Since none of them knew what he looked like, however, they were unable to tell which passenger was Dr. Nurbakhsh. Thus, they began asking every man on the bus who looked about the right age if he was "Dr. Nurbakhsh."

When they eventually got to the shaikh, who was sitting towards the back of the bus, he smiled and politely told them that he didn't know any "Dr. Nurbakhsh," especially one who would warrant such attention. Unsuccessful in their efforts to locate the shaikh, the darvishes returned with disappointment to the khanaqah to let the master know what had happened.

Once the bus arrived in Shiraz, Dr. Nurbakhsh decided to set out for the main cemetery of the city where he was sure he would find an old friend of his, a *qalandar* named Darvish-Farzi for whom external achievement and reputation were meaningless. Dr. Nurbakhsh spent the night in the cemetery with this wandering darvish, then set out for the khanaqah in the morning, his unspoken message being that he was "no one" and did not wish to be accorded any special treatment. Sufism, for him, was meant to be simple and straightforward, not a matter of ceremony and outward display.

Later, in the master's room, Dr. Nurbakhsh learned why Munes Ali Shah had sent for him. Now that he had completed his medical degree, the master informed him, he was to return to Kerman to practice medicine there as a way of serving the people with whom he had grown up.

The province of Kerman had always served as an important center for the Nimatullahi Order, being the burial place of Shah Nimatullah Wali and numerous other masters of the path, and Munes assured Dr. Nurbakhsh that he would benefit greatly from his stay there, just as the people of Kerman would benefit from his presence.

Dr. Nurbakhsh gladly accepted this news and prepared to leave right away.

The letter had come for Dr. Nurbakhsh shortly after his return to Kerman.

His original plan had been to set up his own medical practice in the city of Kerman. But the letter changed all that. It came from the director of the only hospital in Bam, a town not far from the city of Kerman. He had heard about Dr. Nurbakhsh's return home and was writing to offer him a position as his assistant director. The director explained in the letter that he'd already made plans to perform the pilgrimage to Mecca and desperately needed someone to run the hospital in his absence. He begged Dr. Nurbakhsh to accept, pleading that he knew of no one else who could handle the position.

Not wishing to disappoint the director and having no set plans, Dr. Nurbakhsh decided to accept the man's offer and left for Bam a few days later. It was dark by the time he arrived, so he decided to spend the night at the home of a darvish he had known and respected for years. In the morning, accompanied by the darvish, Dr. Nurbakhsh traveled to the hospital where he waited among the patients for his appointment with the director of the hospital. A long time passed before he was eventually shown into the proper office. The director, unaware of who Dr. Nurbakhsh was and thinking him a new patient, proceeded to inquire about his illness. Without saying anything, Dr. Nurbakhsh reached into his coat pocket, removed a letter of introduction that had been given to him by the head of the medical school in Tehran, and handed it to the director.

After he had read the letter, the director glanced up over his glasses and this time took a careful look at the man sitting before him with his disheveled hair, unshaven face, and ill-fitting clothes. The director obviously couldn't believe that this person was the doctor to whom he was supposed to turn over his hospital. Looking down, he read the letter a second time and then a third time before finally accepting the reality of the situation. At that point, he stood and shook Dr. Nurbakhsh's hand, welcoming him to the hospital. He proceeded to explain that regulations required him to take his replacement to the mayor of the city to be approved.

As tactfully as he could, he suggested that Dr. Nurbakhsh might therefore wish to take a bath, shave, and change his clothes before the visit. Dr. Nurbakhsh replied that the only clothes he had were the ones he was wearing, the rest being shipped with his other things from Tehran, and that he didn't have enough money left to go to the public baths. Embarrassed, the director changed the subject by asking Dr. Nurbakhsh where he was staying. He only became more embarrassed and shocked, however, when his replacement informed him that he was staying with an old friend, a *qalandar* who lived in the poorest section of town. This was too much for the director who insisted that Dr. Nurbakhsh stay in the hospital until he could find a suitable place of his own.

At the mayor's office, Dr. Nurbakhsh's reception wasn't much more auspicious. The moment the mayor set eyes upon him, he decided that this disheveled man couldn't possibly be of any importance and promptly ignored him, beginning a discussion with the director of the hospital about some other matter entirely. In the middle of their discussion, there was a knock on the door and a highly respected and well-to-do resident of Bam was shown into the mayor's office.

As soon as the man noticed Dr. Nurbakhsh sitting in the back of the room, he rushed over to him, ignoring both the mayor and the director of the hospital, and beseeched the shaikh for permission to kiss his hand. Both the mayor and director were shocked and thoroughly confused by the man's actions. Seeing their confusion, he apologized for ignoring them and explained the spiritual position held by the unkempt, humble man in the back of the office.

With this, the mayor offered his sincerest apologies to Dr. Nurbakhsh for slighting him and begged his forgiveness. Dr. Nurbakhsh just
smiled and told the mayor there was no problem. Then he excused himself and returned to the hospital with the much-relieved director to assume his new position.

If any of the darvishes in the Order had the idea that the master had sent
Dr. Nurbakhsh to Kerman out of displeasure with him, they were soon
dispelled of this misconception by the letter Munes sent to him shortly
after his departure from Tehran. This letter, which was addressed to all
the darvishes of the Order in the southern part of Iran, bestowed upon
Dr. Nurbakhsh the responsibility for the spiritual affairs of the entire
province encompassing Kerman and Baluchistan.

In the letter, he referred to Dr. Nurbakhsh as "the substance of sincerity and purity" and went on to point out that "in both natural science and
philosophy, he has attained the highest degrees, at the same time practic-
ing physical austerities and night vigils far beyond what his body could
be expected to endure. Most important of all," he concluded, "with God's
grace and approval, Dr. Nurbakhsh has attained divine ethics. Indeed, it
can in fact be said that he is extraordinary, even unique, in this day and
age."

As Munes Ali Shah intended, this letter was read by all the darvishes
in that area and eventually by most of the darvishes in the Order, clearly
indicating that Dr. Nurbakhsh was to be his eventual successor. On a
number of occasions after that, when asked about who his successor would
be, Munes responded by saying that he knew of no one except Dr. Nurbakhsh who would be capable of carrying such a heavy load. He also
stressed that in the present day and age, with more and more people
becoming familiar with scientific knowledge, the master would have to
be someone who understood such things, who could deal with others on
this basis, and no one was better suited for that task than Dr. Nurbakhsh.

While the idea of Dr. Nurbakhsh becoming master pleased the younger
generation of Nimatullahi darvishes, those among the older generation

who had long resented him found it increasingly difficult to accept this decision, so much so that Munes felt it necessary to warn Dr. Nurbakhsh at what was to be one of their last meetings that he had many ambitious enemies who wished him ill, a fact of which Dr. Nurbakhsh was already well aware.

7.

Master of the Nimatullahi Order

The morning of June 14, 1953, Dr. Nurbakhsh received a phone-call from Tehran: Munes Ali Shah, honored master of the Nimatullahi Order, had passed from this world a short while earlier.

Dr. Nurbakhsh's first act was to send telegrams to the shaikhs of the Order informing them of the master's death and of Munes' authorization of Dr. Nurbakhsh to assume the position of master. News of the master's death spread quickly among the darvishes of the Order, and soon a number of them set out for Bam to renew their initiation vows with the new master.

Three days later, a memorial service was held in Bam at which Dr. Nurbakhsh delivered the eulogy, his first public act as master. That evening, upon arriving home, he found one of the local villagers outside waiting for him. After the man had greeted the doctor and paid his respects, he told him that he'd come to get help for his daughter who had fallen ill. Although he knew about the death of the doctor's master, he went on, he nevertheless hadn't lost hope that the doctor would be willing to help him, so he had remained by the door waiting, trusting in God.

Though Dr. Nurbakhsh was totally exhausted from the turmoil of the past three days, he told the man to begin walking home, explaining that he had some business to take care of first but that he would then ride his bicycle and catch up to him. Overcome with gratitude, the man kissed the doctor's hand and left for home, his heart eased.

Inside the house, Dr. Nurbakhsh washed up and changed his clothes. Just as he was about to leave to attend to his patient, a group of darvishes from Mahan and Kerman arrived at the house. Tired and in a distraught state, they had come to be consoled by the new master and to renew their initiation vows with him. Seeing Dr. Nurbakhsh with his bicycle, however, about to depart, they became bewildered, for the tradition had always been for the new master to stay home for a few days to receive those who wanted to come pay their respects and express their sympathies. Thus, they could not understand why he would be leaving, especially so late at night.

Dr. Nurbakhsh greeted the darvishes warmly and showed them into the house, where he served them tea and some food and made sure they would be comfortable in his absence. He then explained that he knew they were confused and troubled by his leaving, but that he had to attend to a patient who was in need. As a doctor, he could not neglect the people who came to him for help, often as a last resort. The first duty of the darvish in the world, he reminded them, is to help God's creatures with no thought of oneself or of reward or gain. But he promised that he would try to get back as soon as possible.

By the time Dr. Nurbakhsh returned home a few hours later, yet another group of darvishes, this one from Zahedan, had shown up to see him. Nimatullahi darvishes from all over Iran were inundating him with telegrams, expressing their loyalty. Some asked for permission to come to Bam to renew their initiation vows; others, upon learning of the master's death, simply set out for Bam, like the ones who'd just arrived.

The next morning, Dr. Nurbakhsh sent off another telegram informing the darvishes that he was on his way to Tehran to arrange for the
traditional memorial service performed on the fortieth day after the
master's death, and that from there he would travel to Kermanshah where
the master's tomb would be located. He asked all the darvishes to remain
in their own cities and promised to visit as many of them as possible after
his trip to Kermanshah, adding that he would send shaikhs to those cities he couldn't visit so that the darvishes there would also be able to
renew their initiation vows.

Shortly after Dr. Nurbakhsh's arrival back in Tehran, a special ceremony
was held with all the shaikhs of the Order during which a document was
read aloud attesting to the fact that Dr. Nurbakhsh was the sole successor to Munes Ali Shah and the rightful master of the Nimatullahi Order.
Each of the shaikhs was then asked to sign the document. Once they had
done so, the master called a handful of the men into his room and informed them that it was no longer appropriate for them to hold the
position of shaikh in the Order. He knew that once he took away their
position in the Order these men would try to stir up trouble, but since all
of them had signed the document acknowledging him as master, there
would be little they could do, at least openly.

Dr. Nurbakhsh's removal of these shaikhs, most of whom were more
concerned with the externals of Islam and outward shows of piety than
with the inner path, constituted but the first step in his efforts as master
to restore the spirit of Bayazid, Abu Said Abu Khayr, and Abu Hasan
Kharaqani to Sufism and free it from its domination by fanatical, exo-
teric mullas.

Back in the fourteenth century, Shah Nimatullah had revived the
tariqat (sufi path) in Iran, awakening numerous disciples all over the
country who he then guided in the integration of such inner practices as
"purgation of the self" and "purification of the heart" with an outer code
of humane ethics and service to society. After Shah Nimatullah's death
in 1431, his son, Burhan al-din Khalilullah, moved the center of the

JEFFREY ROTHSCHILD

Nimatullahi Order to the Deccan in India where it remained for over 300 years. During this time, the people of Iran came to pay less and less attention to spirituality, and Sufism in Iran declined to the point that only a few sufi Orders remained, none with more than a small number of followers.

Then, in 1775 A.D., the master of the Order at that time (Reza Ali Shah) directed his most advanced disciple, Masum Ali Shah, to return to Iran and reestablish the Nimatullahi Order there in an effort to awaken a sense of spirituality among the Iranian people again.

Through Masum and his closest disciples—Nur Ali Shah (who would eventually succeed him as master of the Order), Fayz Ali Shah (Nur Ali Shah's father and an important shaikh of the Nurbakhsheyye Order before his initiation by Masum into the Nimatullahi Order), and Mushtaq Ali Shah (a noted musician of the period), numerous people throughout Iran were initiated onto the sufi path. Everywhere they traveled—Shiraz, Isfahan, Kerman, Kermanshah—Masum and his companions attracted hundreds and sometimes thousands of followers, leading to a flowering of interest in the sufi path.

The orthodox clergy (*ulama*), however, could not tolerate the growing number of darvishes with its implicit threat to their power and control. Sufism brought with it a freedom in the pursuit of Islam that the orthodox clergy took as a challenge to their authority. Therefore, in their own minds, they had no choice but to destroy it or at least severely limit its development. They did so by harassing and eventually eliminating the most charismatic of the Nimatullahi masters and shaikhs.

Masum Ali Shah, for example, was banished unceremoniously from a number of cities in Iran such as Shiraz and Isfahan. After being expelled from the latter, he made his way to Khurasan along with Nur Ali Shah and a few devoted disciples. Outside a small village between Isfahan and Kashan, the travelers stopped to rest and Masum meditated for a long time. When he finally raised his head, he declared, "The police captain in Isfahan has not yet finished bothering us. A few of our body parts still have to be cut off. Anyone wishing to save himself should leave now." Upon hearing this, all of Masum's companions departed except for Nur

Ali Shah. Shortly afterwards, two guards sent by the governor of Isfahan galloped up, seized the two sufis, and cut off their ears as proof of their capture.

Eventually, Masum and Nur Ali Shah made their way to Najaf and then Karbala in Iraq. Then, while on a pilgrimage to the tomb of Imam Reza in Mashad, Masum was arrested, imprisoned, and finally executed. Later, Nur Ali Shah (who had succeeded Masum as master of the Order) and his companion Mushtaq Ali Shah were also expelled from a number of cities. In 1791, on a visit to Kerman, Mushtaq was martyred outside a mosque after the chief Imam there issued a *fatwa* authorizing his execution and exorted the congregation to stone him to death as an infidel.

Nur Ali Shah fled to Shiraz after this but was soon forced to leave the country for Karbala. The King of Iran at the time, however, brought pressure on the governor of Karbala to expel Nur Ali Shah who then set out on the pilgrimage to Mecca, a journey on which he was to die while passing through the city of Musul in Iraq.

With the deaths of Masum Ali Shah, Mushtaq Ali Shah, and Nur Ali Shah, the flowering of the Nimatullahi Order that had followed its return to Iran came to an end, and the spiritual path of Sufism once again began to stagnate under the constricting control exerted by the orthodox clergy.

Dr. Nurbakhsh's aim after becoming master of the Order was no less than the revival of the intensity of aspiration and love that had been reawakened by Masum Ali Shah and Nur Ali Shah in the eighteenth century and that had originally characterized the sufi path back in the tenth and eleventh centuries. Following the example of Shah Nimatullah, Dr. Nurbakhsh set down for the first time in centuries a code of behavior (*adab*) to be observed by all Nimatullahi darvishes, wherever they lived, emphasizing selfless service to society and the cultivation of truly humane ethics. As part of his efforts to free Sufism from any pretense or outward displays of piety, he called for the wearing of traditional clothes rather than any special costume and required each darvish to have a job in the world so as to contribute to society, seldom initiating anyone who did not. In the same spirit, he also forbade the use of drugs such as opium and hashish in the khanaqah, which until then had been common, and banned the practice of forty-day retreats and seclusion from society.

To return Sufism to its true roots in the tenth century, Dr. Nurbakhsh knew, he would first have to bring it into the twentieth century: and his work had just begun.

8.

THE PRESENT–INTERVIEW
AT THE OLD WINDMILL

FOR ALMOST a decade now, the Old Windmill has been the home of the master. Located in the county of Oxfordshire, the Old Windmill consists of twenty acres of land covered with hundreds of apple trees, a large variety of flowers and plants, and various animals including a peacock, two cats, and a watch dog. Its name comes from the stone tower attached to the main building, a structure that once functioned as a working windmill but now bears a greater resemblance to Martello Tower in James Joyce's *Ulysses*.

Inside this main building, on the ground floor facing the entrance to the Old Windmill, is the sitting room where Dr. Nurbakhsh spends most of his time. There isn't much furniture in the room, a good thing given how small it is. A bed, upon which the master sits or reclines when here, stands in the far left corner of the room. Behind it is an enormous glass picture window. In front of the bed is a small desk at which the master can usually be found working on his latest book or project. Directly opposite this desk is the only chair in the room, probably a concession to the various non-darvishes who come to see him since the darvishes themselves almost always sit cross-legged on the floor when there. On the opposite side of the room is a wood-burning fireplace that is often blazing away except during warm summer months.

All over the walls of the sitting room—which is almost always filled with flowers whatever the time of year— are various works of art and objects related to spirituality, many of them gifts for the master from the constant visitors who come to see him. Prominent on the wall in back of his bed is a photograph of Munes Ali Shah, along with numerous works of Persian calligraphy. One of these, directly behind him, is a quote declaring, "It was no joke when Bayazid claimed, 'I am safer with one of my repudiators than with one of my own disciples.'"

The interview with Dr. Nurbakhsh took place on a Sunday morning in late December of 1997. There had been a wedding the day before at which he had presided, and he was in a particularly good mood that morning. Acting as a translator during the interview was Dr. Nurbakhsh's eldest son, Alireza.

After checking that the tape recorder was working properly, I glanced over at the master, who nodded, and then began the interview.

Jeffrey Rothschild: Before we get to my questions about Sufism, I'd like to clarify one point from the interviews we did last year.

During our final interview, you described your eldest son by saying, "Alireza holds a doctoral degree in Philosophy from the University of Wisconsin [at Madison] and was trained by me personally. At present, he is shaikh of the London khanaqah and the representative of the Order there. Most of my work, especially the journal *Sufi*, is under his management."

You then made it clear that you had unquestionably chosen Alireza to be your successor as master. Is this correct?

Dr. Nurbakhsh: [answering in English] Yes! It is my will.

JR: That's certainly as clear as possible!

I'd like to move on now to my questions about Sufism if that's all right. [Dr. Nurbakhsh nods in agreement.] I'm sure you've been asked this question any number of times in the past, but for the record: after over 50 years experience in Sufism—as a seeker, disciple, shaikh, and then master, how would you define the sufi path or what it means to be a sufi?

Dr. N: To be a sufi means to be in love with the Truth (*haq*). And for someone to love the Truth—in other words, God—that person has to love all human beings and serve them, regardless of their race, religion, or nationality. At the very minimum, being a sufi means not disturbing or bothering anyone and tolerating without offense other people's disturbances, other people bothering you.

JR: And what is the most important thing a disciple should know or do in following the sufi path?

Dr. N: You must tell yourself the truth. And you must tell the master the truth as well. In other words, sincerity. You should always be sincere.

JR: What, if anything, does Sufism have to contribute to contemporary society or culture?

Dr. N: Contemporary culture is very much focused on materialism, on the love of money and material things. And humanity has completely forgotten the Truth. Sufism can help remind people of the importance of loving and caring for others. By doing so, it can help to create love and peace among the different nationalities of the world.

JR: Shah Nimatullah claimed, "All those whom the saints have rejected, I will accept, and according to their capacity, I will perfect them." You too have said that you will accept those who other sufi masters have turned away. Why is this?

Dr. N: Because if that person is a thief, after being initiated, he'll steal less. If he stabs people, instead of sticking his knife in three centimeters, he'll stick it in only one centimeter, and so forth. And that's enough.

JR: How does Sufism compare to other mystical paths? What makes it different from them?

Dr. N: Most paths would claim, "We are the Truth." We would say that everyone is expressing the Truth—if, that is, they are saying it with sincerity. If they are, then everyone is expressing the Truth...because the Truth is one.

JR: You have said many times, "Be happy, be content," as have a number of other sufi masters. Why is this?

Dr. N: On the gate to Rumi's khanaqah, it is written, "If you don't have a Beloved, seek one; and if you have a Beloved, then be happy and rejoice." If a person genuinely loves the Truth and after seeking has found it, there is no reason for that person *not* to be happy. They have to be happy.

JR: Is religion essential to spirituality?

Dr. N: [answering only after a long pause and then clarifying that he is speaking solely of Sufism] Religion is the beginning stage of the sufi path. When someone advances to the higher stages of the path, then that person knows whether religion is required.

JR: [to Alireza Nurbakhsh] Tell the master if there's anything I ask about that he doesn't want to discuss, he should let me know.

[After hearing the translation of my statement, the master says something to Alireza who laughs loudly and then translates: "The master says not to worry about it; he's far more clever (*nawgalaw*) than you"—at which we all start laughing.]

JR: In your book *Sufism: Meaning, Knowledge, and Unity* (p.12), you quote a passage from Sarraj's *Kitab al-loma* that says, "In a book devoted to the history of Mecca, Mohammad ibn Eshaq relates that before the advent of Islam, when no one was circumambulating the *kaaba*, a man who was a sufi arrived one day from a distant city. He entered that sacred precinct, made the circumambulation, and then went on his way." Does Sufism, in fact, pre-date Islam—as this passage seems to suggest?

Dr. N: Without question, the first time a human being started to contemplate or think about the Truth, that was sufficient to make it a quest for the sufi path.

JR: Between 800 and 1000 A.D., there were an extraordinary number of advanced sufis, such as Bayazid, Hallaj, Shibli, Abu Said Abu Khayr. Why was this? And why never before then or after?

Dr. N: Well, before that time we really don't have much of a historical record of what went on in terms of Sufism. In stories about the pre-Islamic period, there are some references to Sufism, especially in the writings of Firdusi, who was an Iranian poet. Though he himself lived in the Islamic era, his stories are about a period that pre-dates Islam, and he makes a number of references to Sufism. But there's really not much of a historical record.

Alireza Nurbakhsh: And why never afterwards?

Dr. N: The caliphs and mullahs...[Dr. Nurbakhsh interrupts Alireza's translation here, saying in English "not mullahs, but religious leaders, the religious authorities." Alireza corrects himself and then goes on.] The caliphs and religious leaders realized that the democracy and liberty associated with Sufism went against them and were dangerous for them. So they tried very hard to prevent Sufism from developing.

JR: When I was with you in Iran years ago, I once asked in my broken Persian if Bayazid was a *"khayly bozorg"* (very big) sufi, and you told me that "in Sufism, greatness lies in being small, not big." Who were the "smallest" sufis of the past?

Dr. N: A lot of the greatest sufis have been totally unknown to people.

JR: Of the ones we know about then, who were the closest to God?

Dr. N: Whoever was closer to nothingness was closer to God.

JR: [not being able to accept the master's reluctance to answer the question] And who were the ones closest to nothingness?

Dr. N: You'll have to go ask them yourself when you die. [All three of us laugh at this. I am about to give up and go on to the next question when Dr. Nurbakhsh interrupts me.] The most important thing, the known facts, are that the words of Bayazid and Abu Hasan Kharaqani and Abu Said Abu Khayr, as well as their deeds, had a major effect on Sufism and exerted an important influence on succeeding generations.

JR: Sufis believe that everything in the universe is a manifestation of God's Will and that nothing happens contrary to His Will: is this accurate?

Dr. N: You'll have to ask a philosopher.

JR: Well, you have written that "God is pure good." How then do sufis account for all the suffering and horror in the world, all the terrible things that happen to people?

Dr. N: These things all come from human beings themselves and have nothing to do with God. Human beings create this suffering for themselves—because, for the time being, all the nations of the world have put aside God and worship money in His place.

[After Alireza translates the master's answer, the master looks over at me and adds in English, "Now in the world is the time of dollars, not God."]

JR: But why does God let this go on? I suspect that many people turn away from God or come to doubt His existence because they look at the world and see these terrible occurrences and wonder how God could let such things happen.

Dr. N: They don't understand God well enough to ask this kind of question. [after a pause] What seems ugly to us may be beautiful in fact, and what seems beautiful to us may be ugly in fact. In the world of Sufism, though, there is no absolute bad given that everyone is a part of God's creation.

JR: Can you explain or reconcile the two apparently contradictory views of the world in Sufism: one as an empty, illusory place that leads one away from God and the other as a reflection of God's Being. Both of these views, for example, are expressed in your poetry.

Dr. N: The path to God consists of many, many stages, thousands of different stages, and in each one, the sufi will talk about his own state so that it may seem...[Here, Dr. Nurbakhsh interrupts Alireza's translation of his answer and says in English, "Today I speak something; tomorrow I speak something that's not the same." Then he starts laughing.]

JR: On a more serious note, what does it mean to "die before you die"?

Dr. N: It means that you die to your own egocentricity and become alive in God's Being. Because in truth, there is nothing but God.

JR: Speaking of the subject of dying, someone recently asked me this question, and I wasn't able to answer it. So let me ask you: If you don't follow the sufi path, or some spiritual path, in this life, have you missed some kind of "window of opportunity" that you'll never have again? Or do we get another chance after we die?

Dr. N: No, you've lost it completely, forever!

JR: In regard to what happens after we die, what is the difference between someone who does not follow the spiritual path at all, someone who is on the spiritual path sincerely striving but doesn't finish it, and someone who has finished the path?

Dr. N: [answering before Alireza has even had a chance to translate the question] The bird that manages to escape from its own cage, even if it doesn't reach its ultimate destination, has priority over, an advantage over, all those birds who are still captive in their cages.

JR: And can you elaborate on what that advantage is?

Dr. N: The more you're removed or have escaped from ego-consciousness, the closer you are to the Truth (*haq*).

JR: And does everyone end up at the Truth eventually? Do we all end up in the same place?

AN: How could we if…[interrupting himself] All right, I'll ask the master.

[There is a long pause before Dr. Nurbakhsh answers the question.]

Dr. N: All these different individuals don't really exist. All there is…is one Reality.

JR: So individual consciousness doesn't go on after we die? In other words, is there any individual consciousness after death?

Dr. N: The drop of the Ocean when it reaches the Ocean has lost its "dropness." But at the same time, it doesn't lose its "waterness." [Dr. Nurbakhsh begins laughing again here, very loudly.]

JR: You said at a recent conference in London that no Westerner can truly be a sufi. Did you really mean that? And if so, why?

Dr. N: The first principle of Sufism, the most important aspect of it, is being removed from egotism. And when it comes to Westerners, their egos, their egotistical tendencies, are very strong. That's what I meant.

JR: And in other cultures, there's not as much egotism involved?

Dr. N: [nodding] In Eastern cultures, it's much less egotistical.

JR: Hundreds of years ago, a sufi master said, "Sufism was once a reality without a name; now it is a name without a reality." You also have said recently that Sufism no longer exists, that Sufism is dead. Is this in fact so?

Dr. N: If you consider the number of people who are supposed to be sufis, let alone who truly are sufis, in contrast to the whole population of the world, it's just basically nothing. That's why I said it's dead.

JR: Whereas in the past it was different?

Dr. N: Yes.

JR: Will that change? Will we ever go back to the way it was?

Dr. N: Everything is possible.

JR: You have made it clear in any number of places, as have many other sufi masters, that the *nafs* (self) is the biggest, if not the only, barrier veiling us from God. Yet in your book *The Psychology of Sufism*, you quote a passage from a well-known sufi text saying, "The spirit needs the *Boraq* [the horse on which Mohammad made his night journey to God] of the *nafs* on its journey of ascent to the spirit's domain, for it cannot go by foot....the spirit needs the *nafs* in order to reach the limits of the *nafs*, which in turn needs the two characteristics of passion and anger if it desires to travel higher, or indeed, if it seeks to go back down." (pp.33-4)

Clearly then, the *nafs* serves an important function on the path to God and destroying it or "killing" it is not the point....

AN: No, transforming it is the point.

JR: So the *nafs* somehow helps in transforming itself?

Dr. N: It's with the help of the *nafs* and your ambition that you go towards the Truth. But once you reach the Truth, there is no *nafs* left. The truth is like a light in the distance: you want to reach the light, but by the time you get there, you're completely burned away.

JR: In another place in *The Psychology of Sufism*, you talk about there being two different entities beyond the *nafs*: heart and soul. Can you explain the difference between the two of these?

Dr. N: These are not actually "entities" or "places" in a person. Heart and soul are not the locus of something inside you, but rather stages on the sufi path.

JR: And soul is a higher stage than heart, closer to God?

Dr. N: [answering in English] Yes, that's right.

JR: With your permission, I'd like to ask a few questions of a more personal nature now.

[Dr. Nurbakhsh nods.]

JR: When you were a professor at Tehran University and the director of Ruzbeh Hospital, did the people working with you know that you were a sufi master?

Dr. N: They knew about me and knew that for me working there was service to other people.

JR: And did any of your students want to be initiated?

Dr. N: [shaking his head] I tried as much as possible not to mix the two worlds.

JR: For a good part of your life, you've been writing poetry about the sufi path, and most of these poems have been written in traditional Persian verse forms, such as the *ghazal* and *tarjiband*. Lately, though, you have been writing poems in more free forms. Is there some significance to this?

Dr. N: When a sufi whose basic priority is Sufism happens to be a poet, he doesn't decide what kind of poems he'll write. It isn't forced; it comes from God—sometimes in one form, sometimes in another.

JR: To me, your poetry seems to contain the truth of Sufism far more than your prose writings. Is this in fact so?

Dr. N: Poetry is the language of the heart, whereas with prose, the intellect is all mixed up in it too.

JR: You laugh a lot and tell a lot of jokes—often to reveal things it seems. Could you tell one now?

Dr. N: They asked me, "Who is the real sufi?" I said, "He was here, but he left." [Alireza and I both start laughing again.]

JR: One final question and we'll be done. What advice would you give to people about life, not necessarily just darvishes on the path but anyone who might be reading this book?

[Alireza translates my question, but the master answers it in English.]

Dr. N: To love one another and help one another.

Just as I ask this last question, the late morning sun emerges from behind the clouds and light begins to pour down upon me through the glass window behind the master. Then, as he finishes his answer and the interview is over, the sun just as suddenly disappears again behind the clouds.

A fitting end to an interview with the Bestower of Light.

Selected Poems
from the
Divani Nurbakhsh

TRANSLATED BY ALIREZA NURBAKHSH,
HOSAIN KASHANI, AND J.M. ROTHSCHILD

Jeffrey Rothschild

Each Moment, Each Breath, Is a Treasure

Pour us an overflowing goblet, O Cupbearer,
    for the moment should be treasured.
In the unfolding of time and space,
    each moment, each breath, is a treasure.

The revolving of the heavens
    spared no one.
Out of all the toil and boil in the world,
    each moment, each breath, is a treasure.

Fill the goblet with wine,
    for the lover is not anxious
About the passing of time:
    each moment, each breath, is a treasure.

Before the throne of love,
    reason falls silent;
Leave behind all words, all speech:
    each moment, each breath, is a treasure.

This day we will spend
    in revelry and drunkenness,
For by the next, no trace of us will remain:
    each moment, each breath, is a treasure.

The *rendan* at our banquet
    have no care for tomorrow,
Knowing that in the hidden and the revealed,
    each moment, each breath, is a treasure.

Each moment, each breath, that's passed
    with wine and the Beloved,

BESTOWER OF LIGHT

Listen to Nurbakhsh:
    that moment, that breath, is a treasure.

Love's Speech

The speech of love soars beyond words and their meanings;
    love speaks through a different voice, in a different tongue.

My rival challenges me, demanding that I speak of love,
    but for a deaf heart, what answer is there but silence?

He whose heart is aware of the lovers' world
    hears only the whisperings of love and kindness.

Love speaks in a language unknown to ordinary people:
    leave behind their tiresome chatter with all its headaches.

He who denies love will never grasp these words;
    nothing we could say would ever move his ignorant heart.

In the way of loving-kindness, there is no idle talk;
    only the bankrupt chatter behind every door.

Nurbakhsh, from love's breath your speech is eloquent,
    embraced by the heart of every clear-sighted gnostic.

Jeffrey Rothschild

Love's Uproar (Hi-O-Hu)

From the heart of every atom,
    I hear "the Friend, the Friend".
Do not see even the atom,
    for there is nothing but Him.

The whisperings of reason and love
    all come from the breath of a single reed-player.
The intellect debates and engages in idle talk,
    but love seeks the uproar of *Hi-O-Hu*!

The Beloved is in love's market-place,
    searching and seeking,
While the impoverished lover is among the people of the city,
    disgraced for no reason.

I asked the master: if the path to the Truth is one,
    what then are all these decorations?
They are merely window-dressing, he replied,
    for the sake of color and fragrance.

If you wish to behold His face,
    then seek that eye capable of seeing the Truth,
For desire is a fickle vagabond,
    every moment at a different door.

Manifest, the Ocean is called
    bubble or wave;
But in reality all is water,
    whether droplet, stream, or sea.

The Beloved is the Bestower of Light;
    borrow an eye from Him

Bestower of Light

So that you may clearly see
His splendor displayed everywhere.

From Him

All these wondrous forms in the world
are from Him.
This pleasant, embodied imagination
is also from Him.

Eye is from Him, light from Him,
the power of sight is from Him.
Seeing and the seen are from Him;
all vision is from Him.

Decision is from Him, strength from Him;
action too is from Him.
The path is from Him; coming and going,
each departure and each arrival, all are from Him.

Generosity and being are from Him;
cause and effect are from Him.
Joy and grief are from Him;
the wound is from Him, the salve from Him.

Cage and shackles are from Him;
bait and snare are from Him.
The bird is from Him, the garden from Him;
melodies, high-keyed and low, are from Him.

"I" is from Him, home from Him;
service and aspiration are from Him.
Wealth is from Him, the hand from Him;
the warmth of the hearth is from Him.

All of creation subsists through
    the aspiration of love;
The binding of atom with atom and all the particles
    of the universe are from Him.

Nurbakhsh, from whom is this fervent breath of yours?
If you listen, I will tell you: this, too, is from Him.

The Lamp of Love

At the banquet of the soul, wine is forbidden
    for those who are not hung-over and languishing:
This is the recommendation of the Master of the Holy Fire,
    not an absolute decree.

Whoever follows us on feet
    of surrender and contentment
Will not be excused if he finds fault
    with what we do.

To whom should I say this: no one
    truly has the taste for traveling the path,
Though the way of love is easy
    and the goal not far.

Leave behind cleverness and reason;
    be full of yearning:
For lovers, the mysteries of the Captivator of hearts
    do not remain veiled.

Many are near, yet far,
    far away from us;
And many are far away, but near

and not truly separated from us.

In the dark night of multiplicity,
    what guide is there but love?
With the lamp of love,
    night's darkness is never pitch black.

O Nurbakhsh, do not reveal the secrets of the *rendan*
    to the pious ascetics,
For the bows of those captain's ships
    have no light.

At the Tavern's Door

We are here at the door of the tavern,
    awaiting the Beloved's desire.
Our only wish now is to discover
    what that Possessor of hearts desires.

A hundred thanks that from the tarnish of multiplicity
    we have been set free.
Now, in the realm of Unity, we are waiting to see
    what the awakened heart desires.

We want nothing now,
    for we're joyful in the tavern:
So what could this blazing sigh
    in our breast possibly desire?

In our quest for the Beloved,
    our hearts were turned to blood, our souls lost:
That cunning Ravisher of hearts,
    what more can She desire?

JEFFREY ROTHSCHILD

Having abandoned reason, we are drunk
    and have no idea
What these sober intellectuals
    from us drunkards could desire.

If people defame and slander us,
    we're not offended,
Only bewildered by what these unaware, raw ones
    could possibly desire.

Whether light is bestowed or not,
    what does it matter?
We are here at the door of the tavern,
    awaiting the Beloved's desire.

The Material and Spiritual Realms

I am my own veil
    and the destination of my heart.
This pain and suffering afflicting me,
    all of it comes from "I".

Who am I? Nothing.
    Do not bother pondering:
All being is one; it is He
    who makes this point through my mouth.

I tell you openly:
    I have no mouth of my own.
He is my eyes, my ears,
    and all my limbs.

Forget Greek philosophy and all talk
    of the material and spiritual realms:

BESTOWER OF LIGHT

In truth, He is all and always will be,
  not "I".

Who am I? Nothing but a dream,
  an image upon water.
It is only though habit
  that you see me in my body.

He is unveiled, manifest
  in the market-place;
Why then should I, this impoverished one,
  be the legend of my time?

The Truth is the Bestower of Light
  to everyone, everywhere.
It is not my fault if you have not
  understood my words.

Love's Secrets

Gone is the time of separation and sorrow, pain and burning:
The illuminated firmament has become as our heart desires.

Now, in the Friend's realm, we are drunk and contented.
We drink down the dregs at night and by daylight sip wine.

If You still plan to torment me, I tell Him, then speak up.
More hardship and blame are to come, He replies.

All my tears and the scorching sighs of my heart would have
Meant nothing if not for the Beloved's grace and kindness.

Spiritual states and ecstasy gave us not a moment's peace,
As if autumn and summer both were spring.

JEFFREY ROTHSCHILD

Praise the honor of the tavern of ruin,
For out of reverence, both king and rag-mender kiss its threshold!

Silence, Nurbakhsh! Why are you revealing love's secrets?
Where love is, no secrets remain.

The Way of the Mad

O minstrel, tonight I have left far behind
    the mind and all reason.
If you play the melody of madness till morn,
    I am ready.

Sighs of longing, the heart's wail:
    for us, these are the song of Unity.
We have abandoned the self, and now
    dwell far from rosary and prayer rug.

No longer do we deal in the wares
    of faith or infidelity:
On the path of loving-kindness and love,
    we have given away the capital of our self-existence.

If you have heard that I am a *rend*
    and devil-may-care: it's true.
But if you are simple,
    I will be simple with you.

In the vat of the heart, I have felt the agitation
    that comes from love's boiling.
And now, I am more intoxicating
    than even a hundred goblets of wine.

O Nurbakhsh, there is no escape

from the chains of love's madness.
But unshackled from the bonds of the ego,
    at last we are free.

The Name of the Friend

Say always the name of the Friend—slowly, slowly;
    with this alchemy change the copper of the heart to gold—
        slowly, slowly.

Drink the wine of Unity in the tavern of Oneness
    so that "I and you" will be taken from your mind—
        slowly, slowly.

Stamp on the head of existence, empty your hands of both worlds;
    thus will you become a confidant of God's secrets—
        slowly, slowly.

Seek the way from a king with the "wealth of Allah" (Nimatullah),
    and sooner or later he will separate you from yourself—
        slowly, slowly.

In love's district impatience should not exist, for difficulties
    will be made easy by surrender and contentment—
        slowly, slowly.

Thousands of tests lay in store for a sincere lover,
    all so that he will come to know love's secrets—
        slowly, slowly.

The one who strives truly will pass through the stations of the way,
    traveling the road of *baqa* after the road of *fana*—
        slowly, slowly.

In the school of lovers, silence is better than speech;
O Nurbakhsh, this statement was made clear—
slowly, slowly.

Negligence

Blood rains from my eyes, for neither tears nor sighs remain.
How strange that everything has come to depend upon a glance.

These raw imaginings, these incessant thoughts:
all were traps; gone now, they led not to awareness.

To whom can I speak of this negligence: that the nightingale's cry
Is not from desire for the face of the rose? What a grave mistake!

That mouth which spoke and declared, "I am a lover"
Was not sincere in love and to the *qiblih* never arrived.

Put aside clay and water! Sell religion and heart!
Select a beautiful idol of perfect royal splendor.

Sit with lips closed; stay silent! Put aside intellect,
Judgment and awareness: seek not a path!

If anyone offers good news that you have arrived
At a destination, ignore them! Have no hope of it!

By relying this way upon the help of love and drunkenness,
Every moment, not just sometimes, you'll be free of self-worship.

BESTOWER OF LIGHT

Love's Bazaar

Who opens his eyes to see You loses his blindness;
  who finds a place in Your lane becomes placeless.

Your face can be seen through Your eyes only—if at all,
  for what can anyone witness with his own?

O You, source of all hope, yet completely free,
  what else in all the world could anyone desire?

The merchant of love's bazaar is none other than the customer:
  where then is the profit in trying to buy and sell?

We are the veil upon Your face; otherwise,
  You would not be hidden or need to be found.

Let anyone reveal love's secrets, for in Your presence
  neither confidant nor stranger exists.

O Nurbakhsh, we have been in disgrace for Him all our life,
  and now no reason remains to disgrace us more.

The Crazy Intellect

Through love, I have reached a place
  where no trace of love remains,
Where "I and we" and the image of existence
  have all been forgotten in yearning and left behind.

Where I am now, there is no news,
  here where no knowledge, no opinion can be found.
In His station, even love is bewildered
  and the intellect is but a meddler, talking nonsense.

JEFFREY ROTHSCHILD

Totally impoverished, I have no trace,
    no sustenance, no self.
Freed from faithfulness and faithlessness,
    I am a stranger to myself and all acquaintances.

Yet only for this can I still be blamed:
    that out of regret for Nurbakhsh,
A cry comes from me,
    "You have gone; how is it I know not where?"

The Image of Existence

Come, so we can wash away the image of existence
    and no longer speak of "I and we."

Come, and like us let your thoughts pass away;
    forget both worlds and be silent.

Come and avoid the shame of knowing;
    send those endless lines of learning from your head.

Come, so we can leave behind all things that can be said
    and blind our eyes to all there is to see.

Come, we will be strangers to all
    and seem mad in the eyes of rational men.

Come, we will empty ourselves of self
    and leave far behind the shame of "I".

Come, and welcome unfulfillment,
    for we have removed the self's desires from the heart.

Come, and be drowned in the Ocean of Unity,

free from all thought of union and separation.

As this world is not even worth a grain of sand,
other than what is old and new, it is nothing.

The Wine-Drenched

Our hearts aflame with love of God,
We wine-drenched ones have no news of "I and you."

Don't speak to us about the sober;
We're crazy with God, separated from everything else.

Untroubled by thoughts about the reason for this and that,
We have no business with anyone in the two worlds.

We're a sea on which all this refuse lands;
Yet we're never tainted, being an ocean of purity.

Unruffled by good or bad, attached only to the Beloved,
We're waves thrown into a fervor by currents of fidelity.

We're the customer and friend of the Cupbearer of the Winehouse;
We're totally annihilated in the tavern of ruin.

Yet we refuse to turn our gaze from the sun until it bestows light,
And to watch the rising of the moon we climb every roof.

JEFFREY ROTHSCHILD

The Venture of Loving

I've pawned my cloak at the tavern and offered up my heart
  to the One who holds all hearts.

Don't ask me why there's so much of this, so little of that:
  I've left behind what I had, much or little, on the Friend's way.

Don't ask me about reason's arguments for this and that:
  I've left such arguments to those who are sober.

In love's district, no trace of faith or infidelity remains:
  I've left this snare to those who still deal in such goods.

The venture of loving has bankrupt my ego:
  I've left unspent nothing in this endeavor.

You ask who I am...nothing; what I want...nothing.
  I've left my fate in the hands of the Friend.

Last night with Nurbakhsh, I emptied love's cup,
  then pawned him away at the tavern.

The People of Loving-Kindness

We are the people of loving-kindness, guides of one another
  through the purity of love's steps, all helpers of one another.

Though embodied in different bodies, we are a single spirit,
  heart and soul, possessors of the hearts of one another.

We are one people, with no "you and I," only "we,"
  all equals in love, all beloveds of one another.

BESTOWER OF LIGHT

Only we may pass through the veil of the royal pavilion,
    all of us inextricably linked, all sympathizers with one another.

Each of us is pledged in devotion to sacrifice ourself for the other,
    all candles and moths, all roses and rosegardens for one another.

Our circle, without doubt, is a sanctum fostering affection,
    all of us drunk, then sober from one another.

The armies of the self have retreated from us, for we are
    both each other's soldiers and commanders of one another.

Our pain requires no physician or remedy:
    we are both each other's cure and the sickness of one another.

If you call upon one here, all will say "yes,"
    for all have one name, one breath, all striving with one another.

Our abode is a house of love for You, full of passion and music;
    we are melodies, reed-pipes and lutes for one another.

O Nurbakhsh, it is from being free of any ego that we are
    so feverishly caught up in serving and dealing with one another.

JEFFREY ROTHSCHILD

The Talisman of the Self

You usurped and plundered my broken heart,
    and gave me instead
A head broken by the stone of desire.

Thousands have fallen, bloody,
    in the district of union with You,
Heart and soul given up, head and feet all broken.

Love for Your face has summoned me
    to divine Unity,
For it has broken all idols, whether hidden or revealed.

Totally drunk, I broke away
    from being
As if a bubble had burst in the sea.

The Cupbearer has sent me to the tavern,
    for I've lost my cup
And broken my goblet:

Perhaps now I will witness again clearly
    the treasure of the Beloved,
Now that my soul has broken the talisman of the self.

O Nurbakhsh, this world for you has been a dream
    in which all of creation
Lies bewitched and hearts are broken.

BESTOWER OF LIGHT

The Land of "I and You"

I have departed finally from the land of "I and you"
    and now sit awaiting a sidelong glance from the Friend.

A lifetime I've spoken solely to tell love's tale,
    never disturbing so much as an ant in anger.

Having gone through the book of time and space,
    I am left distressed with so-called friends, wearied of strangers.

I've torn up the claim of leadership, of being a spiritual guide;
    I've smashed the mirror of mastership and disciplehood.

Tell all these idol-worshippers of my state, tell them
    I've been freed from being the idol of their imagination as well.

I've erased the traces of events from the slate of my soul
    and severed the bonds of "other than God" from my heart.

Not only have I smashed the fetters of mastership and guidance,
    I've leapt altogether from the very trap of existence itself.

Ever since I departed from the land of "I and you,"
    everywhere, He has been my Bestower of Light.

GLOSSARY

baqa: the beginning of the "journey in God" that follows *fana* and the completion of the spiritual path (*tariqat*).

"Having caused the passing away of the disciple's will, God endows such a slave with His will, so that whatever the slave wills is now the will of the Divine. This *baqa* corresponds to the outer *fana* [see entry for *fana*].

"The *baqa* corresponding to the inner *fana*, however, is one in which the very veils that are the temporary essence and attributes of the disciple's self are removed. Here, God neither veils the creation, nor does the creation veil God. The veil has been totally removed, and duality transformed into Unity." (*In the Paradise of the Sufis*, p.24)

Bayazid Bastami (d.874 or 877 A.D.): one of the most famous of all sufis, known especially for his "ecstatic" utterances. He is generally credited with being the exemplar of the "intoxicated" school of Sufism (as opposed to the "sober" school exemplified by Jonayd).

darvish: a word of Persian origin literally meaning "poor person" or "pauper," which is used by sufis to indicate the spiritual poverty or neediness that they initially feel. Since most early sufis renounced worldly possessions, they were often known by this term, although a sufi does not necessarily have to be poor and not every poor person is of course a sufi.

fana: the passing away of the self in God; the spiritual station that marks the end of the spiritual path, of traveling towards God.

"The outer *fana* is the 'passing away of individual action' (*fana-ye afaal*), with the resulting manifestation of Divine action. The one who reaches this station becomes drowned in the Ocean of Divine Action, so that he perceives in all events the action and will of God, seeing neither himself nor any other individual as the one who does or wills any event. He becomes so completely without will that no trace of willing any individual action remains in him.

"The inner *fana* involves the 'passing away of the attributes of the self' (*fana-ye sefat*) and the 'passing away of the essence of the self' (*fana-ye zat*). Sometimes, in discovery of the Divine Attributes, the possessor of this state becomes drowned in the passing away of his own attributes. At other times, in witnessing the exalted effects of the Divine Essence, he becomes drowned in the passing away of his essence." (*In the Paradise of the Sufis*, p.24)

Hafez (d.1390 A.D.): probably the best-known and most beloved of all Persian poets. The erotic imagery and numerous references to wine in his poetry have led some critics to conclude that he could not have been a sufi.

kaaba: the sacred house of God at Mecca, built by Abraham for the worship of the One God, and place of pilgrimage (*haj*) for Muslims.

khanaqah: the Persian word for the house of God where sufis gather.
"The *khanaqah* is by definition the private quarters and gathering place of the sufis. It is a place where those of spiritual states can assemble, the school of their inner journey towards perfection. The seekers of God come there to polish the mirror of their hearts and remove the rust of attachment." (*In the Tavern of Ruin: Seven Essays on Sufism*, p.65)

Kharaqani, Abu Hasan (d.1034 A.D.): an early sufi master who exerted an important influence on the development of Sufism. His fame within sufi circles is partly the result of Rumi's anecdotes about him in the *Mathnawi* [see Rumi entry].

Khayr, Abu Said Abu (d.1049 A.D.): a very influential early sufi master, generally credited with setting up one of the first khanaqahs. Few of his own works are extant, but he is well-known because of the *Asrar al-tawhid* (*The Mysteries of Unity*), a biography of him written by his great-great grandson.

love: "Temporal love arises from the beauty of transient forms. Like them, it too is transient—its only lasting result being the perpetuation of the species. It is the result of the sublimation and refinement of sexual desire. Real or Divine love, however, is a profusion and a rapture from the Absolute Beloved which descends upon the heart of the sincere lover. This lover is like a moth which flutters around the beauty of the candle that is the Absolute, burning away its relative existence in His fire. The lover turns away from himself and perishes, inclines towards Him and becomes alive. When the lover is emptied of self and becomes nothing, he finds eternal life....

"Sufis believe that the foundation of the created world is love. All motion, activity, and light throughout the entire universe as we know it derive from the rays of love, and true perfection must be sought in and through love." (*In the Tavern of Ruin*, pp.25-6)

master: (*morad*, lit. "the desired one") the person who guides travelers on the path toward the "passing away of the self in God" (*fana fillah*) and leads them toward "eternal life in God" (*baqa billah*).

"The master is the object of God's constant attention, and his being is comprised of the Divine Attributes. He knows the truths of Reality and has polished the tarnish of multiplicity from the mirror of his heart. He has journeyed to the end of the way of spiritual poverty and abandonment of self. He is the guide of the spiritual path and the sun of the Truth. He liberates travelers from the dark night of self-worship, and brings them into the brilliance of that clear daylight which in this world is the paradise of the selfless witnessing of the Divine Truth." (*In the Tavern of Ruin*, p.113)

nafs: a technical sufi term usually translated as "self" or "ego," the transformation of which is one of the basic goals of the sufi path.

"Material nature [the aggregate of psychological faculties with which a human being is endowed] is inherited at birth; it subsequently develops into what is termed *nafs* through its encounter with the environment and its exposure to the socialization process in the milieu of family and school. The tendency of the *nafs* is to impose its desires unquestioningly in order to gratify itself. The particular intellect, however, serves both as a restraining force and counselor with respect to the *nafs*, advising it as to the positive actions it should perform and the negative ones it should avoid.

"In reality, the *nafs* constitutes the ego and its tendencies, while the intellect represents a skillful inspector who attempts to guide the ego in satisfying those tendencies when manifested in society without harming people, channeling the *nafs* into directions that are socially acceptable and, at the same time, beneficial to its state.

"All human beings possess *nafs* and utilize it while functioning in society. While certain people are governed by the intellect, the majority are ruled solely by the *nafs*." (*The Psychology of Sufism*, p.11)

qiblih: the direction in which Muslims face during prayer, towards Mecca and the *kaaba*.

pir-e dalil: (lit., "counselor") the assistant and consultant to a shaikh. Traditionally, his function was to reprimand and correct the darvishes, whereas the shaikh's role was to console them. Among the *pir-e dalil's* most important duties are familiarizing those who seek to be initiated with the meaning, method, and aim of Sufism and instructing them in the proper behavior to be observed during the initiation ceremony and in the sufi gatherings at the khanaqah. [For further information, see "The Rules and Manners of the Khanaqah" in *In the Tavern of Ruin* and "The Rules and Manners of Initiation into the Sufi Path" in *In the Paradise of the Sufis*.]

rend (plural, *rendan*): in ordinary usage, a rogue, reveler, or profligate. In sufi terminology, *rend* refers to a person who conceals his inner state so fully that he may have finished traveling the spiritual path yet still appear to be an ordinary person. The term also signifies the sufi who sees into others' hearts and is never deceived by anyone, and who is the master of his own manifestations such that he can create any appearance he wishes.

JEFFREY ROTHSCHILD

Rumi (d.1273 A.D.): the most famous of all Persian sufis; his poetry has now been translated into numerous English versions, most recently by Robert Bly and Coleman Barks. His most important work is the *Mathnawi*, a lengthy multi-volume poem written in couplet form that provides detailed guidance for followers of the sufi path, the best known translation of which is R.A. Nicholson's three volume edition.

Shah Nimatullah Wali (d.1431 A.D.): the master in whose honor the Nimatullahi Order is named and the author of numerous poems, essays, and treatises on Sufism (especially on the works of the sufi philosopher Ibn Arabi), almost all of which were available only in manuscript form until Dr. Nurbakhsh became master of the Order, edited them, and had them published. Few of his works, however, have been translated into English, outside of excerpts contained in Dr. Nurbakhsh's own translated writings. A biography of Shah Nimatullah, together with a translation of one of his best known longer poems, is included in Dr. Nurbakhsh's *Masters of the Path* (along with biographies of Masum Ali Shah and Nur Ali Shah).

shaikh: the person who is in charge of both the worldly and spiritual affairs of a khanaqah, whose orders are to be unquestioningly and unconditionally obeyed by the darvishes of that khanaqah. [See parenthetical note at the end of the entry for *pir-e dalil.*]

tavern (*mai-khana*)/tavern of ruin *(kharabat)*: the term "tavern" symbolizes "the heart of the perfect sufi" or "the house of the sufi master who has realized union with God." The term "tavern of ruin" alludes to "the station of Unity" and the ruination of the attributes of human nature, the annihilation of all human qualities. [For a more detailed account not only of these terms but of numerous other essential technical sufi terms used in Dr. Nurbakhsh's and other masters' writings, see his 15 volume collection *Sufi Symbolism: The Nurbakhsh Encyclopedia of Sufi Terminology*, as well as his five-volume collection of essays entitled *Sufism*, in which the explanations of such terms offered by various sufi masters throughout history have been compiled and commented upon by Dr. Nurba-khsh.]

zekr: a Name of God transmitted to the disciple in a special manner by the sufi master or shaikh.

"Through the inculcation of *zekr*, the master instructs the disciple how to be in continuous remembrance of the Divine....When the disciple becomes continually involved in the remembrance of God, his being gradually becomes liberated from egotistical and selfish qualities and illuminated by the Divine Attributes and Divine Nature....The *zekr* of the sufis, then, is like a flood that gradually eliminates the self-centered qualities and illuminates the Divine Attributes in the disciple's heart. Ultimately, the very illusion of 'self' also becomes swept away and taken by this flood. This marks the end of the path and the beginning of the Ocean of selflessness." (*In the Paradise of the Sufis*, pp.19-20)

BIBLIOGRAPHY

Mazhari, Ali A. 1994. *Chelley-e Nur.* London: Khaniqahi Nimatullahi Publications (KNP).

Nurbakhsh, Dr. Javad. 1978. *In the Tavern of Ruin: Seven Essays on Sufism.* New York: KNP.

———. 1979. *In the Paradise of the Sufis.* New York: KNP.

———. 1980. *Divani Nurbakhsh: Sufi Poetry.* New York: KNP.

———. 1980. *Masters of the Path: A History of the Nimat-ullahi Sufi Order.* New York: KNP.

———. 1981. *Sufism I: Meaning, Knowledge, and Unity.* New York: KNP.

———. 1986-1998. *Sufi Symbolism: The Nurbakhsh Encyclopedia of Sufi Terminology* (Vols. 1-15). London: KNP.

———. 1992. *The Psychology of Sufism.* London: KNP.

Rumi, Jalaluddin. 1977 (1926). *The Mathnawi of Jalaluddin Rumi.* Translated by Reynold A. Nicholson. London: Luzac & Co.

ABOUT THE AUTHOR

Jeffrey Rothschild has a Ph.D. in English Education from New York University and has taught basic writing at Queensborough Community College in the City University of New York for over fifteen years. In 1976 and 1978, he lived for a number of months in the Tehran khanaqah where Dr. Nurbakhsh then resided. Upon his return from Iran, he helped to found Khanaqah Nimatullahi Publications (now KNP) for which he has edited numerous works. He is at the present time an Assistant Editor of the journal *SUFI* and has been one of its most prolific authors, publishing over two dozen stories and articles in the journal since its inception in 1989.

NIMATULLAHI SUFI ORDER

NORTH AMERICA

306 West 11th Street
New York, New York 10014
U.S.A.
Tel: 212-924-7739

4931 MacArthur Blvd. NW
Washington, D.C. 20007
U.S.A.
Tel: 202-338-4757

84 Pembroke Street
Boston, Massachusetts
02118, U.S.A.
Tel: 617-536-0076

4021 19th Avenue
San Francisco, California
94132 U.S.A.
Tel: 415-586-1313

11019 Arleta Avenue
Mission Hills, Los Angeles,
California 91345, U.S.A.
Tel: 818-365-2226

219 Chace Street
Santa Cruz, California
95060
U.S.A.
Tel: 831-425-8454

310 NE 57th Street
Seattle, Washington 98105
U.S.A.
Tel: 206-527-5018

4642 North Hermitage
Chicago, Illinois 60640
U.S.A.
Tel: 773-561-1616

405 Greg Avenue
Santa Fe, New Mexico
87501
U.S.A.
Tel: 505-983-8500

3018 Felicita Road
Escondido, San Diego CA
92029
U.S.A.
Tel: 760-489-7834

1596 Ouest avenue des Pins
Montreal H3G 1B4
Quebec, Canada
Tel: 514-989-1411

1784 Lawrence Avenue West
North York, Toronto,
Ontario, Canada M6L 1E2
Tel: 416-242-9397

EUROPE

41 Chepstow Place
London W2 4TS,
England
Tel: 0171-229-0769

95 Old Lansdowne Road
West Didsbury, Manchester
M20 8NZ, England
Tel: 0161-434-8857

Kölnerstraße 176
51149 Köln
Germany
Tel: 49-2203-15390

50 rue du Quatrième Zouaves
Rosny-sous-Bois 93110
Paris, France
Tel: 48552809

116, avenue Charles de Gaulle
69160 Tassin-La-Demi-Lune
Lyon, France
Tel: 478-342-016

C/Abedul 11
Madrid 28036
Spain
Tel: 350-2086

Ringvägen 5
17237 Sundbyberg
Sweden
Tel: 46-8983-767

REST OF THE WORLD

87A Mullens St.
Balmain 2041,
Sydney, Australia
Tel: 9555-7546

63 Boulevard Latrille
BP 1224 Abidjan,
CIDEX ,1 Côte d'Ivoire
Tel: 410510

Quartier Beaurivage
BP 1599 Porto-Novo
Bénin
Tel: 229-21-4706

SHOT
IN THE
DARK
ANNA
BRITTON

CANELO CRIME

First published in the United Kingdom in 2023 by

Canelo
Unit 9, 5th Floor
Cargo Works, 1–2 Hatfields
London SE1 9PG
United Kingdom

A CIP catalogue record for this book is available from the British Library.

Print ISBN 978 1 80436 524 3
Ebook ISBN 978 1 80436 525 0

Cover design by Lisa Brewster

Cover images © Depositphotos

Look for more great books at www.canelo.co

Printed and bound in Great Britain by Clays Ltd, Elcograf S.p.A.

1

For John

Run.

Her foot slips on a patch of wet leaves. There's a wrench from her knee to her hip as she slams down onto her hands. She scrambles back to standing. Pain flares with every step, but she cannot stop. She clenches her fists and runs on.

Breathe.

The cold air is harsh against her throat. Trees steal the scant light of the moon, illuminating the forest in sharp shafts. She can hear rough panting behind. She stumbles, imagining it racing over the undergrowth. Nimble on four legs.

Run.

The desperate struggle for each breath becomes mingled with sobs. Her hurried steps shorten. She pauses beside a tree and wipes her face on her sleeve. She shouldn't stop. Every moment she's still, it gets closer.

Climb.

Running is no longer an option. She hauls herself up into the tree, hefts her weight onto the lower branches and reaches again. Steadying herself on her uninjured leg, she climbs higher. Her arms shake, her fingers numb except for the sting where one of her fake nails snapped off. Her palms slip over the rough bark.

Fuck.

The dog crashes into the trunk. Ignoring how her joints twist and ache, she pulls her legs up as it snarls and thrashes. Through the great cloud made by her breath, the dog hurls itself at the tree. It leaps and claws. Dirt and foamy spit coat its white fur. Its bulging eyes are fixed on her, but she has climbed out of reach.

Breathe.

Her legs cramp. She shifts and pain blooms in her thigh. Dipping her fingers into cracks in the wood, she leans her forehead on the bark and resettles her weight. The dog growls, snapping at the lower branches of the tree. She can almost shut it out. She focuses on the pulse of blood in her ears, the hot air whistling over her lips.

Breathe.

The chase is over. The moon is bright, its beams shifting as the wind shuffles the few leaves left on the near naked trees. Sweat cools on her forehead. She shivers and hugs closer to the thick trunk. Frigid air presses into her neck. Her scarf disappeared somewhere during the chase. She needs to call someone, get help, but her limbs are heavy. Her eyelids droop.

Click.

She jerks upright. Pain lances down her leg but she twists, squinting through the forest. Her eyes struggle against the changing light, the natural movement of the trees. She has only heard that sound once before. Blood leaps in her veins. It's not just her and the dog in this forest.

BANG.
BANG.
BANG.

Her arms drop. The tree turns, bark scratching across her face. Her heart lurches as the last of her balance deserts her. Her fall is not gentle. Branches that had been her salvation batter her back and scrape her arms. She thumps into the ground. Twigs crunch, and the dog pants. She cannot run. She closes her eyes as moist breath stutters over her face.

Day 1

Tuesday, 10 October

Call connected at 8:20.

'Yes?'

'Mr Dunlow? It's Karl.'

'What do you want? I'm on my way out.'

'Sorry, but I was checking the grounds this morning and I found a body.'

'What?'

'Sir, I found a—'

'I heard you. A body of?'

'A girl.'

'Good God. Where?'

'Down in the forest, sir. Round on the east side.'

'Christ almighty. Who is it?'

'I don't know. It's hard to tell.'

'How did they die?'

'I think they were shot.'

'Have you called the police?'

'They're on their way, sir.'

'I'll be at the office. Don't give them the number unless they ask.'

Timothy. Sent 8:46.

Come home. Now.

Terence. Sent 8:52.

Hi, Dad. I've booked the hotel for another couple of nights. Can it wait?

Timothy. Sent 8:53.

This isn't a discussion. Come home.

Call connected at 9:02.

'999, which service do you require?'

'Oh God. I don't know.'

'That's alright. Can you tell me what's happening?'

'It's awful, fucking horrible. I need an ambulance. I don't know. I think it's too late.'

'Can you tell me where you are?'

'On the Northwood Housing Estate. I'm up at the end of the car park. I found it, I found her near the bins.'

'Can you tell me what you've found?'

'A girl. A little girl.'

'Right. And what's happened to her?'

'God, I don't know.'

'Is she breathing?'

'I don't know. I don't know.'

'Can you check? Cup your hand around her nose and mouth.'

'You don't understand. Fucking hell, I can't go in there again.'

'Try to explain to me what's going on.'

'It's horrible. I came down to put my rubbish into the big bins, and I saw that someone had put a bag down the side. I grabbed it, and it opened. And then she fell onto the floor. She's so small. And she's dead. I think. I think so.'

'Okay. An ambulance is on the way. Can you please make sure that no one else goes near her?'

'Yeah, I can do that. I'll stand here.'

'I'm going to stay on the line with you until the ambulance arrives.'

'Please, yes. Thank you.'

'They're about twelve minutes away. Now, can you tell me about the cars parked around you?'

Gabe

Juliet ducked under the blue-and-white tape, her heels sinking into the soft ground. She would never admit to wearing inappropriate footwear, but I couldn't see how she remained upright. Probably sheer force of will. My boots twisted with each step over the damp ground.

Mist hung in the air, defusing the long rays of sunlight filtering through the trees. Under different circumstances, this would be a peaceful place. A private sanctuary for the residents of the ancestral estate. Birds chirped above a forest floor blanketed with orange leaves.

I shoved my hands deep into my coat pockets as I followed Juliet along a well-trampled path. Cold burrowed into my bones. I tried not to shiver. I didn't want to piss off the officers who had already been here for a while.

'Damn freezing.' Juliet had no such qualms. The collar of her light blue coat was turned up, her blonde hair tucked neatly into a scarf.

I jogged a couple of paces to catch up with her, carving my own path. The ground was less slippery away from the many footprints of others who had walked this way before us. Running parallel, a tight line of striped tape marked off another route through the trees. That one would be much more pristine.

'You take the lead on this case,' Juliet said, just out of earshot of a couple of uniformed officers.

'Alright. I will.'

This marked a change. Juliet hadn't wielded her seniority over me in the few months since my arrival, but I'd deferred to her in all the cases we'd worked together so far. I'd been waiting for her to give this push, determined to prove I could be more than a helpful sidekick.

I ran my tongue around my teeth and plastered a bland smile on my face as we walked up to the uniformed officers. 'Good morning.'

'Morning, ma'am,' said the older of the two. He stood with his broad chest puffed, his hand gripping the radio on his hip. The slender

7

officer beside him couldn't keep a pinched wince off her face. Most likely, her skin was usually a gentle brown. Shock had turned it sickly gold.

'I'm Detective Sergeant Gabe Martin. This is Detective Inspector Juliet Stern.'

'You're Gabe?' The male officer's eyes widened, darting between the two of us. 'And you're DI Stern?'

Juliet and I had elicited similar reactions before. I couldn't be sure why. Two female detectives? But everyone in the force was used to working with women by now, and this officer's partner was female. It could have been the shortening of my name, but I wasn't going to use my full name to avoid a bit of gender confusion during introductions.

More likely, Juliet's reputation preceded her. It was one thing to bitch about the detective who made extra work for everyone during a case, and quite another to face her in the flesh. I'd heard the rumours before I moved here. Juliet didn't look like the demon they made her out to be. She was always well-groomed, her straight, shoulder-length hair perfect, her clothes and nails matching. Her face settled naturally into a smile. Only a trusted few, and I counted myself among them, got to see that there wasn't some horrible beast waiting underneath the calm veneer to confirm all the whispers.

Juliet smiled, her eyes crinkling at the edges, but her voice was brisk. 'We certainly are. Could you show us to the body?'

The younger officer flinched, her hand flying to her mouth. She must be new. More experienced officers learnt to school their expressions to indifference even when faced with the worst things a human being could do to another.

'It's a mess, this one,' the older officer said.

He patted his partner's narrow shoulder and turned on his heel. The grey hair receding from his forehead twinkled with droplets of water as he led us over to another taped-off section of forest.

'Can you tell us what's been established so far?' I asked.

'We've marked the victim's flight path.' He pointed over at the long stretch cordoned off to our right. 'The ground was churned up, but we've had the groundskeeper helping. Guy knows his stuff.'

A tall man stood talking with another couple of uniformed officers. His light brown hair rose in a tangled mane around his head. He wore a knitted jumper under a long green coat, both patched and worn. All colour was leached from his face in the early morning light.

8

'Apart from that, we've got the body and where the shooter might have been standing.'

'Are forensics on their way?' Juliet asked.

'They've been delayed, won't be here for a few hours. Something else has cropped up.'

'Right.' Juliet pursed her lips. 'Can you keep a scene guard up until they arrive, and manage the log?'

'Yes, ma'am.' The uniformed officer looked faintly offended that she thought he might do anything else.

'I'm sure you're handling things until they get here.' I pulled my notepad out of my pocket. 'Can you tell me what you've ascertained so far?'

The officer stopped in front of the next round of tape, turning his back on it. His knuckles were white around his radio, like a toddler clutching compulsively at a security blanket.

'Looks like the girl was chased by an animal through the forest. A big dog, probably. We have both sets of prints.' He paused, considerate of my hand racing across the paper. 'I can't tell you much about the victim. She's Black, in her teens maybe. Couldn't get at any ID without disturbing the body. From the look of her clothes, she's not a runaway or living rough.'

'Thank you.' I ignored Juliet's foot twitching on the spongy ground. 'Anything else?'

'There's no sign of the animal but there's lots of tracks and evidence.' He ran a hand through his hair. A drop of displaced water trickled down the side of his face and trembled on his stubbled chin. 'Like I said, it's a mess. You'll see for yourself.'

He held up the tape and gestured us through. I tucked away my notepad as I dipped underneath, my stomach clenching. Confronting a dead body was never a pleasant task, but one described so consistently as out of the ordinary was bound to be its own special brand of grim. The officer let the tape snap into place behind us and strode over to his partner.

'Was that necessary?' Juliet picked her way across sprawling ivy and clumps of withering flowers.

This had been a point of contention since we'd worked our first case together. 'You know I like to hear from officers on the scene.'

'And what exactly did you learn that you couldn't have figured out yourself?'

'Nothing this time, but one day.'

Juliet grinned, slipping her slender fingers into a pair of crumpled plastic gloves. 'One day, they'll amaze us both.'

'Exactly.' I breathed into my gloves before tugging them on.

We'd reached the inner cordon. Inside, a body lay crumpled at the base of an oak tree. Juliet held the tape high, all signs of levity wiped from her face.

'Talk me through it. What do you see?'

I set my muddied boots on unmarred patches of moss, swallowing the tightness in my throat. 'There's a lot of disturbance on the ground. Confused footprints, animal and human.' I looked up at the tree, rather than at the body. This wasn't standard protocol, but I needed a moment. I pointed through the branches. 'Looks like there's blood further up. Maybe she climbed the tree before she was shot.'

I glanced over my shoulder. Juliet stood beside the tape, her hands burrowed inside her coat and her grey eyes fixed on me. Her face was expressionless, so I hadn't gotten anything wrong yet.

'There's blood spatter on the trunk up there.' The bark was stained inky red, impossible to miss in such large quantities. 'Looks like she fell from the tree and hit branches on the way down.' I lowered my arm, following her progress. The wood was splintered and broken.

'She climbed the tree because she was pursued?' Juliet asked.

'Presumably. Forensics will help us get a clearer picture.'

I pressed my lips together and took a few short steps over to the body. It lay awkwardly on its side. I had to stand a metre away to avoid the surrounding blood and broken branches. Even approaching from behind, I could tell the uniformed officer hadn't lied; it was a mess.

'Looks like she was shot three times in the back. All went straight through, if the damage to her clothes and amount of blood is any indication. If we're lucky, the bullets might be lodged in the tree.' I breathed through my mouth. 'Black, female. I'd say late teens, early twenties, from her clothes.'

One of her arms was slung over her back, clearly dislocated. The fabric of her coat was slashed and torn, run through with blood and crushed leaves. I walked over to her other side.

'Her face has been mauled by an animal.' I crouched down and made myself look. The skin was torn, flesh pulled from the bone in wet chunks. Her black hair tangled behind her bloodied ears. 'It looks like there are teeth marks around the worst areas. Most likely a dog. What other animal could do this around here?'

Juliet had mentioned wild horses as we drove over. This was the first time I'd visited the far edge of our patch that stretched into the north-east of the New Forest. I'd looked over at her, expecting the wry smile that accompanied her dry wit, but her face was set as she flicked through emails on her phone. I still wasn't sure huge animals were allowed to roam free in this rustic place, but at least we hadn't encountered any yet.

'Let's assume it's a dog for now.' Juliet approached on the other side of the body. 'How long do you think she's been here?'

I stood up. 'Not long. Can't have been dead for more than a few hours, but forensics will be able to give us a more accurate time of death.'

Small creatures had not yet made their homes in the broken flesh. I looked away from the victim's face. Blood was so thick over her chest that it would have been impossible to tell the colour of her top if one shoulder of her coat wasn't thrown back, revealing the baby-pink fabric. She'd landed badly, held on her side by the strange angle of her arms and splayed legs.

Juliet pointed at where the victim's hip jutted from the ground. The bulge under her jeans was too square to be displaced bone.

'Looks like there's something in her pocket.' Juliet glanced over her shoulder, but we were hidden by the thick trunks of trees. 'Forensics are being too slow. We need to know who she is now.'

'Juliet!' I hissed, as she bent and edged her gloved fingers into the tight fabric.

'Your lead has been temporarily rescinded.' She worked her hand around to the right angle, careful not to move the body. 'If anyone's going to get bollocked for this, it's me.'

I crossed my arms as she slid out a purple purse. Anyone else would be disciplined for such flagrant disrespect of an active crime scene. Juliet might be too, but it didn't affect her. She carried on working either way, and her track record made anyone think twice before taking serious action against her.

She retrieved evidence bags from her coat pocket. Before she dropped the purse into one, she unzipped it and pulled out a card.

'This is Melanie Pirt. Seventeen years old.'

I looked down at the body as Juliet sealed the evidence bags and wrote on the outsides. Melanie Pirt. How did she end up here?

With each step away from the body, the muscles in my shoulders unwound. We walked over to the two uniformed officers we'd spoken to before, whose hands were clasped around steaming cups. Their mouths dropped open when Juliet held out the evidence bags.

'Give these to the forensic team when they get here. I extracted them from the victim, Melanie Pirt's, pocket.'

'You touched the body?' The grey-haired officer gripped the bags, pressing Melanie's provisional driver's licence into the clear plastic.

'We generally do that to figure out who they are,' Juliet said.

I winced but covered it up with a cough. That wasn't strictly true. No other detective would dare touch a body before forensics had gone over it.

'Do you want us to inform the family, ma'am?' the female officer asked, recovering quicker than her partner.

'Actually, we'd like to do that later.' It was always helpful to note their reactions. I nodded over her shoulder at another cordoned-off area. 'We're going to take a look at where the shooter was standing now.'

The younger officer fell into step beside me, leaving her colleague behind. No doubt he was creating excuses for when the forensics team arrived. Juliet would, quite fairly this time, get the blame.

'What can you tell me about this area?' I asked.

'There's shell casings and footprints, one of them very clear. Doesn't look like the killer went over to the body. Far as we can see, they shot from a distance and left. We've taped off as far as we could track the footprints into the forest. They didn't head towards the manor or any other outbuildings.'

I pulled out my notepad and the uniformed officer waited while my pencil scratched across the paper. Juliet peered at the cordoned-off area, then walked over to the groundskeeper.

'Sorry, ma'am. That was rude, before.' She smoothed a non-existent strand of escaped hair back into her neat, black bun. 'I'm PC Alice To, and that's PC James Knowles.'

'Not a problem.'

I crouched to look at the boot print inside the cordoned-off area. It was a perfect indentation. Big, probably belonging to a man. We'd know more once the forensic team made a cast. I couldn't see the shell casings, but I trusted they were there.

I straightened and made a note about the boot print. Behind Alice, Juliet tapped at her phone and the groundskeeper loped away along the well-used path.

'You've done good work here today, Alice.' I wrote down her and her partner's names. 'Is there anything else that might help with our investigation?'

'No.' Alice bit her lip. 'She must have been so scared.'

My stomach lurched. I shoved my notepad into my pocket to hide the tremor in my hands.

'It gets easier,' I said.

It was a kind lie.

Jordan. Sent 10:30.

Babe, where you at? xx

From: Juliet Stern **juliet.stern@mit.gov.uk**
To: Madison Campbell
madison.campbell@mitadmin.gov.uk
CC: Gabriella Martin **gabriella.martin@mit.gov.uk**
Date: **10 October, 10:50**
Subject: **Operation Chalice – Next of kin**

Maddy,

Please find out the next of kin for the victim – Melanie Pirt, aged 17.
Please also arrange an interview with the residents of the Dunlow
Estate.

I hope you enjoyed your training yesterday. I expect you to be fully
health and safety compliant at all times.

Juliet

Gabe

Back at the station, I shared a lift with Juliet up to the seventh floor. The main open-plan space was empty of other detectives and officers, which confirmed why forensics were taking their time. Another case must have come in.

I dropped my coat off in the side office I shared with Juliet and retraced my steps across the main space. Our assistant, Maddy, didn't look up as I passed. Her hands flew across her keyboard, her wavy brown hair falling in curtains on either side of her face. I walked through to the stairs and descended to the third floor, then hurried down a corridor, skirting past closed doors and keeping my head lowered near open ones. I swung my hands at my sides, maintaining the illusion that I was taking a casual stroll through the station.

I turned a corner and pushed through a heavy door. I pulled the bolt across to lock it, then pushed through a second door. I let it swing shut while I fell to my knees and vomited into the toilet bowl.

This had been an acceptable reaction the first time I'd encountered a dead body. Paul Willis, the other DI who worked on our floor, had rubbed my back as I'd emptied my stomach. He told me the kind lie then, that I'd get used to it. I'd worked extra hard on that case to prove my abilities weren't affected by my initial involuntary reaction.

This shouldn't have been happening anymore. With more cases than I could count on two hands solved and filed away, I should be as unaffected as Juliet or Paul when I encountered a dead body. It was always going to be unpleasant, harrowing sometimes, but I should have gotten past reacting so viscerally.

I held out hope that I'd get over this someday. For now, I came here to do what had to be done. This was the only toilet in the station that was not only a single cubicle but had two doors to deaden the sound of my retching. No one needed to know about this. I was weak enough already in too many of their eyes.

That was the hazard of my history being on public record and working with professionally nosy individuals. My colleagues had to have looked me up, but at least no one had tried to talk to me about it.

I pulled a few sheets of toilet roll from the holder and wiped my mouth. It was only in this first moment that my past intruded, that my body forgot it was thirty-one and reverted to the reactions I'd had when I was seven. For the rest of the case, every time I saw Melanie's lifeless body or shredded face, I would feel nothing more than a twinge of sadness or distaste.

It was particularly galling that nothing other than the feeling at this moment was similar to what happened when I was a child. The blind panic, the rising nausea, the desperate fight to find a safe place. I didn't know why dead bodies triggered it. I hadn't seen one back then.

My arms were shaking, but I felt steady enough as I pushed onto my heels and stood. I braced one hand against the wall and pressed the button to flush. Reaching around the cistern, I pulled out the air freshener I'd stashed there and filled the cubicle with the chemically sweet spray.

I escaped the pungent combination of flowers and vomit in the outer room, a space big enough for a sink and bin. Swilling water around my mouth, I stared into the mirror bolted above the basin. My sallow skin shone with sweat. I cupped water into my hands and splashed it over my face, running my fingers though my cropped hair. A few passes with my blunt nails and it looked the same as when I'd walked into the station this morning, the dark brown strands swept back from my forehead.

There was a knock at the door as I gargled and spat.

'One minute,' I called.

I took another gulp of water. My brown eyes were bloodshot, but not too badly. I'd washed the sweat off and the cold water had returned some of the colour to my cheeks, even if it was in blotchy patches rather than a healthy glow. I blew my nose and popped an extra strong mint on my tongue.

I unlocked the outer door with a prepared smile on my face for whoever was waiting. It dropped when I spotted Juliet leaning on the far wall. I couldn't tell if the stench of vomit and fake flowers had followed me.

'We've got an address for the next of kin.' She passed over my coat then started walking along the corridor.

I tugged on my coat as I followed her. If she was happy to ignore me using a toilet so far from our office, then I was happy not to ask how she knew to find me here. Despite her prickly outer shell, Juliet was one of the people least likely to pity me, but I wasn't going to share details if I didn't have to.

Her spotless heels clacked on the floor as we walked towards the lifts. Her hair was immaculate despite the mist in the forest. She was totally unaffected by what we'd seen at the Dunlow Estate.

I sucked hard on the mint dissolving on my tongue. I couldn't force my body out of this reaction, but I could do the other parts of my job just as well as everyone else. Better, if some of Juliet's success rubbed off on me. This hang-up from my childhood wasn't going to ruin the only job I'd ever wanted.

Call connected at 12:15.

'Hello, Dunlow Consultants. How can I help you?'

'Hello there. Can I please speak to Mr Timothy Dunlow?'

'May I ask who is calling?'

'My name's Maddy. I'm calling on behalf of Detectives Juliet Stern and Gabe Martin. They need to arrange a time to talk to Mr Dunlow about an incident on his property.'

'Please stay on the line. I'll connect you.'

BEEP. BEEP. BEEP.

'Yes?'

'Hello there. Is that Timothy Dunlow?'

'Speaking.'

'Hi, my name is Maddy. I'm calling on behalf of Detectives Juliet Stern and Gabe Martin.'

'My assistant told me. Do you know who it is yet?'

'I'm sorry?'

'The body. Do you know who it is?'

'I'm sorry, Mr Dunlow. At this time I can't discuss any details of the investigation.'

'There was a body found on my property and you can't tell me who it is?'

'Unfortunately no. But I was calling to arrange for Gabe and Juliet to come and have a chat.'

'A chat?'

'Yes. They'd like to talk to you about the investigation. Is there a time later today when they could come to see you? Work or home is fine.'

'I don't think that's necessary. Someone's died, but it has nothing to do with me.'

'Still, Gabe and Juliet would like to talk to you about a few things. They could come to you, or you could pop into the station.'

'Christ, no. They can come to the house. I'll be home at half five.'

'Great. I'll tell them to come just after.'
'Fine. Is that all?'
'Yes. Thank you for assisting with the investigation.'

The Refuge – registered charity no. 3950478

WEEKLY SUPPORT MEETINGS

Come along to our friendly and supportive weekly
meetings run by trained counsellors

A space to:

Rest and recover

See that you are not alone

Seek guidance and advice

Tell your story in a non-judgemental space

Every Wednesday at 7 p.m.

St James's Methodist Hall

**The Refuge – providing healing services for those
affected by physical and emotional abuse**

Gabe

'Maddy's set up a meeting with Timothy Dunlow this afternoon. He's the owner of the estate.'

'Good.' I checked my mirrors before turning right. 'What do we know about him?'

Juliet laid her phone on her lap and rolled her shoulders. She'd been focused on the device for most of the short drive. I'd been working with her long enough to know this wasn't rudeness, but an unwillingness to let any moment go to waste during an investigation.

'Not much yet. Filthy rich, obviously. Owns the estate and the surrounding land. He has a reputation for being ruthless in business, but I'm not sure exactly what his company does. Some kind of consultancy. He has two sons, Leonard and Terence. Wife died a few years ago. Cancer. He's not involved in politics, not in the local paper much, doesn't get involved in the community.' Juliet paused while I merged with traffic. 'Maddy said he was a shit when she called him.'

'Did she actually say that?'

'It was the subtext.'

I turned right, as directed by the silent satnav. Juliet insisted that if I wanted it on, I wasn't allowed to force her to endure the tinny voice as well. 'Have the Dunlows got any guns?'

'Many.' Juliet tapped her nails on her knee, her eyes sweeping over the blocks of flats and stunted trees coasting past the window. 'The groundskeeper, Karl, told me they have an outhouse full of them. I've asked the forensic team to take a look when they finally get there. There are dogs on the estate too. Part of Karl's job is looking after them. Apparently, they use them on the hunt.'

Everything needed to kill Melanie was primed and waiting on the estate. I pulled my grey Vauxhall Astra into a car park overshadowed by several tall buildings and reversed into a visitor's space.

'Timothy Dunlow is definitely a person of interest,' Juliet said, as she climbed out of the car. 'But I can't see a connection between him and Melanie.'

'Hopefully he'll clear that up for us this afternoon.'

'Case closed by dinner?' Juliet raised one pale eyebrow.

'Ideally.'

I locked the car and we walked through the car park to the front of a block of flats. The area our station covered was a mix of urban and rural, stretching between the City of Southampton and the surrounding areas, right over to the north-east of the New Forest. The obscenely wealthy in Dunlow's neck of the woods had little reason to mingle with those who lived in more built-up areas, like the estate Melanie Pirt had lived on. Juliet was right, it was hard to see the connection between the seventeen-year-old and the middle-aged man. They lived in relative proximity but, in reality, inhabited different worlds.

This was one of the nicer housing estates. Most of the residents owned their properties or had lived here long enough to take pride in their surroundings. Balconies were filled with bright pots, the plants coming to the end of their season but eking out the last of the sun. Rubbish bracketed the bin store, but the paths were clean and any graffiti was contained to council signs.

It reminded me of home until I closed my eyes. Then, the ever-present cries of gulls reasserted themselves. That was a sound rarely heard in north London, but it couldn't be escaped this near to the sea.

'You want to take the lead in here as well?' Juliet swept through the unlocked front doors and unfastened her coat as she climbed the stairs.

I couldn't see her face, but knew she'd be smirking. If there was one part of this job where I excelled over Juliet, it was interacting with a victim's family. She could maintain a mask of sympathy when sitting dumbly, but if she got too talkative she'd start asking about movements and samples far too quickly. It wasn't that Juliet didn't know where the line was, but she disregarded it. If there was anyone as concerned with seeking justice as her, it was a victim's nearest and dearest, but that didn't manifest in the same way as it did for a seasoned detective. I'd only sat in on one of these meetings before suggesting I take over. It was not appropriate to discuss blood spatter with the recently bereaved.

At least Juliet was here. I hadn't been working on the force for more than a month when someone described these moments before a conference with the families of the deceased as the long, lonely walk. It wasn't quite so lonely with another officer by my side, even if it was someone as forcefully tactless as Juliet.

Outside a blue door on the fifth floor, I undid my coat and adjusted my ID badge. Who knew what the worst part of our job was, but this had to be near the top. Melanie had lived with her grandmother, so we were unlikely to be faced with a suspect. All that awaited us here was a life-altering conversation.

There was no knocker or doorbell. I rapped on the wood and stepped off the bristly welcome mat. Juliet clicked her phone onto silent.

'Yes?' The door half opened, revealing a stooped Black woman. Her white-grey hair was pulled into a tidy bun and thick glasses balanced on the end of her nose.

'Hello. I'm Detective Sergeant Gabe Martin and this is Detective Inspector Juliet Stern. Is this the residence of Melanie Pirt?'

'Yes. Is she in trouble?' The elderly woman gripped the door, pressing the edge into the folds of her floral print dress.

'Might we come in for a moment?' Better not to get into a discussion of this nature on the doorstep.

Melanie's grandmother pulled the door wide. I gestured for her to lead the way along a narrow corridor. She moved slowly, balancing between slipper-clad feet and a sturdy wooden stick.

In the living room, photos covered the walls, the old and more recent mingling in gaudy frames. A young Black girl waved from behind polished glass, hair contained by tight plaits. Older incarnations of the same face pouted, her lashes impossibly long. The room smelt of stale cigarettes. One butt rested in an ashtray on a round table beside the reclinable chair Melanie's grandmother lowered herself into. She leant her stick on an ancient electric heater. Juliet and I sat on the sofa opposite, sinking into the soft cushions.

The old woman fiddled with a remote, turning off the already muted TV, while I slid forward to perch on the edge of my seat. I didn't want to have this conversation while slouching.

'How are you related to Melanie?' I pulled out my notepad and rested it on my knee.

It was always best to check. One of Paul's favourite stories was how, as a fresh-faced PC, he'd broken the news of a break-in to the wrong person. Juliet couldn't understand why he would willingly divulge the details of one of his mistakes, and that was part of the reason she wasn't invited out to the pub with the others on our floor.

'I'm her grandmother.' She knotted her hands together on her knee. 'Ida Pirt.'

'Thank you, Ida.' I made a note, then put down my pencil. 'We're here because there has been an incident, and we think Melanie may have been involved.'

Ida's hands tightened, wrinkling the fabric of her skirt. 'Is she in trouble?'

'Early this morning, a body was found on the Dunlow Estate in the New Forest.' I maintained eye contact. 'I'm sorry to have to tell you this, but we believe it's Melanie.'

Shock pulsed through Ida's body. She sat back, her mouth forming soundless words. Her dark eyes filled with tears that spilled onto her wizened cheeks.

'Is there someone we can call for you?' I asked.

Ida batted at her glasses, letting them fall onto the chain looped around her neck. She wiped her face. 'Evie, next door.' She thumbed at the wall to her left.

'I'll go.' Juliet rose in one fluid motion and let herself out of the flat.

'Ida?' I waited for her to focus on me. I resisted rearing back from the expression of unadulterated pain on her face. 'How can we contact Melanie's parents?'

'They're dead.' Her voice was blunted by years of loss.

'I'm sorry.' I pressed my thumb into the corner of my notepad. 'Is there anyone else we should contact?'

Ida shook her head. Brittle strands of hair clung to her forehead as fresh tears filled her eyes. 'We only had each other.'

The front door swished open and a squat white woman entered the room. In contrast to Ida's neat dress, she was in a stained pair of dungarees and her light grey hair corkscrewed around her wrinkled face.

'Ida?' Her Irish accent was strong. 'What's the matter?'

'It's my Melanie,' Ida croaked. More tears snaked down her cheeks, making dark tracks across her skin. She reached out a shaking arm and

Evie grasped her hand, engulfing it in both of her own. Evie's knuckles were warped by arthritis. Gripping so tightly must have hurt, but she didn't let go.

'Ida?' I stood, not quite managing Juliet's grace. 'If it's alright, we'll come back tomorrow morning? We have a few more questions.'

'Yes, that's fine,' Evie answered for her. Ida had closed her eyes, retreating into herself.

'I'm so sorry for your loss.'

Neither woman replied. I walked out of the flat, slotting my notepad into my pocket. Juliet waited in the hallway. I pulled the door shut and followed her down the winding stairs.

'That was unpleasant.' Juliet walked out to the car park. 'But at least we know she's not a suspect. I can't see her running around a forest.'

That was all this meeting was about for Juliet; a chance to sound out the next of kin and remove them from the investigation early on. I unlocked the car and let her climb inside while I stared at the block of flats, wondering which balcony belonged to Ida. She already knew grief, had buried a child when Melanie's parents died. Would that make losing her granddaughter anymore bearable?

'Hopefully she'll be more talkative tomorrow,' Juliet said, once I'd climbed into the car.

I punched the station postcode into the satnav and waited for the map to load. I was learning our patch and used the colourful maps as a guide despite Juliet's disdain. She was engrossed in her phone by the time I pulled out of the car park.

Everything she'd said was true. That had been an unpleasant experience, we could rule Ida out of the investigation, and it would be helpful if she was able to talk to us tomorrow. But it was callous to focus on those things while a woman mourned the loss of her beloved granddaughter.

I wasn't thinking of the case as I drove away from Ida's flat, but the young woman who featured in the photos on Ida's wall. Her smile sat in my mind alongside the mauled body lying in the woods.

BIKERGUY.

Up for a ride. Message with pic.

Swipe.

LIANE40.

Looking for friendship and laughs.

Swipe.

T65.

Message if you like it rough. No time wasting. Pic a
must.

Swipe.

KIMWAITSFORNOWOMAN.

Message for a meet up. Don't waste my time if you
don't want something serious.

Swipe.

OLLIEOLIVER4.

Looking for something good in a mad world. Will
meet for fun.

Tap.

Unknown number. Sent 14:34.

I did what you asked. Pay up.

Gabe

'The autopsy will be delayed,' Juliet said, as I walked into our office. She was glaring at her computer, her chair tucked under the desk sat snugly opposite mine.

I passed her the black coffee I'd made in the empty staffroom. 'There's another case?'

Juliet had been busy in the few minutes I'd stepped out to make our drinks. I leant on the end of my desk and sipped my coffee, drinkable immediately because of the amount of milk I'd sloshed into it. On the opposite wall stretched a pitted cork board where Juliet had pinned up the scant evidence we'd gathered. This was part of the reason we shared the office; Juliet liked laying out evidence in this way and she claimed she didn't want to keep calling me in to look over it with her. I'd decided she also didn't like working alone, despite the way she alienated most of her colleagues.

Many of the names pinned to the board – Karl, Leonard, Terence – had no attached picture yet. Timothy Dunlow sat above them all, scowling from a photo nabbed from his company website. I could see why he had a nasty reputation. If this was the best picture a professional photographer could capture, then he wasn't a man prone to gentler moments. His full head of white hair was swept away from his forehead and his colourless skin was crisscrossed with lines, the most pronounced lying between his impressive eyebrows.

The only other image pinned to the wall was a satellite map of the Dunlow Estate. Dark green forest crowded a square of grass in which sat a sprawling manor. The sight of the shooting was marked with a silver star. The twine Juliet favoured sat dormant on the top of one of the filing cabinets, crammed into the space behind her desk. She had a multitude of bright colours, one of which would be stretched across the wall once we had some links to work on. Paul joked this was the reason Juliet was so adept at catching killers – she worked like one.

'There's been another murder,' Juliet said.

I froze mid sip. I'd not worked on a serial killer case yet, hadn't tested whether I was detached enough to deal with that.

I stared at Melanie's name until my stomach stopped swooping. 'Is it related?'

'No. It's a little girl.'

Relief swamped me. Whenever possible, I avoided working cases that involved a child. Since our case came in first, I wouldn't be reassigned. Paul's partner, Nicole, was on maternity leave. In her absence, I'd occasionally been pulled over to his team for complicated crimes.

Juliet tapped the side of her black coffee, as though that would help it cool quicker. 'It's going to slow everything down; uniforms are already being reassigned. We won't have the resources we need.'

I sat heavily in my chair. 'For heaven's sake, Juliet.'

'What?' An expression of genuine confusion replaced her glare.

'A child has died. You don't have to be so mercenary about it.' When I'd first worked with Juliet, I'd kept these comments to myself, but witnessing how everything else bounced off her made me bold. 'Don't you have daughters?'

Juliet wrinkled her nose. 'That has nothing to do with this.'

I shook my head. I didn't let many of the things Juliet said bother me but at the start of each case or whenever we heard about some new atrocity being dealt with elsewhere, we butted heads like this. She felt almost nothing, while the amount of feelings I kept inside threatened to rip their way out. This was why it was best for me to stay away from cases with children.

Juliet looked out to the quiet main floor. 'You can't feel everything, Gabe.'

I took a sip of coffee and wiggled my mouse in place of a reply. I couldn't tear myself apart over every person killed and family broken, but it would be worse to feel nothing at all.

From: Madison Campbell
madison.campbell@mitadmin.gov.uk
To: Juliet Stern **juliet.stern@mit.gov.uk,** Gabriella Martin **gabri-ella.martin@mit.gov.uk**
Date: **10 October, 16:41**
Subject: **Operation Chalice – Press release**

Juliet and Gabe,

Here is the draft press release for the Dunlow Estate murder:

A murder investigation has been launched following an incident on the Dunlow Estate in the New Forest.

Police were called at approximately 08:15hrs on Tuesday, 10 October to reports of a body found on the Dunlow Estate. An ambulance was called to the scene but the woman, believed to be aged in her teens, was pronounced dead at the scene at 09:00hrs.

No other details have been released yet but police are anxious to speak to anyone who may have been in the area at the time.

Next of kin have been informed. Formal identification awaits. A post-mortem examination will take place in due course.

A crime scene remains in place.

Detective Sergeant Gabriella Martin is leading the investigation and said: 'I am keen to hear from anybody who may have been in or around the Dunlow Estate or surrounding area on the night of the 9 October. If you have any information, please contact the incident room.'

No arrests have been made; enquiries continue.

Let me know if there's anything you want changed,

Maddy

Gabe

Gravel crunched underfoot as we climbed out of the car and onto the wide driveway. The double fronted house faced a well-tended lawn, the faded peach stonework bathed in late afternoon light. The surrounding forest created long shadows across the grass.

Light spilled from several sash windows. Juliet and I walked towards the manor, the entryway visible through narrow panes of glass either side of the front door. Polished wooden flooring stretched towards the back of the house.

'You're in the lead still,' Juliet said, as I lifted the brass door knocker.

I let it fall with a loud thunk. 'Step in if you notice something I don't.'

I wasn't too proud to ask for help. Juliet might be a consummate failure at talking to victims' families, but she was one of the best at wheedling the truth out of perpetrators of violent crimes. It was her face: kindly looking and open. Killers and rapists placed Juliet firmly into the 'not a threat' category. Most of them only realised their mistake once it was already too late. Her benign smile hid an exceptionally quick mind, one that spotted inconsistencies in a story long before anyone else.

I wanted to prove myself, but that wouldn't make me lose sight of what was important: bringing Melanie's killer to justice, stopping them before they could hurt anyone else. That was one similarity between Juliet and I; we would do anything to find the truth.

Timothy Dunlow emerged from one of the rooms at the back of the manor. He'd had time since arriving home from work to loosen his tie, but he was imposing in a tailored inky blue suit. He frowned through the glass as he opened the door. The wind had obviously changed while he was pulling that face.

'Good afternoon, Mr Dunlow.' I held out my hand, summoning a tight smile. 'I'm Detective Sergeant Gabe Martin and this is Detective Inspector Juliet Stern. Thank you for meeting with us.'

Dunlow took my hand and gripped it firmly. He looked the kind of man who would have been to a seminar about the appropriate pressure to use when shaking hands to impress upon everyone his importance and power. There would have been a follow-up workshop in never giving those lesser than you permission to use your first name.

'I didn't have a lot of choice.' His voice was a low growl that would cut across any boardroom.

'Still, we're grateful you made time for us,' Juliet said, as he pumped her hand. Her lips were upturned, but there was a hardness around her eyes as Dunlow turned and led us into the manor.

I unbuttoned my coat, gentle heat lapping over me. It was the same in all posh houses, or at least in the ones where the owners had enough money for the upkeep. They didn't endure draughts or blasting radiators. These opulent places were like carefully maintained zoo exhibits; the environment rigidly controlled to maintain the inhabitants' constant comfort.

Dunlow led us to a sitting room at the back of the house. The view through the windows showed the sun setting over lawns surrounded by tall trees. I wondered whether it was intense dislike of the outside world that led Dunlow to shut it out so thoroughly with dense forest in every direction, or if he liked living in a civilised oasis in the middle of all that green.

I wouldn't have been able to stand the quiet, the lack of humanity. I liked the occasional walk around places like this, but returning to a home blanketed in every direction by hundreds of others was a comfort. My rented maisonette was on the edge of my comfort zone; not in the city proper but built up enough that I felt swaddled by the surrounding humanity.

Every piece of furniture in the sitting room was clearly far more expensive than all the items in Ida Pirt's flat. Dunlow settled into a highbacked armchair near an empty fireplace. Scorch marks on the back panelling proved its usefulness, but Juliet and I were not the kind of guests he would light a fire for. A drink rested on a table at his elbow, something amber in a low glass. He didn't offer us anything.

We sat on a sofa opposite. The cushions were so highly stuffed that they barely gave way as they took our weight. I pulled my notepad out of my pocket and rested it on my knee.

'It would be helpful to our investigation if you'd answer a few questions.' I sensed Dunlow wouldn't appreciate any padding. 'Can I ask who was on the estate last night?'

34

'Myself.' Dunlow looked at one of the long windows rather than at either of us, his words delivered in a bored drawl. 'My younger son, Leo, slept in the den over the garages. Karl would have been somewhere on the grounds.'

'And your other son, Terence?'

Dunlow's eyes snapped to me. The barb had landed. I'd let him wonder how much digging we'd done about his family.

'Terence was away at a wedding. He's coming home later today.'

'Great.' I made a note to check that alibi. 'And what did you do yesterday evening and last night?'

'I got home from work at seven and had dinner with Leo at around eight.' Dunlow picked up his glass and swirled it. 'Afterwards, I worked for a couple of hours and then I went to bed. I read a book and fell asleep at around eleven.'

'Can anyone confirm your whereabouts after you ate with Leo?'

'Why would they need to?' Dunlow stared flatly at me, drink cradled in one hand.

'At this point, it would be helpful to rule you out as a suspect,' I said.

Dunlow's eyes continued to bore into mine. They were blue, incredibly light. Combined with his white hair and bushy eyebrows, they gave him a washed-out quality.

Juliet flicked her hair over one shoulder. The movement grounded me. I wasn't a young woman annoying an older man, but a detective with every right to be here.

'No. Leo and I both enjoy our privacy.' Dunlow took a sip of his drink, supremely unconcerned that he had an uncorroborated alibi on the night a young woman was murdered on his land. It was either the arrogance of the untouchably rich, or something more sinister.

'I see.' I made a show of writing a note. 'When did you hear about the body?'

'The groundskeeper called me this morning, before I left for work.'

'And you didn't wait for the police?'

Dunlow placed his drink on the coaster, fine beads of moisture forming on the lower half of the glass. 'I didn't see any reason to stay.'

'Okay.' Next time I thought Juliet was heartless, I needed to remember this guy. 'You may already be aware, but the victim was shot three times. Did you hear gunshots in the night?'

'I sleep with the window closed.' Dunlow gave no reaction to hearing an unknown person had been shot. He either already knew or didn't care. 'I heard nothing.'

'Right. We're aware there are several guns on the property. When was the last time you used one?'

Dunlow's resting expression of a deep frown remained unchanged. 'Weeks ago.'

'Good.' I made a note as Juliet shifted beside me. I didn't think that meant anything. Dunlow was impressively shut down, even she wouldn't have gotten any more from him. 'We haven't been able to formally identify the body yet, but we can confirm it is that of a young Black woman. Is there anyone who matches that description who would have had reason to come onto your property?'

'No.'

I tapped my pencil, holding Dunlow's gaze. 'How old are your sons?'

The lines on his face lengthened, the first sign that he felt anything other than aggrieved tolerance for my questioning. 'Terence is twenty-four and Leo is eighteen.'

'Would Leo have had a girl over?' I asked.

'No, he would not.' Dunlow's hand flexed on his knee. 'Leo doesn't mingle with many girls as he goes to an all-boys school. Besides, he knows my views on dating while he's in education.'

'Which are?'

'It's an unwanted distraction.' Dunlow hadn't raised his voice, but there was a ring of authority to his words.

Juliet leant back beside me, folding one leg over the other. She raised her eyebrows; not antagonising, but clearly disbelieving.

Dunlow's expression soured. His hand shot out and he grabbed his drink, taking a gulp of the doubtless expensive and well-aged liquor.

'Would you mind if we had a chat with Leo?' I asked.

Dunlow was a strong suspect, made no less so by his lack of alibi and disdainful attitude, but his son was also on the property last night. Since Leo was a similar age to Melanie, it wasn't too much of a stretch to assume he was the reason why she was on the estate, no matter what his father might insist to the contrary.

Dunlow pulled a phone out of his jacket pocket. He thumbed at it, then tossed it onto the table beside his chair.

'He'll be down in a minute.'

'Great.'

I noted the phone make and model. Not because I needed to, but because some interviewees found excessive notetaking uncomfortable. When I looked up, Dunlow's eyes were directed at the pad on my knee. He wasn't as untouchable as he wanted us to believe.

'What is it you do for a living, Mr Dunlow?' asked Juliet.

He glared at her. The pressure of his attention was lessened once his focus was removed. Perhaps that was Juliet's intention.

'I run a company. We manage mergers.' Dunlow's tone implied he'd reached heady new heights of boredom. 'We work as an independent third party, getting the best deal for all involved.'

That explained his reputation. Dunlow might claim to advocate fairly but in every business transaction, and especially ones of this nature, someone was going to get shafted. It wouldn't be whoever wrote the larger pay cheque.

'You do well from it?' Juliet asked.

'I do well,' Dunlow parroted.

He looked like he'd smelt something unpleasant. Juliet wouldn't have forgotten the wealthy's distaste for discussing money, but apparently Dunlow was having the same effect on her as he was on me. We wanted to rattle him, make him feel uncomfortable.

I twisted when the varnished wooden door opened behind us and a young man entered the room. Leo looked nothing like his father. Unruly hair fell over his forehead in auburn waves and his skin was a smooth olive tan. His eyes were a muddy brown behind glasses made to look like old NHS prescription frames. I doubted they cost under a hundred quid. Where his father fully inhabited his broad frame, Leo was lanky and coltish.

Juliet and I stood as he hurried around to the front of the sofa. He shook our hands in turn, his long-fingered grip loose. His other hand was held close to his stomach, wrapped in a bandage. He'd changed from whatever preppy uniform his school deemed appropriate into a faded green hoodie and jeans.

'Hello, Leo. I'm Gabe Martin and this is Juliet Stern.' I didn't use our full titles as Leo looked terrified enough, his eyes wide as he sat down in a chair beside his father's. 'We're detectives, and we have a few questions about an incident on the estate last night.'

'Okay.' Leo fidgeted in his seat, his uninjured hand playing around his mouth. His lips were chapped, like he'd been biting them. 'I don't know anything, though. Dad hasn't told me what's going on.'

'What did you do last night, after you had dinner with your father?' I asked.

'I went over to the den above the garage.' Leo's gaze darted into the empty space between me and Juliet.

'What did you do there?'

Leo's eyes flicked to me before he bowed his head, his fingers catching a loose thread at the edge of his bandage. 'I played on my Xbox, read a bit, then I went to sleep.'

'Can anyone confirm this?'

'No.' Leo squirmed in his seat, displaying the correct response to not having an alibi during a murder investigation.

'You didn't play a game online with friends?' I prompted.

'No.' Leo shook his head. Beside him, Dunlow picked up his drink and took a sip.

'Did anyone visit you last night?' I kept my eyes on Leo but saw Dunlow's knuckles whiten around his glass.

'No,' Leo said.

'A girl did not come to visit you?'

Blood crept up his neck and over his cheeks in uneven patches. 'No.'

'I've already told you this,' Dunlow said.

I made a note of Leo's lack of alibi, not quite ignoring Dunlow but not acknowledging him either. 'Did you hear anything in the night?'

'I don't think so.' Leo sucked his lower lip. 'I went to sleep at about elevenish and I didn't wake up until seven this morning.'

'You didn't hear gunshots?' I asked.

Leo flinched, his hair falling into his eyes. He pushed his glasses up his nose and drew the hair back from his forehead in a careless tangle. 'What?' He looked between Juliet and me. 'Someone was shot?'

'Did you hear gunshots, Leo?' I asked again.

He dropped his gaze and shook his head. 'No. I didn't hear anything.'

'Okay.' I turned the page in my notepad, the paper scraping as I pulled it over the binding.

'Sorry, Leo. I didn't catch that.' Juliet leant forward.

I'd missed him mumbling something into his chest. His eyes darted over at his father.

'Are they alright?' Leo licked his lips. 'The person who got shot?'

'No, Leo,' I said. 'Unfortunately, they passed away.'

All colour drained from his face. He sat back in his chair, hands falling to his lap. Juliet straightened, her nails tapping on her knee. I didn't have to ask if Leo's reaction was as damning as it seemed. He knew something about what happened last night.

'Any more questions?' Dunlow placed his drink on the coaster. He didn't quite judge the distance and the drink leant to one side, condensation running down onto the table.

'A couple.' I turned back to Leo. 'What size shoe are you?'

'Eleven.' Leo blinked slowly. 'Same as Dad.'

That was helpful oversharing. 'And how did you hurt your hand?'

Leo looked down at the bandage. As if in a daze, he wiggled his fingers. 'One of the dogs bit me.'

'When was this?'

'Days ago.' Leo spoke in a monotone. Since I'd confirmed Melanie's fate, he'd drifted away.

Dunlow had noticed too. He sat forward in his chair. 'Anything else?'

'We'd like to take DNA samples from both of you.' I pulled the swabs and tubes from one of my voluminous coat pockets.

Leo straightened. 'Why?'

'It's to eliminate you as suspects,' I explained. 'You can refuse, but we'll have to note that you're not willing to comply with our investigation.'

'It's fine.' Dunlow snatched the sample kits from me and shoved one at Leo. 'Let them do what they want. Then they'll get out of here.'

Disconnected spots of blush stole across Leo's face, either for his father's rudeness or his disinclination to submit to DNA testing. He did as he was told though, awkwardly unscrewing the pot with one hand and dropping in the swab he'd passed around the inside of his cheeks.

Juliet and I stood as Dunlow passed back the kits. Leo stayed seated, his face downturned, but his father jumped up and led the way to the front door.

'Thank you for your cooperation,' I said as we walked out onto the gravel. 'Once we have more details, we'll be in touch.'

Without replying, Dunlow shut the door. A bolt thudded into place, and through the glass I could see him striding towards the room we'd just left. Leo would no doubt get a bollocking for being an open book. Dunlow was right about one thing; the windows didn't let any sound in or out.

'God, I hope it was him,' Juliet said, as we walked over to the car.

Involuntarily, my face twitched into a smile. 'Very professional.'

I couldn't deny how satisfying it would be to smash through Dunlow's smug demeanour. It was a shame Leo had thrown himself so firmly into the ring of suspects. There was no denying he knew something he wasn't telling us.

'We passed the groundskeeper's cottage on the way in, right?' I asked, as we climbed into the car. 'Let's hope Dunlow's attitude hasn't rubbed off on him too much.'

'Karl was pleasant when I spoke to him earlier.'

I looked over at Juliet as I turned the key in the ignition. Her calling someone pleasant, and not in a derogatory way, was unusual. She didn't offer anything more, already engrossed in her phone.

I turned the car in a wide circle across the gravel drive. The curtains in every room at the front of the manor had been drawn shut.

My Lion. Sent 18:04.

Mel, you need to message me – I don't care what you said. Are you alright? I have to know you're okay xx

Gabe

The groundskeeper emerged from the forest as I parked the car to one side of the long driveway cutting through the trees. His light brown hair rose in a wild thatch around his head. He crossed his arms over his chest as we climbed out of the car.

'Hello again, Karl. Let me introduce Detective Sergeant Gabe Martin.' Juliet dipped her head towards the ivy-covered dwelling beside our car. It was tiny compared to the manor; one storey and there could only be a couple of rooms. A muddy four-by-four was parked in its shadow. 'Is that your cottage?'

'Yes.' Karl made no move to invite us inside, even though it must have been where he was headed before we'd arrived. 'You got some more questions for me?'

'We do,' Juliet said.

'I thought you might.' Karl unfolded his arms and turned around. 'I'll show you where the dogs are and all.'

I followed behind him and Juliet. His boots were caked in mud. It was hard to gauge the size while he was on the move between the long shadows cast by trees. Big, anyway.

Within seconds of walking, I would have been lost without a guide. The trees around us all looked the same: extra leggy without an abundant covering of leaves.

'You manage the grounds?' Juliet asked.

She had changed into a pair of flat trainers. That was the closest she'd get to confessing her footwear this morning had not been perfectly suited to romping through a forest.

'Yeah.' Karl nodded, his mussed hair swaying. 'The gardens are easy, they're just grass, and Mr Dunlow likes the forest left as is.'

'How often do you walk through the forest?' I asked.

'Every day. I walk the dogs all around the place.' His accent was gentle, a soft Yorkshire lilt. He may have grown up there but had lived south long enough that he'd lost most of the distinctive tones.

Karl led us into a barn that loomed between trees. The air smelt of wet fur, but it was warm after the chill wind outside. A few dogs yipped at us from behind waist-high wooden gates, but they quietened when Karl waved his hand at them. Only one remained intrigued, a snout snuffling along the top of the gate.

'Can you tell us what you did yesterday evening?' I pulled out my notepad.

Karl stopped walking in the middle of the barn. He leant against a wooden post that stretched up to the high ceiling, one of his ankles crossed over the other.

'I fed the dogs at about seven and tidied up a bit. They were all here then. After that I went back to the cottage. That must have been about nine. I had something to eat and went to bed.'

'Can anyone confirm this?' I asked.

'No. I live alone.'

Another suspect with no alibi. This was becoming a worrying pattern. At least Karl looked concerned, his stubbled jaw jutting.

'Did you hear anything during the night?'

'I didn't hear gunshots, if that's what you mean.'

I made a note. Karl wasn't a complete dickhead like his boss, but he certainly wasn't happy we were here. I'd spoken to witnesses who were scared, who were worried about saying anything in case they got in trouble. Karl wasn't acting like them, but there was an edge to his answers.

'Did you notice anyone entering the estate?' I asked.

'No. The gate's got a system; the button's attached to my phone so I can let people in no matter where I am. If someone had come in that way, I'd have known about it.'

'Would you know if someone let themselves in?' I asked.

'No.' Karl scratched at the side of his head. 'There aren't many keys though. Mr Dunlow and the boys have got them. Maybe one or two others.'

'Could you give us a full list of the people with keys?' Juliet pulled a business card out of her pocket. 'You can email it over.'

'Fine.' Karl stashed the card in his worn coat without looking at it. 'I don't think the girl came in through the gate.'

'How do you think she got in?' I asked.

'There's a stone wall all the way around the land, but it's not too high and it's crumbling in places. If someone wanted to get in without

43

anyone knowing, they could climb it.' Karl kicked at the hay under his boot. 'Mr Dunlow doesn't care all that much about someone getting onto the grounds. The main house has an alarm and the dogs are down by me. I've told him a few times he should get CCTV but he's not keen on it. He told me to keep my nose out, that he doesn't want to be watched all the time.'

I wasn't sure Dunlow would have phrased it in such a polite way. I made a note to have the walls around the estate checked. If Karl was right, Melanie might not have been running randomly through the forest while chased by a dog, but towards somewhere she knew she could escape.

Although, I didn't know how she could have found her way in the dark even if she wasn't pursued. Melanie was a city girl, like me. We were immediately disorientated once surrounded by nature.

Juliet wandered over to the back wall of the barn. Shelves of dog food and toys stretched across it.

'What happened this morning?' I asked.

'I got up early, like usual. About six.' Karl turned slightly to keep both me and Juliet in his line of sight. 'I noticed there was a problem when I came to feed the dogs. Lucy was missing.'

He pushed away from the post and led me over to an empty stall near where Juliet was snooping. In the next space, the interested Alsatian bounced onto its hind legs. It wagged ecstatically when Karl rested his hand between its ears.

'Can you describe Lucy?' I asked.

'She's a big dog, bigger than Artie here.' He patted the dog absently. 'White Shepherd. Beautiful, but a brute. She doesn't like anyone apart from Mr Dunlow. He spoils her. She's the one that bit Leo the other day.'

'Does Leo like the dogs?'

'Yeah.' When Karl smiled, a dimple formed in his left cheek. It made him look younger, early thirties rather than late. 'He's great with them. It shook him up when Lucy turned on him.'

'Did he get the bite seen to?' That would be one way to check Leo had been bitten when he said he had. It didn't seem like Karl was lying, but he could be a far better actor than Leo.

'I had a look at it. It wasn't nasty, no worse than I've had before. I told him if it started swelling or itching he needed to go to the hospital, but he wasn't too bothered.'

'What did you do when you noticed Lucy was missing?' I asked.

'Nothing. I wasn't too concerned. The dogs get out occasionally. They like the woods, but they come back when they get hungry or lonely. I had a quick look around the barn but I won't feel worried unless she's missing for a few days.'

'She's still not returned?'

'No.' Karl scratched between Artie's pointed ears. 'If you ask me, she was the dog that did that to the girl's face. I didn't get a good look, just grabbed the dogs and called the police, but I wouldn't be surprised if you found some white fur. Lucy's a terrible moulter.'

Her stall had clumps of discoloured fur in the corners. The side panel shuddered as Artie's tail thumped into it.

'Why have you got plastic gloves out here?' Juliet pointed at an open box on the top shelf.

Karl swallowed. 'Sometimes I have to help the dogs, you know, do their business. It's an anal gland thing.'

'Say no more.' Juliet walked away from the back wall, her lips downturned in disgust.

I flipped over a page in my notepad, suppressing a smile. 'After you noticed Lucy was gone, you went into the forest?'

'Yeah. I took a couple of the dogs with me, Bane and Wolfie.' Karl stepped away from Artie's stall to point at two others. 'We walked the route I take most mornings; around the edge of the estate, then back through the middle of the forest.'

'What did you do when you found the body?'

'I didn't find it.' Karl rubbed at the stubble on his chin. 'Bane did. He came running over, barking like crazy and pulling at my arm until I followed. Like I said, once I saw the body, I got the dogs away and called the police, then Mr Dunlow.' He paused. 'Whoever did it, I don't know if they're stupid or didn't know I walk through the forest every day, but that girl was going to be found.'

I noted that down. None of the suspects we'd talked to seemed unintelligent, but Karl made a good point. Why would anyone leave a body where it would be discovered?

'How did Mr Dunlow react when you told him about the body?' Juliet asked.

'Honestly?' Karl looked between us. 'He was annoyed. Doesn't mean he did it or anything. That's the way he always is. He and Terence are too stuck up to talk to the likes of me. I'm not sure Mr Dunlow's got it in him, no matter how much he likes shooting at the range and on the hunt.'

Karl shook his head and walked towards the wide doors of the barn. I quickly scrubbed between Artie's ears. He licked at my wrist.

Juliet kept pace beside Karl, and I hurried to catch up. 'Can you confirm Terence was off the property last night?' she asked.

'Yeah. Ted left yesterday afternoon. A wedding or something.' Karl looked up at the dark sky. The sun had set while we were inside the barn. The only light came from the bright moon. 'Is there anything else? Only, I need to get on. I'm behind as it is.'

'We need a DNA sample.' Juliet pulled a kit out of her pocket.

Without protest, Karl wiped the swab around the inside of his mouth and passed the closed tube back to her. 'Is that everything?'

I wished there was more light, that the nearby trees weren't half-blocking the moon. There was something lurking behind Karl's words. It was like he expected us to have more to ask about.

'No, that's it. Thank you for talking to us,' I said.

Karl strode off through the forest. Keeping him in sight, we followed at a more sedate pace and arrived at the car as he closed the door of his cottage.

'We're not invited in then,' Juliet muttered.

A light came on in one of the rooms. From this far away, it was impossible to see inside. Movement from behind the murky panes of glass could have been the curtains whisking shut.

Jordan. Sent 19:34.

Didn't see you at school – where you at? Please
don't ghost me. I promise I'll do better xx

From: Angela Dobson
angela.dobson@superintendent.gov.uk
To: Juliet Stern **juliet.stern@mit.gov.uk**
CC: David Rees **david.rees@forensics.gov.uk**
Date: **10 October, 19:39**
Subject: **Operation Chalice – Forensic compromise**

Juliet,

David has informed me that you removed evidence from a body at the active crime scene on the Dunlow Estate before the arrival of the forensic team. I don't care that they were delayed by another case, that's no excuse for tampering with evidence.

The manner in which a body is handled at the scene of death can not only alter the appearance of the deceased person but also might influence the subsequent evaluation of evidence. It is vital that you work together with the many other services involved to ensure that the deceased are handled appropriately and this effect is minimised.

This is not the first time I've had to reprimand you for similar actions. I understand that any delays are frustrating, but do not let this get the better of your good judgement.

Thankfully, the body was photographed prior to your arrival at the scene and your retrieval of evidence was properly noted in the scene log. Despite this good fortune, I am surprised this has happened.

If you're accused of something like this again, we are going to have a serious discussion and I may have to take disciplinary action. A copy of this email has been placed on the official murder log.

I hope the girls and Keith are well.

Detective Superintendent Angela Dobson

News archives – violent crime

Man found guilty of murdering his wife and violently assaulting his son

A man who beat his wife to death and left his son in a critical condition in their North Yorkshire home has been convicted of murder and grievous bodily harm.

Matthew Biss, 42, beat Jennifer Biss née Clements, 35, to death with a golf club just before 9 p.m. on 7 May. He beat his seventeen-year-old son, Karl Biss, to unconsciousness.

Neighbours reported hearing a loud altercation between the couple earlier in the evening. The police were called after shouts and screams were heard at around 8 p.m. Matthew Biss was apprehended at the scene.

Paramedics arrived just after 9 p.m. Jennifer Biss was pronounced dead at the scene but Karl Biss was taken to hospital, where he recovered from his injuries. After regaining consciousness, he was able to positively identify his father as both his and his mother's attacker.

Matthew Biss refused to cooperate with police and pleaded not guilty. He has been sentenced to life imprisonment.

Gabe

'You've been busy.' I placed a sweating takeaway container on Juliet's desk.

She'd gotten out the twine. The wall of evidence had been populated with pictures and articles while I was at the Chinese restaurant down the road. Lime green strands connected each of the suspects to Melanie.

Juliet grabbed the container and came to stand beside me. She shovelled a forkful of noodles into her mouth. There were purplish bags under her eyes, which would only grow as this case wore on. I'd tried to express concern for her before. That had resulted in two weeks of curt replies and coldness. The most I could do was ensure she went home at a reasonable time each night and feed her at regular intervals.

'I've been working on our main suspects,' Juliet said between mouthfuls. 'There's not much to follow up on, but I've been digging into their pasts.'

'Anything interesting?' I picked up a spring roll and bit off one end.

'Dunlow is squeaky clean. A few bad reviews on blog sites, but nothing more than you'd expect from a man who's helping big companies squash smaller ones. He's a member of the local shooting range, like Karl said. No previous convictions, not even a speeding ticket.

'Leo goes to an all-boys private school. I've emailed to find out more about him but there's nothing on him in the system. No idea how either of them would be connected to the victim.'

She chewed on her noodles. 'I've put Terence on the board too. I've emailed to check his alibi, but we can discount him for now.'

'What about Karl?' I nodded towards a picture of the grounds-keeper that must have been taken a while ago. His hair was squashed under a graduation cap. The photo was surrounded by notes and articles.

'There's a lot he didn't tell us.' Juliet stabbed her fork at him. 'He's not from around here, has moved from job to job despite a first-class history degree. He's been working for Dunlow for just over a year, the longest he's stayed anywhere. He grew up in Yorkshire, was left without family when his father killed his mother with a golf club. Beat Karl half to death too.'

'Sad story.' I bent down to read the article. Karl's father scowled from a black-and-white mugshot. He didn't look anything like his son; his face twisted and hair shaved close to his scalp. This explained Karl's wary reticence. He wouldn't want us rummaging around in his past.

'A history of violence in the family,' Juliet corrected. 'He's emailed over the list of people with keys to the estate, but we need to speak to him again.'

I moved away from the wall of evidence and picked up another spring roll as I sat down at my desk. 'I don't see him as a killer, no matter what his father did. Why would he have called in the body if he'd killed Melanie? He knows those woods better than anyone, could have hidden her if he'd wanted to.'

Juliet chucked her empty container into the bin and sat down, her chair angled towards the wall of evidence. 'Maybe he was lying about that too. Maybe the others go into the forest more than he said, and he knew he couldn't hide the body forever.'

'I thought you liked him?' I used my grease-free hand to wiggle my mouse, bringing my computer to life. 'What motive would he have had to kill Melanie?'

'What reason did any of them have to murder her?' Juliet asked, ignoring my first comment. 'And why was Melanie even on the estate?'

'Leo knows something.' I looked over at his photo on the wall.

'Definitely.'

'The pathologist might be able to give us something to go on,' I said, reading an email. 'They can see us tomorrow afternoon. And maybe Ida will be able to help us form a connection between Melanie and one of these men. If not, we'll have to talk to them again and hope one of them slips up.'

Juliet nodded, her lips pushed to one side as she stared at her computer screen. I glanced at the wall, my eyes drifting to Karl's picture. He and I both knew what it was like for a life to be marred by horrific violence. And what it was like to be judged because of it.

51

Gabe. Sent 19:53.

I'll be done at work soon if you're still up for meeting?

Ollie. Sent 19:54.

I am. I'm looking forward to it x

Gabe. Sent 19:59.

Same. I'll be out of here at about 8:30. Meet you then?

Ollie. Sent 20:01.

Sure. I'll get you a drink in x

Call connected at 20:27.

'Hello?'

'Hey, it's me.'

'Juliet? You're calling late.'

'I wanted to let you know a new case has come in.'

'Right.'

'That means I probably won't be able to get away this weekend.'

'I know what it means.'

'Keith. Don't.'

'Don't what?'

'Don't be like that.'

'Fine.'

'What will you tell the girls?'

'What I always do. Your mummy loves you. She's sorry she can't be here but she's busy making the world a better place.'

'Good. Thank you.'

'They miss you.'

'I miss them. I'll call tomorrow, talk to them too.'

'Okay. Love you.'

'I've got to go. Bye.'

Unknown number. Sent 21:46.

You're home now. Where's my money?

Gabe

'Believe it or not, this isn't something I usually do,' Ollie gasped.

His chest rose and fell with his laboured breaths, his flawless bronze skin shiny with sweat. In the streetlight filtering through my thin curtains, I could just about see the dark patterns of tattoos twisting across his shoulders.

'But this is what you need, right?' he murmured.

'What do you mean?'

I didn't want to reply to his previous comment. This was something I did on a semi-regular basis, my craving for human contact and the moment of forgetting that sex allowed me overtaking my pathetic inability to form lasting relationships. Discussing that would dramatically reduce the chances of this happening again, and I already wanted it to.

Ollie turned his head towards me, his back flat on the mattress. I couldn't read his expression in the darkness, but his lips pulled into a gentle smile. 'You're wounded, somehow. I can see it in your eyes. And this is what you need, so how could I not give it to you?'

I blinked, my heart constricting. He was flaying me, pulling back my skin and peering at the darkness within, the pain wedged between my ribs. I hoped he was particularly perceptive, rather than my inner damage being obvious to everyone.

Normally, when someone got this close to the truth, I'd push them away. But I didn't want Ollie to leave. It wasn't that he was a warm body; I'd been temporarily comforted by them before. Ollie was different. Even before we'd fallen into bed, I'd felt calm. He might see too much, but he handled that insight carefully.

'Will you stay?' The vulnerability of the question almost choked me.

Under the covers, Ollie's hand found mine. He threaded our fingers together and squeezed.

Still smiling, he rolled his head to look up at the ceiling. 'How could I say no?'

Day 2

Wednesday, 11 October

BODY OF LITTLE GIRL LEFT IN A BIN – READ AN EXCLUSIVE
INTERVIEW WITH THE WOMAN WHO FOUND HER...

Scroll.

DERELICTION OF DUTY? – POLICE REFUSE TO COMMENT
AFTER A YOUNG GIRL IS KILLED...

Scroll.

WHAT MORE COULD HAVE BEEN DONE? – SHE WAS AN
INNOCENT CHILD...

Scroll.

My Lion. Sent 8:02.

Mel, please don't ignore me. I'm scared x

Call connected at 9:04.

'Hello, Detective Inspector Juliet Stern.'

'Hi. I'm returning a call. It's Laura, Mr Dunlow's personal assistant. Is now a good time?'

'It is. I believe you have a key to the Dunlow Estate?'

'I do.'

'When did you last use it?'

'Let me check the calendar. I needed some paperwork and Mr Dunlow was away, working with clients in London. Okay. Yeah. Must have been the 2nd of this month.'

'And you have the key now?'

'Um, let me check my purse. I keep it on me just in case Mr Dunlow needs me to get anything. Yes, it's here.'

'No one could have removed it between your last visit and now?'

'I don't think so. I keep my bag with me at work, and I live alone.'

'Thank you, Laura. Could you tell me what you were doing on the night of the 9th?'

'Oh, you need to know that? Well, I had dinner with a friend and after we went for drinks. I got home at about midnight. I can show you the receipt for the Uber?'

'That would be helpful. My assistant will be in touch.'

'I can give you the meal receipt as well.'

'Sure. Thank you for your time, Laura. If you notice anything or want to tell me about something you see or hear, please use this number.'

'Um, okay. Can I ask? Everyone here is talking about what happened. Mr Dunlow's not in trouble, is he?'

'We are following multiple lines of enquiry.'

'Okay. It's just, Mr Dunlow's not a murderer. I know he's not always the kindest boss and some people don't like him, but he wouldn't kill someone.'

'Thank you, Laura. I'll be in contact if we have any more questions.'

Gabe

'Unprompted, she told me her boss might be a shit human being, but he isn't a murderer.' Juliet finished telling me about her conversation with Dunlow's receptionist as we walked up the stairs to Ida's flat.

'Interesting she would jump to the conclusion he's a suspect.'

'That's what I thought,' Juliet said. 'Could be that, unconsciously, she actually does think he's capable. Or, he's such a dickhead that she's gotten used to people thinking he's worse than he is, and she doesn't want our judgement clouded.'

We reached Ida's floor and walked over to the blue door. From the outside, there was no way of telling the inhabitant's life had monumentally changed. I knocked and unbuttoned my coat. Seconds later, the door half-opened.

'Hello, Ida. I hope this is a good time?'

She stared at me with bloodshot eyes, but pulled the door wide and led us through to the living room. The smell of cigarettes was much stronger. Several bent butts rested in the ash tray. Candles flickered on top of the electric heater, surrounded by pictures of the same smiling young woman.

I sat strategically on the edge of the sofa so that I didn't sink. Juliet crossed one leg over the other, her face set in a calm smile. People who met her at times like this might think she was kind and sympathetic. The illusion lasted as long as she didn't open her mouth.

Ida sported the dazed look of the recently bereaved. Despite their physical differences, Ida's blank expression reminded me of my mum. For months of my childhood, she'd retreated into an invisible shell, her eyes unfocused even when she spoke to me.

I swallowed. I didn't need to think about that now, or ever. I pulled my notepad out of my pocket and set it on my knee.

'We would like to talk about the incident on the Dunlow Estate that we believe involved Melanie and ask you a few more questions,' I said. 'If there's anything you don't understand or don't want to answer right now, just let me know.'

Ida stared impassively at me. I gulped, my throat dry. I would have liked a glass of water, but I couldn't ask. Ida's negligence was of a different nature to Dunlow's, but no less impenetrable.

'Firstly, I want to apologise. The autopsy of the body found on the Dunlow Estate has been pushed back to this afternoon, so we have been unable to make a formal identification. However, we are reasonably sure it's Melanie.'

'Do you need me to come look at her?' Ida's voice was a hollow croak.

'That's not necessary.' We wouldn't put her through that unless we had no other option. 'We found Melanie's purse in the victim's pocket, and the coroner will check her dental records.'

'I would like to see her.' Deep creases formed around Ida's eyes.

I faltered. If she insisted, we couldn't stop her.

'Ida?' Juliet clasped her hands together on her knee. 'The victim was shot, but an animal was also involved. Identifying Melanie would be incredibly unpleasant.'

'She would want you to remember her as she was,' I added. 'Rather than what was done to her.'

A tear tracked down Ida's face. She seemed to barely register the new information about her granddaughter's death. 'Whatever you think is best.'

Juliet's stark stating of facts had been effective at both sparing Ida pain and moving the interview along. I could learn something from that.

'Yesterday, you told me that Melanie's parents had passed away.' I waited for Ida to refocus on me. Her gaze had strayed over to the pictures on the heater. 'Could you tell me about that?'

'It happened four years ago,' Ida said in a dull monotone. 'Her father was a drinker, always drank and drove even though Suzanna, my daughter, begged him not to. They weren't married, and I thought one day she would grow tired of his mess and leave him. I came to this country with my husband because it offered opportunities we couldn't dream of in Nigeria. I wanted Suzanna to take advantage of them too, but then she got mixed up with him.

'That evening, he won big at cards. He was drinking into the night. Suzanna wanted to get a taxi home, their friends heard them arguing about it before they left the pub, but she was a soft girl, too soft, and she always did what he said. He managed two roads before he crashed into a lamppost. He was killed instantly. Suzanna died in the ambulance on the way to the hospital.'

'I'm sorry,' I said.

'Melanie was alone at home, waiting for them. She heard the sirens. She said she knew, but I wonder if every time her father was out drinking, she was waiting for bad news. After that, she came to live with me.'

'What was her life here like? Did she have many friends?' I flipped a page in my notebook, happy to move away from her parents' deaths.

'Melanie was a quiet girl, head in her books most of the time.' Ida frowned. 'She had a boyfriend. Jordan.'

'Do you know his last name?' I asked.

'Something like Hines, Himes.' Ida's bloodshot eyes narrowed. 'He didn't come here. I didn't approve of a boyfriend at her age.'

'I see.' I noted the possible surnames. A boyfriend was more likely to know the intimate details of a teenager's life than a grandmother. 'Ida, can you think of any reason Melanie would have been on the Dunlow Estate two nights ago?'

Ida shook her head, burying her hands in her skirt. 'She told me she was out with friends, that she was going to stay the night.'

Ida obviously loved her granddaughter but had little idea of what she was up to.

'I'm sorry to ask you this, but can you think of anyone who would have wanted to harm Melanie?' I asked.

Ida's eyes filled with tears. 'No one. I don't know who could have done this to my sweet girl.'

The front door clicked open. Evie appeared in the living room doorway, her wizened face falling into a scowl when she spotted Juliet and me. Her hair was bound into a tangled bun and her dungarees were a sombre black.

'Could we take a look at Melanie's bedroom?' I asked. We needed to gather evidence, but it would give the women a chance to comfort one another in peace.

'It's the second door on the left,' Evie said. 'Would you like a drink?'

Juliet stood. 'Water would be lovely.'

'Tea, please. Milk, no sugar.' My thighs complained as I rose. 'We won't be long.'

'Have you moved anything in Melanie's room?' Juliet asked.

Ida closed her eyes in a long blink. 'I haven't been in there at all.'

'Good.' Juliet swept out of the room.

I offered Ida a smile but her face was turned to the hastily erected shrine. Evie's narrowed eyes tracked me out of the room.

The smell of cigarettes receded as I walked into Melanie's bedroom, replaced by cheap body spray and fresh linen. I closed the door behind me.

Juliet had already pulled on a pair of plastic gloves and was picking through the bookshelves surrounding a narrow window. The bed had been made in a hurry, the purple duvet pulled over a rumpled sheet. A pile of folded laundry sat on a wooden chair beside a desk covered in an assortment of books and make-up. Above the bed, notes and pictures were tacked to the wall. Odd song lyrics preached unfailing love and quotes from celebrities demanded I did my best.

I pulled a selfie from the wall and slipped it into my notepad. Melanie's hair hid under a knitted hat, her eyes shining with uncontained glee. It was clearly a picture she'd liked. If we were going to pin a photo to our evidence wall, it might as well be one she'd preferred.

'Nothing here.' Juliet flicked through the last book and replaced it on the bottom shelf. She walked over to examine the desk.

I turned to the chest of drawers beside the bed. A mirror rested against the wall, pony figurines lined up across the top. Their manes were coated in dust. I examined the undersides and found nothing but stickers proclaiming their country of origin. I replaced them and opened the top drawer. Nose wrinkled, I picked through Melanie's bright underwear. My fingers met nothing but soft fabric. I patted through the clothes in the next drawer, tops and vests folded into neat piles.

The third drawer stuck. When I reached behind colourful jumpers and leggings, I found a box. I slipped it straight into an evidence bag. No wonder it was hidden. Ida, who didn't even want her seventeen-year-old granddaughter dating, would not have approved of her stashing condoms in her bedroom.

Juliet placed a couple of bags beside mine. She hadn't found much; a condom wrapper pulled from the bin and a packet of cigarettes. I labelled them carefully, my pen smudging on the uneven surface.

Leaving them on the duvet, I got down on my hands and knees while Juliet rifled inside the wardrobe. I worked through boxes of old school books and dusty jeans shoved under the bed.

I replaced the last box and sat back on my heels. 'Nothing.'

'It would have been handy if there was a secret diary, detailing exactly who she planned to meet.' Juliet shut the wardrobe doors.

'That would have been incredibly helpful.'

My legs protested again as I stood. Round two with Ollie this morning had been unexpected yet pleasant, but I needed to conserve my energy on work days.

I slid the evidence bags into my coat pocket and followed Juliet through to the living room. Evie bustled in with drinks as we sat on the sinking sofa. She poured each of us a cup of tea from a pot patterned with yellow flowers. Juliet took hers without a word. She knew better than to refuse anything from a family member, even a drink she claimed tasted like warmed pond water.

Ida set her cup on the table beside her chair. The ashtray had been tidied away and a window cracked open. Yellowing net curtains moved in the breeze. 'Evie wanted to talk to you.'

Ida's friend sat in another armchair, her misshapen hands cupped around her drink.

I placed my cup on the floor and pulled out my notepad. 'What did you want to tell us?'

'Ida told me Melanie was shot.' Evie's dark brown eyes flicked over to Ida, and her face hardened. 'I think Jordan did it.'

Ida gasped, and a trickle of tea escaped her cup. She didn't seem to notice it shoring up against her fingers.

Evie did. 'Ida, you've scalded yourself.' She jumped up and took the drink. 'Come on, let's run your hand under cold water.'

While Evie hurried Ida out of the room, Juliet and I exchanged a glance. I didn't think it likely Evie would have any great insight into Melanie's life, but she might have picked up on something. Older people had a tendency to go unnoticed. Evie bustled back into the room, the sound of water flowing cut off as she shut the door to the kitchen.

I sat forward. 'Why do you think Jordan did it?'

'He used to hit Melanie.' Evie perched on the edge of the armchair. 'She was scared of him. She didn't want to be his girlfriend anymore.'

'How do you know he hit Melanie?' I asked.

'She showed me the bruises on her legs one day when Ida was down at the shops. Made me promise not to tell. Like I would. Knowing her granddaughter was involved with the same kind of scum that killed her daughter would have broken Ida's heart.'

'What makes you think that Jordan killed Melanie?' I asked.

'She was trying to get rid of him. I told her, he was no good for her. Anyway, she liked someone else. I think Jordan found out and killed her.'

I scribbled notes. 'Do you know who she'd developed feelings for?'

'No.' Evie's nostrils flared. 'She was being secretive. I noticed her texting one time, and she told me to mind my own business. She called him "My Lion".'

'Lion?' I looked at Juliet. It didn't take a genius to crack that code. She took a sip of her tea and grimaced.

'Do you have any idea why Melanie would have been on the Dunlow Estate?' I asked Evie.

'No. None of us know anyone over that way.' She chewed her bottom lip. 'I reckon Jordan lured her there and killed her where he thought no one would find the body.'

That edged close to Karl's theory. Jordan might not have known the woods were well patrolled. There were stretches of land we'd passed as we drove over to the Dunlow Estate that looked untouched.

The kitchen door opened and Ida shuffled into the room. She sank into her seat and Evie refilled her cup.

'Thank you for talking to us, and for letting us look at Melanie's room.' I took a gulp of tea and stood up.

Juliet rose and passed her cup to me. I didn't know if it was advisable to leave her, but I walked through to the kitchen. The sides were clear except for a microwave meal for one defrosting on a plate.

'We hope to have access to the analysis of Melanie's phone soon,' Juliet explained. I drank my tea while pouring hers into the sink. 'She was carrying it when she died. Do you have any idea what her passcode is?'

'I wouldn't know anything like that,' Ida said.

'That's okay,' I said as I walked back into the room. 'Thank you, Ida. We'll be in touch, but if anything else occurs to you, give us a call.'

'I'll show you out,' Evie said.

I smiled at Ida once more, but she had looked away. Flickering candlelight briefly caught on the damp patches beneath her eyes.

We followed Evie to the front door. She marched right out into the hall.

'There's something else you need to know.' She reached past me to pull the door shut. 'Ida sees what she wants when it comes to that girl. She doesn't see the truth.'

'What do you mean?' I asked.

'What I mean is; maybe she was a little too like her mother and hung around with the wrong sort of person. Maybe she did something they didn't like and brought this on herself.'

Evie grabbed the doorhandle and let herself back into Ida's flat. The letterbox rattled as she slammed the door.

Juliet raised one elegant eyebrow, a grin rising to her lips.

'Not here,' I said, turning towards the stairs.

Evie might trust that conversations wouldn't be overheard in a communal hallway, but the last thing we needed was a complaint about how one of the detectives on a murder case was bad mouthing a victim's friends and family.

I couldn't help voicing one theory. 'Do you think "lion" could be the passcode for Melanie's phone?'

From: Alice To **alice.to@police.gov.uk**
To: Gabriella Martin **gabriella.martin@mit.gov.uk**
Date: **11 October, 11:06**
Subject: **After work drinks**

Hi Gabe,

A few of us are heading to the Scholars Arms after work tonight.
I'd love to buy you a drink to say thanks for being so kind to me
yesterday.

Pop in if you're free!

Alice

Unknown number. Sent 11:37.

Give me my money.

DRUNK DRIVER KILLS HIMSELF AND PARTNER IN CRASH

Residents of Milo Street were woken in the early hours when a Ford Fiesta collided with a lamppost situated in the middle of the road. Both police and ambulance were called, but the driver, Daniel Sithole, was pronounced dead at the scene. The passenger, Suzanna Pirt, was rushed to hospital but she passed away en route.

The couple are survived by a teenage daughter who is now being cared for by her grandmother. She was at home at the time of the crash.

Daniel Sithole, who had a previous conviction for drink driving, was unlicensed at the time of the accident as it had been previously revoked by the police. Neighbours reported seeing him driving recklessly on many occasions, sometimes with both his partner and daughter in the car.

A spokesperson for the local police said, 'This was a tragic incident where two people were killed. If you have any information or dash cam footage you think will help with this enquiry, please contact the incident room.'

Gabe

I was pinning Melanie's selfie on the wall when Juliet huffed into our office, a sandwich in each hand. She passed one to me.

'We need to hustle.' She tore open her lunch. 'The pathologist held up the autopsy, but they'll refuse to see us if we don't arrive on time.'

I pulled at my sandwich's plastic casing as I sat down. Eating didn't hold much appeal, considering our plan for this afternoon. I bit off one corner. The bread was thinly sliced, the cheese tasteless.

'What did you think of Evie's assessment of the boyfriend?' Juliet didn't look at me, her eyes on her computer screen.

I swallowed. 'If there are marks on Melanie's body, we'll have something to work with. But we only have Evie's word that Jordan was hurting her.'

'There might be something on Melanie's phone.' Juliet clicked her mouse and our printer hummed to life. 'I've requested it be looked over by the IT team as soon as possible and I passed on your tip about the passcode.' She picked up the piece of paper. 'You didn't ask where Ida or Evie were when Melanie was killed.'

'I thought we agreed Ida wasn't involved? She wasn't about to murder her only remaining relative. And Evie was too small to have made that boot print.'

'They could be accomplices.' Juliet snipped at the paper.

'You're messing with me, right? Evie might not have liked Melanie, but I can't see her disapproval becoming a plot to kill.'

'Yes, I'm not serious. Although I would love to have Evie in for a formal interview. She'd be a firecracker.' Juliet stood up and pinned pieces of paper to the wall. One was a newspaper clipping reporting the death of Melanie's parents. 'Try not to let your vision get clouded by how innocent anyone seems though. Those women might have loved Melanie and they might have not committed the murder themselves, but this wouldn't be the first time someone did something stupid or reckless and got someone they loved killed.'

The already unappealing sandwich turned to paste in my mouth. 'You think I should have pushed harder at Ida's?'

Juliet shrugged. 'We got good information. Don't beat yourself up. Just don't be afraid to ruffle some feathers. You're a natural at kindness, which will get some people to open up and was probably the right tack earlier, but sometimes you'll need to be harsher.'

I bit my lip. One thing that had become apparent after working two minutes together was that I was the softer touch. I had to remember Juliet wasn't telling me to be like her, but that there were times when her more direct approach would get better results.

Juliet stepped back from the wall. She'd attached a grainy picture of a thin, white boy to the board. A cigarette dangled from his lips. 'The boyfriend is Jordan Haines,' she told me. 'I've asked Maddy to arrange a meeting with him. Evie might be wrong about the beating and the new beau, but Jordan knew Melanie well. He might be able to tell us why she was on the estate that night.'

Juliet wound more lime green twine across the board, connecting Melanie to a growing web of names. I turned to my sandwich before her smiling face could morph into the mutilated mess I'd seen on the forest floor.

Ollie. Sent 13:02.

I am not a booty call. Meetings must have some kind of food involved from now on xx

Gabe. Sent 13:15.

Does breakfast count? x

Ollie. Sent 13.16.

Cheeky. I can't do tonight. Tomorrow? xx

Gabe

'Shall we begin?' Derek asked.

He and his assistant stood on one side of the examination table, Juliet and I on the other. Melanie's body lay under a beige sheet between us. Derek pressed the record button on a shiny Dictaphone.

An extra strong mint burned on my tongue. Strip lights bounced on the white wall and floor tiles, glinting off the metal instruments on a table to our right. No one could mistake the purpose of this room, but that wasn't why goosepimples were rising across my arms.

I rolled my shoulders. Derek was one of the nicer pathologists. He was in his late forties, with marks of smiles around his eyes. The lights reflected off the hairless brown dome of his head. Despite Juliet's predictions of doom as I'd driven over, he hadn't been too much of an arse when we'd signed in two minutes late.

'We can't stay for the whole autopsy,' Juliet announced. 'We've got to dash for an interview with a suspect after the external examination.'

I tried not to sag too obviously with relief. I had no idea what Juliet was talking about, but I'd take any task over witnessing a complete investigation in this room.

Derek sighed. 'David and the rest of the forensic team can't be here either. You'll all have to depend on the recording and photographs, for the most part.' He gestured at the young man hovering near the edge of the table, a clunky camera held in his hands. 'Roland's earning his keep today.'

The blond man blushed but pressed his lips together in concentration when Derek spoke again. 'There is a lot of damage to the body we'll have to sort through. Let's go from the top down.'

Without ceremony, he lifted the sheet away from Melanie's face. Juliet stilled, holding her breath for a beat before exhaling. A chemical smell overlaid any lingering scent of blood or decay. Roland's camera clicked.

It wasn't as bad as I'd expected. Melanie's face was largely intact, the worst of the damage clogged with twigs and dirt. Only one part of her chin bone flashed through the meaty gore, bright against her dark brown skin.

Removed from where she had been left for dead on the forest floor, I could see the similarities to the photos at Ida's flat. This was definitely Melanie Pirt. I felt a twinge of sadness for Ida. She'd been wracked with grief, but there would have been a kernel of hope that we'd gotten this all horribly wrong.

'The victim's face was mauled by an animal.' Derek poked at the mangled flesh with a metal probe. 'We believe this happened shortly after she died, due to the amount of blood in the wounds and the pattern of clotting. We'll send off samples to confirm.'

'Would an Alsatian make sense?' I focused on unmarked pieces of Melanie's face while Derek placed cotton swabs and carefully moved sections of flesh into plastic bags. A patch above her artfully plucked brows was smooth.

'I don't know my dog breeds well enough to tell.' Derek tilted his head to the side. 'If you got me a picture of the jaw and teeth, I could guess. Once we find the animal, the vet will be able to say for certain.'

'Great.' I pulled out my notebook, lifting it higher than necessary to block out Melanie's face.

'Do you have any idea how long the gap was between her dying and being found?' Juliet asked.

'Could only have been six or seven hours.' Derek pulled the sheet further down Melanie's body.

Hand tight around my pencil, I braced myself before looking. A modesty strip had been placed across Melanie's breasts, leaving the bullet holes in her torso visible.

'Looks like the victim was shot three times from behind.' Derek picked up a metal rod and worked it into the bullet wound closest to him. He did the same to the others, Roland's camera the only sound in the cool room. 'The bullets all went through but one ruptured her stomach. The victim would have died quickly, perhaps even before she hit the ground.'

Small mercies. At least I could tell Ida that Melanie wouldn't have suffered for long.

I pressed the mint hard into the roof of my mouth and repositioned my notepad as Derek pulled the sheet down to examine Melanie's genitals. Juliet's face was still, her eyes on Derek's hands.

'The victim had sex earlier in the day. Unprotected, it looks like.' Derek pulled the sheet up, covering most of Melanie's torso. 'We'll take samples from the area for testing later.'

'Right.' I made a note to ask the boyfriend about that. If Melanie hadn't had sex with him, that gave him a clear motive for murder.

Derek moved to the bottom of the table and lifted the sheet over Melanie's feet. The joints of her big toes jutted, like she'd worn too many pairs of heels while the bones were developing. Derek bunched the sheet up to expose her thighs.

'The bruising here is recent, presumably sustained during the chase. A ligament was torn.' Derek moved a clean probe away from a deep purple stain on the inside of Melanie's right leg. 'These are less recent.' He pointed at a patch of dull circular bruises on her thighs. 'Looks like someone had been punching her. Could be self-inflicted, but these markings are consistent with a fist. It would have been difficult to punch herself hard enough from that angle.'

Ida was wrong then; someone did want to hurt Melanie. They already were.

'Good work,' Juliet said, as Derek laid the sheet over Melanie's body and pressed a button to stop the recording. 'Sorry we have to shoot off.'

He and Juliet moved away, dumping their gloves in a bin as they discussed when the full report would be ready. I shoved my notepad into my pocket, ignored by Roland as he clicked through the photos he'd taken.

One of Melanie's hands had been left exposed. It was delicate, the joints slender. The palm was no doubt torn and bruised, but looking at the back of her hand, I could imagine a whole, undamaged body lay beneath the sheet. The only indication of anything wrong was one missing blue acrylic nail, snapped from her middle finger.

'Gabe?' Juliet called from over by the door. 'You alright?'

I pulled the sheet over Melanie's hand and hurried across the room. Derek walked back to the body, so didn't witness my fingers shaking as I tugged off my gloves and threw them in the bin.

'I'm fine.' I held the door open for Juliet. She swept through, her lips a thin line.

She was right; I couldn't feel everything. A young woman had been murdered and that was terribly sad, but I needed to focus if we were going to catch Melanie's killer. If I wanted to get the job done and successfully lead my first case, then I needed to toughen up and start asking harsh questions.

Keith. Sent 14:46.

Juliet, can you give me a call when you get this? We need to talk x

Juliet. Sent 15:11.

I'm working.

Keith. Sent 15:12.

You can't drop your responsibilities because there's an interesting case.

Keith. Sent 15:13.

I can see you've read my message.

Keith. Sent 15:13.

You shouldn't ignore me, Juliet.

Call connected at 15:48.

'Hello?'

'Hello. Is that Ida?'

'Yes. Who is this?'

'It's Detective Sergeant Gabe Martin. Ida, we've met with the pathologist. I'm sorry to tell you, but we can now confirm that the body found on the Dunlow Estate was Melanie.'

'Oh.'

'I'm truly sorry for your loss.'

'You still don't think I should come to see her?'

'It's not a good idea.'

'If you say so.'

'Would you like me to pass on your details to our bereavement services?'

'No, I don't think so.'

'We have specially trained officers who can liaise with you about the case.'

'I'd rather talk to you.'

'Well—'

'We're going to have a memorial. I know how these things work, I've seen it on TV. We won't be able to bury her for a while, but we want to do something.'

'It may take some time for her body to be released, at least until the initial stage of the investigation is over.'

'I thought as much. We're going to have a service at my church next week.'

'That's good.'

'I'd like it if you would come.'

'Oh. Once you have everything decided, send me the details. I'll try to be there.'

'Thank you.'

'Is there anything else, Ida?'

'You'll catch him? The man who did this?'

'We're doing everything we can to bring the person who killed Melanie to justice.'

'Good.'

'We'll release a short statement to the press later, naming Melanie as the victim and appealing for witnesses.'

'Will it be in the papers?'

'It might be.'

'They got that poor little girl on the front today.'

'Yes. Ida, I'll be in touch if we have any news.'

Gabe

'Jordan Haines is in meeting room two.' Maddy popped her head into our office, her green fingernails gripping the doorframe. Her hair was tied into a bun on top of her head, but stray locks curled around her ears.

'Thanks, Maddy.' Juliet locked her computer and stood.

I shoved a last bit of a Mars into my mouth. Pictures of White Alsatians filled my screen. It wasn't a popular breed. If we couldn't find the dog, I'd have to contact a breeder and ask them to take a picture of their dog's teeth. An odd request, even from a detective.

'Are you happy to sit in?' I asked, as we walked out into the open-plan office area.

'It's fine.' Maddy's brown hair bounced with every step, despite her attempt to confine it. 'He was such a charming young man on the phone, I wouldn't want to miss the chance to meet him in person.'

Juliet laughed as I let them walk on ahead. The main part of our floor was much busier than it had been earlier in the day. A large picture of Krystal Barrett, the young girl found in the bin store, was stuck to the far wall. Her broad smile was punctuated by missing teeth and her plaits were lopsided. Smaller pictures of her parents flanked her. They looked drab, ordinary. Certainly not the kind of people you'd suspect of killing their own child.

Only Juliet felt the need to decorate evidence walls with twine. Even if she wasn't in the minority, there wouldn't have been much wrapped around pins out here. Paul and his team had decided that one of the parents killed their daughter while the other looked on. Their main job was figuring out who the guiltiest party was.

A gummy feeling of guilt clogged my insides. Maybe I could have been helpful if this case had been assigned to Juliet and me, offered another perspective before everyone piled blame onto the parents. Experiences I tried to lock away could have shed a different light.

I shook myself. My involvement would have been a hindrance rather than an asset. Anything to do with kids was too close to home. I needed to focus on Melanie's murder, which was turning out to be far more difficult to unpick than any other case I'd worked on. We had too many suspects, far too few alibis, and no real evidence. Hopefully, Jordan would give us something concrete to work with.

We took the lift down to the ground floor, Juliet tapping at her phone and Maddy fiddling with a loose button on her cardigan. I gripped my notebook. I'd shed my coat upstairs, leaving my standard jumper and chinos. I wished for the protective bulk. If needed, I was going to implement Juliet's advice to be harsher. That wouldn't be a comfortable experience. Layers would have hidden a multitude of nervous ticks.

The lift doors slid open and we walked across the foyer. The front wall was made up entirely of glass. Normally it looked out onto a sleepy side street far from the bustling docks and shopping centres, but today a crowd milled on the pavement.

'The press is lurking,' Maddy murmured, as we averted our faces. 'They want to know more about what happened to the little girl.'

I wrinkled my nose, but smoothed my face to blankness as Juliet opened the meeting room door. The strong odour of cigarettes greeted us. The walls of the boxy space were painted an inoffensive cream and the furniture was picked from a mass-order catalogue. Jordan slouched on a square sofa. Behind him, peeling posters warned against a life of drug-related crime.

Jordan looked up as we entered, wearing a bored scowl. He had buzzcut dark blond hair and his pale skin was littered with blemishes. Juliet and I sat on the sofa opposite him, while Maddy perched on a chair off to one side. Jordan's grey eyes darted between us under eyebrows with asymmetrically shaved chunks. He leant back but his fists were clenched, the muscles of his arms tense under his off-white school shirt.

'Jordan, I'm Gabe Martin and this is Juliet Stern. We're detectives leading the investigation into an incident on the Dunlow Estate on Monday night. Maddy Campbell is here as a witness, as you're under eighteen. If you want to stop at any time or feel uncomfortable, please let us know.' I flipped over to a clean page in my notepad. 'You are not under arrest or caution, but we think you may be able to help.'

'I don't need her here.' Jordan's voice was high, whiney like metal cutting metal. He jerked his head towards Maddy. 'I don't know why I'm here. I don't know anyone over there.'

Maddy widened her eyes. Since Jordan hadn't demanded she leave, I'd keep her in. If we had to lean on anything said here in court, Maddy would confirm we hadn't coerced or scared Jordan. Not that he would admit to such weakness.

'Still, we'd like to ask you a few questions.' I rested my pencil on my pad. 'Can you please tell us about your relationship with Melanie Pirt?'

'Mel?' Jordan looked between Juliet and me. 'What's this got to do with her?'

'Could you answer the question?' Juliet's tone was mild, but I could sense the tension building behind her seemingly kind eyes. I might think Jordan was doing his best impression of a hard man, but she'd think he was a little shit.

Jordan looked ready to mutiny, his thin lips pressed together and his partial eyebrows furrowed, but then he relaxed, his hands flexing on his knees.

'She's my girlfriend. Kind of. We've been together on and off for two years. Lately more off than on.'

'Why's that?' I asked. It might be too much to hope Jordan would spontaneously confess he'd beaten Melanie, but he might say something accidentally incriminating.

'She gets clingy, demanding stuff from me, but then she can't hang out for weeks.' Jordan's pimple-lined jaw jutted. 'Her gran doesn't like me. We can't always hang out at mine, so we drive around in my mum's car. Mel gets annoyed when we do that.'

Apparently, Melanie hadn't told her on–off boyfriend about how her parents died.

'Were you and Melanie sexually active?' I asked. Those condoms could have been intended for Jordan, but his motive for murder increased if he was being refused sex or knew she was intimate with someone else.

'Yeah.' Blood flooded Jordan's cheeks. He was a child running around in an almost man's body.

'When did you last see Melanie?' I asked.

'I dunno.' Jordan kicked his heel into the sofa. 'We met up Sunday night, and I think I saw her at college after that. She wasn't there today, or yesterday. I texted and she ignored me.'

I made a note of that. 'What did you do on Sunday night?'

'Argued.' Jordan kicked the sofa again.

'What did you argue about?' I asked.

'Stupid stuff.'

'Did you have sex?'

Jordan glared at me. 'No.'

'You said you saw Melanie at school on Monday?' I moved on.

Juliet shifted beside me. I gripped my pencil, not sure if she was uncomfortable on the lumpy padding or if the movement meant something. Surely she didn't expect me to press harder for a full explanation of Jordan's argument with Melanie? That would alienate him, and he was just about cooperating as it was.

'Yeah,' he said. 'She wouldn't talk to me.'

'What did you do Monday night, after school and until the next morning?' I asked.

'I dunno.' Jordan scrunched up his face. 'I went home, watched some TV. My dad was around so I went up to my room.'

'Why did you go up to your room?'

'I don't like hanging out with him.' The corners of Jordan's mouth pulled down. 'I like it when it's just me and Mum.'

'So you went up to your room?' I gestured for Jordan to carry on.

'Yeah. I did some homework, went down for dinner but ate it in my room. I watched TV and fell asleep.'

'Can anyone confirm your whereabouts?' I asked. We didn't need another shaky alibi.

'Mum and Dad were downstairs.' Jordan sat up, planting his feet on the floor. He looked like a startled rodent, suddenly alert. 'What's this to do with? Why are you asking for my whereabouts?'

'Jordan?' Juliet tilted her head to one side. 'Did you ever hit Melanie?'

I schooled my features to nothingness while Jordan's fell open like a book. Blood flooded his cheeks, his eyes narrowing as he gritted his teeth.

'No.'

'Never?' Juliet poked.

'No,' Jordan ground the word out.

Juliet sat back, her lips pursed. I wasn't sure what had made her jump in. Maybe she wanted to gauge Jordan's reaction before we told him what had happened to Melanie.

And his reaction was telling. I'd bet he was the one hitting Melanie, or he had a good idea who was and was protecting them for some reason.

'Jordan?' I laid my pencil on my notepad. 'We invited you here because there was an incident on the Dunlow Estate on Monday night. Melanie was involved.'

Jordan's face slackened. 'Where is she? What do you mean, an incident?'

'I'm sorry to have to tell you this, but Melanie was shot and killed.'

Jordan's mouth fell open. Slowly, his fingers dug into the cheap fabric covering his thighs, his nails turning white.

I leant forward. 'Jordan, do you know anything about what happened? Is there anything you want to tell us?'

His chin trembled and his hands gripped harder. 'Do you know who did it?' His voice raised in pitch as he fought tears.

'We're in the process of an investigation.'

'So no, right?' He released his trousers and lifted an arm to hide his face in the crook of his elbow. 'Guys live there,' he muttered thickly.

'You said you didn't know anyone from the Dunlow Estate,' Juliet interjected.

Jordan lowered his arm, exposing the dampness around his eyes. 'I don't,' he spat. 'But I know there are guys living there. One of them goes to the posho school. Mel was texting someone new. Whoever it was, he was stalking her. Texting and calling her all the time.'

I picked up my notepad. 'Any idea who this was?'

'No, but it must have been someone from that fancy estate.' Jordan sniffed. 'Mel was scared. He wanted to meet up all the time. She thought he was a loser, she felt sorry for him, but he wouldn't let her go.'

'How long had this been going on for?' I asked.

Jordan huffed, his breath shuddering. 'I dunno. As long as me and Mel had been on the rocks, so a couple of months.'

I pressed my lips together, wondering how to ask my next question without antagonising Jordan or causing any further distress.

'Was Melanie having sex with anyone else?' Juliet asked.

That was one way to do it. Jordan flicked his watery eyes towards her in a death-glare.

'No.' His voice was at its lowest, verging on a growl. 'She wouldn't dare.'

I glanced at Juliet. 'I don't think we have anything else to ask today, Jordan, but would you mind coming in if we have any other questions?'

Jordan rubbed his knuckles across his eyes, the fight Juliet raised in him dissipating. 'What other questions? That stalker did it.'

'We'll look into that,' I said.

He stood abruptly. 'We done here?'

'Let me show you out.' Maddy jumped up and held the door open.

Jordan stormed out of the room. He was a tall young man, and one glance confirmed he wore big trainers. The once white fabric was murky with greens and browns.

I leant into the low cushions of the sofa. Strange that a piece of furniture would have been designed to make users so uncomfortable.

'That was interesting,' Juliet said.

I rubbed my face. 'Why did you jump in to ask about whether he'd hit Mel? And about her having sex with someone else?'

'You were building rapport with him, no matter how tenuous. As soon as you asked about either of those things, it would have broken down.'

So it wasn't that Juliet wanted me to be harsher with every suspect, or at least not right now. I had to learn when to strike.

I flipped my notepad shut. I had more pressing things to think about than my career progression. 'He seemed genuinely shocked when I told him Melanie's dead.'

Juliet hummed. 'We've got another suspect with no real alibi, but we might have a motive. He was definitely jealous, even if he didn't know who of.'

'I don't believe he didn't hit Melanie. Who else would have been doing it?'

'This mysterious stalker?' Juliet stood up. 'Do you think Jordan killed her?'

I rose to my feet. 'No.'

I didn't think the crying young man who'd sat across from us was able to fake his emotions so completely. Despite his anger and his swagger, I couldn't picture him shooting his girlfriend three times and leaving her for dead, no matter how jealous he'd been.

Maybe Jordan was right, and someone had scared Melanie. What if they were also hitting her? Jordan might be an innocent bystander, no matter how much he looked and tried to act the part of something darker.

From: Dean Ashmore
dean.ashmore@staugustus.sch.uk
To: Juliet Stern **juliet.stern@mit.gov.uk**
Date: **11 October, 16:39**
Subject: **Leonard Dunlow**

Dear Juliet,

Let me first say that I do hope Leonard is alright. He's at a critical point in his studies and it would be such a shame for his attention to be affected.

In relation to your questions – Leonard is a wonderful student. I teach him music, in addition to being his form tutor, and he's an incredibly hardworking and courteous young man. The only after-school club he engages in is Orchestra, where he plays piano. He's well liked by his peers, if sometimes a tad quiet. I haven't noticed any recent changes in his behaviour.

His father is a valued parent governor. I don't know the man well. At parent conferences, he has been pleased with Leonard's progress. He's quite demanding of his son, but no more so than any other parent.

I didn't teach here when Terence attended but I've asked the other teachers and they remember him as an outgoing and dedicated student.

Let me know if you need any more details,

Dean Ashmore

Published 11 October – police.uk

Dunlow Estate Victim Identified

Detectives investigating the shooting on the Dunlow Estate in the New Forest on the night of Monday, 9 October have formally identified the victim as seventeen-year-old Melanie Pirt. They continue to appeal for witnesses and information.

2 shares

No comments, be the first to make a comment.

Published 11 October – police.uk

Northwood Housing Estate Victim Identified

Detectives investigating the murder on the North-wood Housing Estate in Southampton on the morning of Tuesday, 10 October have formally identified the victim as seven-year-old Krystal Barrett. They continue to appeal for witnesses and information.

128 shares

78 comments

Call connected at 16:52.

'What? Why on earth are you calling me?'
    'You know why. I need my money.'
    'I'll get it to you.'
    'When?'
    'I don't know yet. In case you haven't noticed, there's a murder investigation happening. I can't do anything suspicious right now.'
    'I need that money. I want out of—'
    'Shit. Dad's home. Don't call me again.'

Gabe

'We'll get reports on Melanie's phone tomorrow,' Juliet said. 'Should be able to take a look at her purse as well.'

'Good.' I jumped up from my desk. Since the interview with Jordan, I'd been full of restless energy. We had another suspect but were no nearer to finding any answers. 'Let's talk through what we've got so far.'

The wall was decorated with more evidence. Pictures from the pathologist's full post-mortem were tacked up, along with photos the forensic team had taken in the forest. Quotes from interviews, copied from my notebook, were scattered under suspects' pictures.

Juliet spun her chair around and steepled her fingers under her chin. 'I always love a run-through.'

'Jordan has to be a suspect despite his tearful reaction, but I'm more concerned about someone else.' I pointed at Leo's picture. He was in school uniform, his hair gelled back from his face. It made his chunky glasses the most prominent feature. 'I'd like to have another chat with Leo. There's something he wasn't telling us, and he's clearly this My Lion Melanie was seeing.'

'Clearly.'

I frowned at Juliet. 'What am I missing?'

Juliet twisted in her chair and her fingers raced across her keyboard. 'Leo is the most obvious candidate for My Lion, but we have to keep someone else in the frame.'

She turned her monitor to show me a picture of Karl. This one was more recent than the photo tacked to the wall. His hair tangled in a wild halo around his face.

'Remind you of anything?' Juliet asked.

I deflated. One thing I'd been reasonably certain of was the identity of Melanie's secret admirer. 'I thought you liked Karl?'

Juliet rolled her eyes and pushed her monitor back into place. 'I didn't say that. I said he seemed pleasant. And even if I did like him, I'd never let that stop me from pursuing every line of enquiry.'

That was what we had to do. Whether I was inclined to consider Karl a suspect or not, he had no alibi, a tragically violent past, and he could have been in contact with Melanie. I was suspicious of Leo, but the simplest explanation wasn't always the right one.

I had a tendency towards trusting my gut. It didn't cause me to do a bad job, but it affected my priorities when investigating a case. Juliet was much more clinical.

'Right. Okay.' I grabbed a pad of post-its from my desk. 'We need to talk to Leo, and let's add another chat with Karl into the mix. And there are some key questions we need to answer.'

I wrote them out on individual post-its and stuck them to the wall.

WHO IS MY LION?

WHO DID MELANIE HAVE SEX WITH?

WHERE IS THE DOG?

WHERE IS THE GUN?

MISSING PERSONS – JUSTIN AND SONIA BARRETT

Police are appealing for any information regarding the disappearance of JUSTIN and SONIA BARRETT on 10 October. If you saw JUSTIN or SONIA after this date, please call your local police station and quote case number 10098756.

Justin is approx. 5'11 tall, 34 years old. He was last seen wearing a dark blue hoodie and torn jeans.

Sonia is approx. 5'7 tall, 29 years old. She was last seen wearing a grey jumper and black leggings.

Both were last sighted on the Northwood Housing Estate in Southampton.

Police ask that members of the public do not approach JUSTIN or SONIA.

Call connected at 17:10.

'Detective Inspector Juliet Stern.'

    'Hi. This is Karl, from the Dunlow Estate. You gave me your card.'

    'Hi, Karl. How can I help you?'

    'I think you should come here. I found the dog.'

    'Have you kept it contained from the others?'

    'No need. It's dead.'

    'I see. We'll be there soon.'

Gabe

'It's over here.' Karl walked ahead of us, my car disappearing behind trees as we trekked deeper into the forest. 'I talked to the forensic team after I called. They were packing up, but I caught them before they left.'

'That's great,' I said. It was much easier to get them to look at something while they were still in situ. 'Thank you.'

'How did you find the dog?' Juliet asked.

Even in knee-high boots, she easily kept pace with Karl. The light was fading, so we used the torches on our phones to find our way. Karl walked confidently through the gloom.

'I was out with Monty and Delilah,' he said. 'Monty started whining at something off the path, so I went over to have a look. Someone tried to bury it.'

Karl seemed unbothered by discovering two bodies in the forest where he walked every day. That could be indicative of guilt, or a chronic lack of it.

'Did you move anything?' Juliet asked.

'Yeah.' Karl stuck his hands in his coat pockets. 'I couldn't tell what it was until I moved some of the stuff. Could have been a dead badger, we've had those before.'

'It's fine,' I reassured him.

Juliet raised her eyebrows at me. It wasn't ideal, since we would have trouble telling if any of Karl's DNA on the dog was from uncovering it or killing it, but that couldn't be helped.

'Just tell the forensic team exactly what you moved and they'll take that into account,' Juliet said.

'I already have.' Karl trudged on. 'But like I told them, if it's DNA you're worried about, mine would have been all over the dog anyway. So would Mr Dunlow's, Leo's too.'

Juliet turned to me again, her eyebrows even higher. I wasn't sure what she was communicating. Karl seemed incredibly upfront. He might have been cagey before, but I chalked that up to unwillingness to talk about his past. I didn't think he'd told us the issues with DNA because he was protesting his innocence. He had much simpler ways of ensuring he wouldn't be considered a killer. Namely, not calling in either body and letting them rot out here.

Juliet slowed, drawing back from Karl. 'David is working this case.'

I grimaced. 'I'll take the lead here as well?'

'Yes, please.'

David Rees was remarkably good at his job. He was also an arse-hole. A stickler for the rules, he'd never gotten on with Juliet. Things had only deteriorated between them after he asked her out and she'd rejected him. None too kindly, if witnesses were to be believed.

A forensic tent had already been placed over the dog's body, along with flood lights. A generator whirred between trees. Juliet's jaw tightened before she stepped inside the tent. I nodded at Karl then followed her, letting the fabric fall shut behind me.

'David?' I plastered a smile on my face.

He straightened up. 'Stern. Martin. You were quick.'

The use of our surnames jarred. Angela hadn't banned them when she became superintendent but had made her distaste clear. We weren't part of some old boys' club anymore, and should cast off the throwbacks we'd carried from when the force was. David got away with it because the forensics team worked on a strange, slightly separate plane.

His ginger hair was tucked into a white body suit; the only part of him visible the circle of his face. His angular nose was sprinkled with freckles. He was about Juliet's height, so towered over me. A fact he might have taken more pleasure in if he noticed anyone other than Juliet whenever she was nearby.

A mound of twigs and leaves lay at his feet. Some of the covering had been cleared, presumably by Karl. Whiteish fur poked through brown leaves, discoloured and matted.

I pulled my notebook out of my pocket. 'What can you tell us?'

'Dead dog, probably the one involved in the attack.' Whenever David looked away from the mound, his blue eyes weren't on me. 'Can't tell you much until we bag up the debris but looks like it's been dead for a couple of days. May have been killed the same night as the girl.'

'How did it die?' I leant forward to peer at the exposed parts of the animal.

'You can see here.' David crouched to point one gloved finger at an area of cleared leaves. 'The fur is stuck together. We think that's a gunshot wound.'

Brown leaves were caked around the furry body. I couldn't tell what was going on underneath, but I trusted David's expertise.

'You okay to work on this tonight?' I slipped my notebook into my pocket.

'Sure.' David stood, staring at Juliet. 'Not like we have anyone waiting at home, right?'

Juliet's face stilled, and she led the way out of the tent. I followed, not bothering to say goodbye. It wasn't like David would have paid attention anyway.

About a year ago, a rumour had circulated that Juliet's husband had left her. So David decided she was fair game. He couldn't comprehend that she might not want anything to do with him, whether or not she was single. He definitely didn't believe that she and her husband were still together, but her husband had moved their daughters out of the city and into a rambling farmhouse near Eastleigh. Juliet visited them at the weekends, when she could.

This happened before I moved here. Maddy filled me in on the personal histories of our colleagues. We didn't think of it as gossip, more essential sharing of information. I was especially grateful when it came to Juliet. It wasn't like she would volunteer any information about her personal life.

'Odious man,' Juliet said, once we were far enough away from the tent.

'You okay?' I checked.

Karl lurked at the edge of the glow cast by the flood lights. He braced his shoulder against a tree while he talked to Leo and another man so strikingly similar in appearance that there was no question of who he was.

'It's fine,' Juliet said. 'Let's see what Leo has to say for himself.'

I accepted her dismissal. Juliet was more than capable of shaking off an unpleasant encounter and getting on with her job. We'd been presented with an ideal opportunity to speak to Leo without his father present. She wouldn't want to miss that, even if David's jibe about her lonely homelife stung.

'Gentlemen,' I said when we reached the group.

An older, slicker version of Leo smiled at us in a way that probably worked wonders on a lot of the women he encountered. If Terence had the same sight issues as his brother, then he wore contacts rather than allow glasses to partially obscure his face or deep brown eyes. His hair was styled into sculpted waves, the same auburn-brown as his brother's. Leo hovered beside him, his head down.

Karl pushed away from the tree. 'You got everything you need? I can walk you to your car.'

'Terence Dunlow.' He walked around the groundskeeper and extended his hand. His grip was firm, his palm smooth. 'Karl tells me you're the detectives on this case?'

Karl glowered behind the older brother. I nodded, tucking my hand in my pocket and wiping it on the inner lining. Terence's hand wasn't slimy, but I couldn't help the uncomfortable sensation his touch provoked. It was the same with all men of his ilk; it bothered me that not a single callous had formed on his hands. He'd likely never done an honest day's work in his life.

'I'm Detective Sergeant Gabe Martin. This is Detective Inspector Juliet Stern.'

'Dreadful this happened here.' Terence looked past us to the hastily erected tent. 'Must have been a terrible shock for you, Karl, finding both bodies.'

The statement was cloaked in concern, but Terence's eyes were hard. The groundskeeper didn't bother to wipe the dislike from his face but jerked his head once in affirmation.

'I'll let you get on.' One more fake smile aimed at us, and Terence turned to walk away. Like a tarnished mirror image, Leo moved with him.

'Leo?' I called out, before they could go too far.

He lifted his head for the first time. His glasses were wide, shiny points of reflected light.

'Can I check? Are you sure you didn't know Melanie Pirt?'

Leo blanched. Before he could answer, his brother's hand clapped onto his shoulder. Terence wasn't smiling anymore.

Leo swallowed, looking at the ground again. 'No. I didn't know her.'

'Only her boyfriend, Jordan Haines, seems to think someone here knew her,' I pushed. 'He thinks someone was obsessed with her.'

In the corner of my eye, Karl shifted his weight from one booted foot to the other. I hoped Juliet was keeping a close watch over him and could tell me whether that movement was prompted by impatience or interest.

'It wasn't me,' Leo said. 'I didn't know her.'

'Is that all?' Terence didn't wait for a reply before steering Leo towards the house. I assumed. It was impossible to tell what direction they were headed in the dark, crowded by countless trees.

I turned to Karl. 'Do you mind showing us to our car?'

I only had a second to wonder if he looked wary before he loped along the path.

'Good work,' Juliet murmured as we followed. 'That's what pushing looks like.' She tipped her head at Karl, just visible in the darkness outside of our torch beams. 'You alright to do that to him too?'

'Yeah.'

Pressing into Leo hadn't been too bad, but the difference between him and Karl was vast. I believed Leo was hiding something and I wanted to irk his entitled older brother, whereas Karl was protecting himself. It would be a lot more uncomfortable poking into the parts of his life he didn't want to speak about. An unspoken code existed between survivors of horrific things; we didn't go delving into each other's business without invitation.

But Karl wasn't someone I'd met at a pub or support group. He was a suspect in a murder case. That overrode any squeamishness about prodding around in his past.

'Is that everything?' Karl asked once our car came into view, parked alongside his cottage. Loud yips and barks sounded from the barn. 'I've not fed the dogs yet, so I need to head off.'

'Just one thing.' I kept my expression neutral, scrunching the silky fabric inside my pocket between my fingers. 'Why didn't you tell us about your parents?'

It was like I'd blasphemed in front of a nun. Karl's head jerked back, his expression clouding. 'Who told you about that?'

'It's all on record,' Juliet jumped in when I waited a beat too long to answer. 'Why didn't you tell us about them?'

'Because it has nothing to do with this.' Karl's hand shook so violently as he pulled his phone out of his coat pocket that it was a miracle he didn't drop it. 'Look, I've helped you out, but now I have to get on with my job.'

He turned and strode away, his face lit by his phone. I walked over to the car, my stomach clenching with guilt.

Juliet climbed into the passenger seat. 'That went well.'

I turned the key in the ignition and pulled on my seatbelt to avoid looking right at her.

'Leo is a lying cretin, I think we can agree.' Juliet's face was lit in the same way as Karl's. 'But Karl is a mystery. Was he pissed we'd uncovered the secret about his parents, or is he hiding something else and he doesn't want us finding more ammunition against him?'

She didn't seem bothered by my silence as we drove out of the estate and onto a narrow country lane. I drove slowly, wary of wild creatures leaping in the way.

Juliet didn't have the same experiences as me, so there was no way she could correctly interpret Karl's reaction when we'd slung his past at him like muck.

He hadn't been pissed. He'd been afraid. Suddenly confronted with something he tried so hard to remove himself from, probably even rarely thought of. We'd returned him to the moment his dad swung the golf club and his world dissolved into screaming pain.

Juliet couldn't see any of that, because she hadn't lived through something traumatic and life altering. But I could. I would bet anything that if someone who lived on the Dunlow Estate had hounded Melanie and led her to her death then it was one of the owners, not Karl.

Unknown number. Sent 18:42.

I'm not fucking around anymore. Give me the money or I'll tell your daddy what you've been doing.

From: Juliet Stern **juliet.stern@mit.gov.uk**
To: Ryan White **ryan.white@hmps.plo.gov.uk**
CC: Gabriella Martin **gabriella.martin@mit.gov.uk**
Date: **11 October, 19:10**
Subject: **Legal visit**

Hello Ryan,

I would like to arrange a legal visit with one of your inmates –
Matthew Biss, prisoner number A2244WN – as a matter of urgency.
He will inform our understanding of the childhood and violent history
of a key suspect in an ongoing murder investigation.

Thank you for your cooperation,

Detective Inspector Juliet Stern

Gabe

Going to the pub was a mistake.

I sat squeezed on the middle of a long bench, surrounded by junior officers and admin staff. All young, all female. They'd let their hair down from tight buns and, by the time I'd arrived, were all on their second or third glass of wine. I'd ordered a small one. Down to the dregs, I was looking for a natural opportunity to leave.

I squirmed, hot thighs pressing alongside mine. It wasn't that I considered these women below me, but I didn't fit in. I didn't switch off easily. My aim wasn't to be alone, but my inability to speak openly about myself eventually drove most people away.

My association with Juliet didn't help. I had a standing invitation to the pub Paul and the others on our floor moored in at most Friday nights, but I'd clocked the way conversations stumbled around me. Juliet was the butt of too many jokes. They couldn't be sure where my allegiances lay.

Invitations out were too infrequent to be sneered at. This night was a bust, but next time I might meet people who I could form friendships with. Of a sort.

I took a sip of my dwindling wine, conversation about children and partners soaring around me. Maddy sat at one end of the table, swilling her glass. The last time I'd seen her this subdued was after her ex-girlfriend tried to storm the station and had to be escorted off the premises.

'Another?' Alice leant across the table, her straight, black hair grazing her shoulders. She was a lot more confident than when we'd met in the forest. After thanking me over and over for being so kind, she'd sat me down between two of our colleagues and promptly dominated conversations around the table.

'I can't stay long.' I laid the groundwork for a premature exit.

Everyone else had settled in for the long haul. Their faces shiny from the moist air inside the pub, they'd strewn their coats over the benches in a mismatched jumble. I'd kept mine on.

'Before you go, you have to tell me something.' Alice rested her elbows on the table and cradled her wine glass in both hands. They were small, like mine. In another situation, I would have asked how hard she had to work to get her colleagues to take her seriously as a petite woman. 'I've heard some strange things about Detective Stern around the station.'

'We don't need to talk about that,' Maddy piped up, her face turning pink.

Alice waved a hand at her. 'This one won't tell us anything, but you work with Juliet every day. You know what she's really like.'

Maddy stared down at her drink. I wished I could communicate how proud I was that she'd withstood the doubtless onslaught of questions about Juliet from Alice and her cronies. Apparently, we didn't gossip together. She actually was only sharing what she knew to help me do a good job.

'I heard she keeps clothes in her desk,' one of the other women piled on. We'd been introduced, but I'd been too concerned her boobs would break free of her glittering top as she lunged forward to shake my hand that I'd not retained her name. 'Heard she barely goes home, works non-stop even when she doesn't have a case.'

That might have been true before I arrived. Juliet had seemed bemused when I'd insisted, a couple of weeks after I'd started working with her, that we leave the office together each night. I ended up working longer hours, waiting for her to check one last detail, but I made sure she went home with at least enough hours left in the day to get a decent night's sleep before she returned to the station outrageously early the next morning.

'What does she have to go home for?' Alice crowed. 'Do you know, it took her three days to even notice her husband had left her? He took the kids too.'

This was why I'd been invited out. Not because Alice wanted to thank me or to be friendly, but because she wanted to know the truth about Juliet. That made me feel less guilty about making a swift exit.

Juliet would be utterly confused by the amount of attention she elicited around the station. She was interested in colleagues only so long as they had something to contribute to a case. I counted it as her making an extra special effort any time she enquired about my plans for the weekend.

I necked the rest of my wine and slid the glass to the middle of the table. 'I've worked with Juliet for about eight months now. There can't be many rumours I haven't heard about her but, I can assure you, few of them are true.'

Pressing my hands on the table and trying not to kick anyone, I made my awkward dismount off the bench. Alice's smile curdled until I added, 'Let me get another round in before I go.'

I ordered a couple of bottles of wine at the bar. There was a cheer as I brought them to the table, some half-hearted attempts from Alice to get me to stay during which I avoided looking at Maddy, and then I was free. I pushed through the pub doors and breathed in the chill night air.

I didn't consider myself a good actor or liar, but I'd gotten adept at denying accusations thrown at me about Juliet. A lot of the rumours were based on truth, but I couldn't see why that was anyone's business. I wasn't about to use her secrets to curry favour.

There was no doubt in my mind that Juliet had more than one change of clothing squirrelled away in our office. Some nights, there was no budging her and she would work on cold cases rather than go home to her lonely flat. There were more Mondays I saw evidence of her working through the weekend than not.

Drizzle blasted me as I turned a corner. The bus was already at the stop. I jogged over to board at the back of the queue, then sat down and watched rivulets of water snake across the glass as the rain picked up. I'd left my car at the station, optimistic I might be over the limit when I left the pub.

Some rumours I could neither confirm nor deny. I'd never asked Juliet what had happened when her husband moved out of the city. It could have been planned. Or she could have walked into her home and found her family gone.

I wrapped my coat tighter around me. I liked solving puzzles, but I'd resigned myself to Juliet being a mystery I would never get to the bottom of. I could protect her from gossips and make sure she went home at a reasonable hour. I couldn't control what she did at home or make her talk to me about her personal life.

I had to trust she was an adult and would ask for help if she needed it. Time and time again, I'd made it clear I was willing to lend a listening ear.

Still, as the bus trundled along busy streets and other passengers murmured sleepily, I worried for Juliet. There had to be something going on for her to be so averse to spending time with her husband and children.

Call connected at 20:51.

'Hello?'

'Hi, Mum. It's not too late, is it?'

'Gabriella, my darling. It's never too late to talk to you.'

'I won't keep you long. Just fancied a chat.'

'I don't mind, love. How are you?'

'Good. I'm working on a new case.'

'Oh, is it that poor little girl? I cried when I read about it.'

'No. It's not that one.'

'Well. Probably for the best.'

'How about you? What have you been up to?'

'Oh, you know, busy, always busy. There's a new foodbank at church I've been helping with. I drive around and give out the boxes. They're always ever so grateful. Poor mites.'

'That's good. How about Dad?'

'Oh, he's fine. Busy at the allotment, bringing home wonderful veggies.'

'He still not talking to me?'

'He'll get there. You know how stubborn he is.'

'It makes no sense. He won't talk to me because I moved away. Where's the logic in that?'

'You think I don't know that, love?'

'Sorry. I shouldn't have a go at you.'

'It's alright. I know it's hard. But he'll come around.'

'Yeah.'

'Do you think you'll come home for a visit any time soon?'

'Maybe. It's really full on at work at the moment.'

'I understand. We're always here.'

'Yeah. I've got to go.'

'Sleep well, darling.'

'You too, Mum. Love you.'

'I love you.'

Gabe. Sent 21:46.

I'm looking forward to seeing you tomorrow x

Ollie. Sent 21:47.

You too. I expect something special in the morning if you keep me waiting again xxx

Gabe. Sent 21:49.

Full English it is x

Ollie. Sent 21:50.

That's not exactly what I had in mind, but it'll do xxx

Gabe. Sent 21:53.

I'll try not to be too late at work, but I don't have much control over it x

Ollie. Sent 21:57.

It's fine. I'm free tomorrow evening. I hope it doesn't sound desperate or anything, but you're worth the wait x

Gabe. Sent 21:59.

Not desperate, but I'll try not to keep you waiting too long xx

Day 3

Thursday, 12 October

Gabe

I walked into our office, two coffees balanced around the fingers of one hand and an evidence bag clutched in the other. Juliet jumped up and grabbed one of the mugs. Today, she'd paired grey trousers with a cream blouse. Her nails were painted a smooth navy.

'I went to see Maddy first thing. She had this waiting.'

There was no need to explain why it was so important I sought out our assistant this morning. I'd known Maddy would need convincing I wasn't going to shun her because of Alice's tactless pursuit of the truth.

'She's a doll.' Juliet plonked her coffee on her desk. Brown droplets dribbled down the side while she rummaged in one of her drawers. She emerged with a pair of plastic gloves that she threw across our desks. 'I'll let you play with that. The report on Melanie's phone has come in as well.'

Before I sat down, I stuck a silver star where the dog had been found on the aerial map of the Dunlow Estate. Not too far from where Melanie died, and in the direction the forensics team had already established the killer walked after shooting. Seemingly towards nothing. There was only a Bronze Age burial ground across the road.

Despite answering one of my pressing questions, finding the dog's body hadn't confirmed or denied anything.

I pulled the post-it off the wall, then dumped my bag, coat and coffee on my desk and chair. Always scruffy next to Juliet, I tugged at my jumper sleeves and ran a hand through my wind-tousled hair. Slipping on the gloves, I pulled Melanie's purse out of the evidence bag. No marks on the purple fabric, even though its owner had sustained such damage. I flipped open the popper and eased the sections apart.

'The passcode worked,' Juliet said, tapping at her keyboard.

'Good.' Internally, I air punched. Without access to Melanie's phone, this case would be even harder.

I extracted an array of loyalty cards from the purse: Boots, Waterstones, Superdrug, The Body Shop. Melanie's library card was battered, but her debit card untouched. I unzipped the change compartment and let coins fall into my palm. Among the dented pounds was a button.

I turned it between my finger and thumb. 'Think this is important?'

It was large and green, probably from a coat. I looked over at a picture of Melanie taken in the forest. Her thick coat was pink, fastened with a zip.

'Could be something.' Juliet's eyes didn't leave her computer screen. 'Or could be a nice button she found.'

Maybe one of our suspects had a coat that was missing a button. I put it down beside the coins and made a note. A tiny thing to build a case on, but we'd gotten nowhere so far. I'd take any speck of evidence I could get.

Turning the purse on its side, I checked the long slot for notes and receipts. My fingertips caught on a slip of paper. I laid it flat on my desk.

'I've got a bus ticket.' I squinted at the faded blue writing. 'Melanie got on a bus near her home at about half seven, which means she was probably on the estate from about eight p.m.'

'That works perfectly with a timeline I'm establishing here.' Juliet beckoned me over to her desk. 'Take a look at these messages from My Lion.'

A TRANSCRIPT OF TEXT MESSAGES FOUND ON MELANIE PIRT'S MOBILE PHONE

THREAD ONE – 08/10

Jordan Haines. 16:04
You coming over tonight? Dad is out xxx

Melanie Pirt. 16:08
I told you I'm not hanging out with you anymore. We're done.

Jordan Haines. 16:09
It's over when I say it is

Jordan Haines. 18:37
Don't ignore me bitch

THREAD TWO – 09/10

Jordan Haines. 8:02
Sorry. I didn't mean it. Don't give up on me babe xxx

Melanie Pirt. 10:35
Leave me alone.

Jordan Haines. 13:14
Maybe I did mean it then. You fucking bitch

Jordan Haines. 13:15
I see you walking around school. You think you're something special

Jordan Haines. 13:17
You're nothing without me

THREAD THREE – 10/10

Jordan Haines. 10.30
Babe, where you at? xxx

Jordan Haines. 19:34
I didn't see you at school – where you at? Please don't avoid me. I promise I'll do better xxx

THREAD FOUR – 09/10

Melanie Pirt. 17:13
Can I come see you later? x

My Lion. 17:14
Today? x

Melanie Pirt. 17:14
Yeah. I need to see you x

Melanie Pirt. 17:16
Please x

My Lion. 17:17
Get the number 36 bus to the stop opposite the entrance to Black Hill farm. Do you know it? x

Melanie Pirt. 17:18
Yeah x

My Lion. 17:19
Wait there. I'll come find you x

Melanie Pirt. 19:33
I'm on the bus now x

My Lion. 19:34
I can't wait to see you x

THREAD FIVE – 10/10

My Lion. 18:04
Mel, I need you to message me – I don't care what you said. Are you alright? I have to know you're okay xx

My Lion. 8:02
Mel, please don't ignore me. I'm scared x

Gabe

'Morning,' I said, as I walked into the break room.

Paul looked up, his hands braced on the countertop. His greying black hair was mussed on one side, like he'd been pulling at the thick strands. His stick leant on the countertop beside him. He'd been injured years ago in a hostage situation and had used a walking aid ever since.

'Is it morning still?' he asked, his deep voice flat.

I looked at my watch. 'Just about.'

He went back to staring at the red light on the toaster. I reached around him to get coffee from the top cupboard. I spooned it out into mine and Juliet's mugs, added sugar to mine, and flicked on the kettle. Its gentle hissing filled the cramped room, comprised of a kitchenette and two ratty sofas.

Paul hadn't moved.

'How's the case going?' Asking went against every inclination inside of me screaming that I should keep my distance, but I would have asked about any other case.

Paul swivelled his head to squint at me, then resumed his toaster-vigil. The always purple skin around his eyes looked almost bruised. 'It's clear cut. All the evidence is there. Just got to bloody find them.'

I wrinkled my nose at the smell of burning toast. The slices jumped up, blackened and smoking. Paul dropped them onto his plate. 'The press is going to have a field day.'

Paul's lack of tolerance for the media was almost as legendary around the station as Juliet's icy bitch status. But he wasn't wrong. Journalists would leap on a high priority murder investigation losing its perpetrators.

'Thank God our case came through first.' The kettle clicked off and I poured steaming water into the mugs. 'I don't envy you spending your days dealing with the press and trawling through CCTV of warehouses.'

Paul dropped his knife, which landed with a clatter beside his toast.

'You alright?' I asked. He couldn't claim I was taking an unhealthy interest in his case. Anyone with eyes had heard the basic facts about Krystal's parents. Her father was a lorry driver, so would have insider knowledge of many industrial complexes.

Paul shook his head, picking up the sticky knife. 'Fine. Just had a thought.' His face brightened. 'You might not have to deal with the press, but I took a gander at that mad wall of Juliet's after you two left last night. You've got too many suspects and no leads.'

'We didn't then.' I poured milk into my coffee. 'We have now.'

Paul scraped more jam over his charred slabs. 'I should have known. You're far too chipper for someone with nothing to go on.'

I picked up the mugs. 'Have a good day now.'

'Yeah, yeah. You too.' Paul waved me out of the room. 'Let's arrange dinner soon. You can entertain the monsters for a night.'

My tentative friendship with Paul was one of the most unlikely things to survive my move here. We'd met when we worked up in north London. He'd always taken the time to talk to uniformed officers, was unfailingly courteous and patient. He paid more attention to me once it became clear I thought about scenes differently to others at my pay grade. When I'd needed encouragement to attempt the detective exam, he'd cheered me on. He moved down here a year before me, probably envisioned me becoming his protegee when I followed. But he'd been allocated someone else to work with before I arrived. Despite his animosity towards Juliet, my working with her hadn't affected our cheerful banter or the occasional meals he invited me to, his home cosy with the shouts of his sons and his wife's gentle questions.

I walked across the open-plan floor towards mine and Juliet's office, trying and failing to ignore the oversized picture of Krystal, bracketed on either side by her missing parents. I fought off a shiver. If there was one person I trusted to bring a child's murderers to justice, it was Paul.

I hadn't lied to him; we'd found something that could help us find Melanie's killer. Alongside the incriminating texts from My Lion, the IT team had uncovered pictures of Melanie's legs. They showed a history of abuse, her brown skin mottled with changing patterns of bruises.

We might not know all the answers, but the evidence from Melanie's phone had brought us a step closer. Someone had been hurting her in the months before she died and someone had encouraged her onto the Dunlow Estate the night she was murdered.

'I've got something else,' Juliet said as I walked into our office.

I placed both coffees on her desk and sat next to her. Since she'd called me over to look at the IT report, we'd been working side by side.

Juliet clicked her mouse and a photo filled her computer screen. It was different to the tearful selfies interspersing the records of beatings. Melanie was laughing. That was clear, even though she held up her hands to cover her face. The photographer's arm was in shot, reaching towards her. Their sleeve was blue.

I looked at the wall of evidence. Leo smiled in his school uniform. A navy blazer squared off his shoulders.

'Exactly,' Juliet said. 'Now listen to this.'

The IT team had also sent over several voice recordings. Juliet clicked on the last in a short list. Static filled the air, then the tinny sound of someone playing the piano. After a sharp inhale, a voice joined in.

I closed my eyes as Melanie sang a verse and chorus of *Amazing Grace*, her breathing heavy after each line. There was something different about hearing voices from beyond the grave. Pictures were static. I struggled with the wealth of video and sound evidence victims left behind. It made them so much more real.

Another verse, and the singing faltered. The piano stopped.

What do you think?

It was good. Really good.

The recording ended. I opened my eyes. Juliet propped her elbows on the table, her coffee steaming into her face.

'That was Leo's voice, right?' My phone vibrated and I thumbed at it. 'That's the tech team. My Lion's phone number is registered to Timothy Dunlow.'

'Looks like you might be right about My Lion. I don't see Dunlow giving Karl a phone.'

I grabbed my mug and took a sip, hiding the smile rising on my face. In such a complex case, if I could be the one to make mental leaps and find the killer first, that had to equate to a job well done. Melanie would be able to rest peacefully and her loved ones move on, knowing her murderer had been brought to justice.

'Both Leo and Jordan have lied to us.' I set down my drink. 'We need to talk to them again.'

From: Paul Willis **paul.willis@mit.gov.uk**
To: Alice To **alice.to@police.gov.uk**
Date: **12 October, 11:53**
Subject: **Operation Toucan – CCTV**

Alice,

This is your next assignment. We have hours and hours of CCTV footage from different industrial complexes for you to look through. Any sign of someone who looks like Justin or Sonia Barrett coming or going from any of the warehouses – flag it to me.

You said you're keen to take the detective exam soon, and this is a good taste of the kind of work you'll be doing if you pass. There's not much running around to catch bad guys, and a lot of staring at a computer screen, trying to spot tiny mistakes.

Enjoy!

Paul

Unknown number. Sent 11:58.

> Do you want me to fuck up your life? Forget about your daddy, how about I tell the police you're a liar? Don't keep me waiting.

Gabe

We watched from the car as Jordan kicked a stone along the pavement, a half-smoked cigarette smouldering between his fingers. His school shirt was untucked and his tie hung loose. He tossed away the cigarette before letting himself into a narrow terraced house. The street was tidy but shabby, flowers planted in short front gardens counteracted by scuffed wheely bins dotted in others.

We'd decided to question Jordan first because the college he attended let out earlier than Leo's private school and he lived closer to the station. There was also a chance Jordan would confess he'd murdered Melanie in a fit of rage after finding out she was seeing someone else, rendering an urgent interview with Leo unnecessary.

'Shall I take the lead?' Juliet spun her phone on her knee. 'This is in no way a reflection on how you've been working, but I have a feeling a brisker approach may be more effective with our young friend. Your softly-softly will work better with Leo.'

I wasn't sure how I felt about this suggestion. Jordan probably would respond better to Juliet and Leo to me, and I wasn't disappointed at losing the chance to practise harsher interrogation techniques. Still, I would have liked to have been the one to prompt the change.

'An important part of leading is knowing when to delegate,' I said.

Juliet grinned and slid her phone into her pocket. 'I shall allow you to delegate this to me then.'

We climbed out of the car and walked towards Jordan's house. I relished being out in the cool air after long minutes of waiting in the car, despite the rotting smell from bin bags piled under a nearby tree. A patch of overgrown grass separated Jordan's house from the road. Juliet led the way over uneven paving stones and rapped on the plastic front door. It didn't take long for a blurry silhouette to appear behind a pane of misted glass.

A thin woman opened the door, her collar bones jutting above the hem of a faded orange jumper. Her hair was a similar dirty blonde as

Jordan's, pulled into a tight ponytail. She had the same feral air as him; a rat trapped in a cage who would take any chance to run.

'Hello. I'm Detective Inspector Juliet Stern and this is Detective Sergeant Gabe Martin. Is Jordan in? We need to ask him a few questions about the murder of Melanie Pirt.'

The woman's eyes widened, darting to the row of houses behind us. This area might not be as well-to-do as the suburb I was renting in, but apparently the neighbours were every bit as nosy. She ushered Juliet and me inside.

'I'm his mum.' She led us through to a cramped living room. 'I know that makes me biased, but Jordan's a good boy. He might not get the best grades or be the most well behaved in lessons, but he wouldn't have hurt Mel. He was nuts for her.'

Juliet pulled off her coat and folded it over the arm of a faux leather sofa that spanned the length of one wall. 'If we could talk to Jordan?'

His mum dithered but left the room. Juliet settled herself on one side of the sofa and I took the other, the inner workings complaining as it took our weight. Glass doors led out onto an overlooked garden, which was as neglected as the patch of grass at the front of the house. Juliet examined the remote on the scratched coffee table and muted the widescreen TV hung on the far wall. I pulled my notepad out of my pocket and flicked to a fresh page.

The floorboards overhead creaked as Jordan came downstairs, his mum walking in his shadow. He took the only remaining seat, a battered recliner under the TV, leaving her to hover in the doorway.

'What do you want?' Jordan had changed into a pair of jogging bottoms and an oversized green hoodie, but he didn't look comfortable. His shoulders were hunched, his eyes bloodshot.

'We need to ask you a few more questions about the nature of your relationship with Melanie Pirt. When we met with you before, you told us you'd not hurt her.' Juliet pulled the pictures we'd printed this afternoon from between the pages of her organiser and spread them on the coffee table. Melanie's thighs were discoloured with blacks and deep purples. 'I'm going to ask you again. Jordan, did you ever hurt Melanie Pirt?'

His mum squeaked, her hand flying to her mouth. Jordan shrunk into his chair. I leant forward and gathered up the pictures. The point had been made. We didn't need to cause Jordan or his mum any more distress.

'I need you to tell the truth,' Juliet said. 'Because, to me, it looks like you were hurting Melanie for a long time. We need you to tell the truth, otherwise we'll come to our own conclusions, and that may cause us to believe you had something to do with Melanie's death.'

'I didn't have anything to do with that.' Jordan's jaw quivered. 'And I didn't mean to hurt her.'

Juliet sat forward, her face intent. 'Tell us what you did, Jordan.'

'I didn't start off doing it. I didn't mean to.' He sniffed and held the sleeve of his hoodie under his nose. 'I loved her, I still love her. But sometimes she would say or do something so stupid, like smile at another guy, and I'd lose it.'

His mum's hand hadn't left her mouth. It was clamped there, her fingers digging into the skin of her cheek. I made a note about her reaction. It would be horrible for any parent to find out their son was beating his girlfriend, but this seemed a little extreme.

'Did you hit Melanie Pirt regularly before she died on the 9th October?' Juliet asked.

Jordan nodded into his lap, a fallen tear creating a dark circle on the pale grey of his jogging bottoms. With a small sound like a mouse being stepped on, his mum fled the room.

'Jordan?' Juliet's eyes hadn't strayed from him. 'Did you have anything to do with Melanie's death?'

'No.' He looked up, swiping the wetness from his face. 'I told you, I didn't kill her. I wouldn't hurt her.' He flinched, confronted by the hypocrisy of his own statement. 'It's stupid. The only reason I ever did stuff to her was because I didn't want to lose her. I wouldn't have killed her.'

I'd heard similar disturbed logic before. Some men beat women because they had a screw loose, but others lashed out because they couldn't see any other way of keeping those they loved close and controlled.

Jordan rubbed his sleeve over his face. 'I told you before; someone up on that estate killed Mel. There's a guy who lives there called Leonard. I think he did it.'

Juliet tilted her head to the side. 'You told us you don't know anyone who lives on the Dunlow Estate.'

'I don't.' Jordan glared at her. 'I looked up who lives there. Leonard's our age, he's a posh private school boy. He's everything I'm not so he's exactly the type of guy Mel would go running to when she was pissed at me.'

Juliet stood. 'We have everything we need.'

'No. Wait.' Jordan jumped up. 'I know this sounds bad and I know I'm not a reliable witness or whatever, but you have to listen to me. Someone up on that posho estate killed Mel, and I really think it was Leonard. It wouldn't have been anyone older; Mel would have told me something like that to make me jealous. Leonard makes sense. He was obsessed with her. The guy couldn't have her, so he tricked her onto the estate and killed her. He's one of those privileged twats. If he can't have her, no one can.'

Jordan couldn't know any of this. He was desperately clinging to any morsel of blame to throw at someone else.

I stood alongside Juliet, while Jordan breathed heavily. He was one second away from shouting or crying.

'Jordan?' I said. 'We'll take this into consideration. Thank you for being honest today. That must have been hard.'

His face crumpled. If Juliet had made one of her caustic comments, he might have come at us, fists flying, but my gentle words broke his façade down. We left him climbing back into the chair, his head buried in his folded arms.

His mum must have hidden away upstairs. We walked through the hall, past a pile of battered trainers, and out of the front door. Soft rain hit our faces as we rushed over to the car. Juliet sat stiff in the passenger seat, watching droplets patter on the windscreen, as I turned on the ignition and twisted the heating dial. Hot air blasted from the fans.

'Do you believe him?'

I blew out a breath. 'Mostly, yes. He was hurting Melanie and I don't think he had anything to do with her death. I'm not sure about his Leo theories though. Seems like he's lashing out at an easy target.'

'I'm not so sure about his claim that Melanie would have told him if she was seeing someone older either,' Juliet said, staring ahead. 'Why would she want to annoy him when the consequence was a beating?'

'Agreed.' I pulled on my seatbelt. 'Leo should be home from school soon. If we get to the estate early enough, we might be able to interview him without his father lurking around.'

Juliet nodded, tugging her seatbelt over her chest. 'Did you see her reaction?'

I flicked on the indicator and turned onto the road. 'Jordan's mum's?'

'Yeah.'

I wrinkled my nose. 'We didn't meet Jordan's dad today, but I wouldn't be surprised if Jordan was copying behaviour.'

'Why does she live like that?' Juliet sighed. 'Why stay with someone who hurts her? Why keep her kid in that place so he will repeat his father's mistakes?'

I waited at a junction for a gap in traffic streaming across the busier main road. I wasn't sure why Juliet was so irked by Jordan's parents' situation. It was unpleasant but unless his mum spoke up, we were powerless. Juliet didn't normally care about the personal lives of the families we encountered, or at least was only interested so far as they gave insight into a suspect's behaviour.

'Not everyone is strong like you,' I said. 'I'm not making excuses, but it's true.'

Juliet turned away, fixing her gaze on droplets of rain dribbling down her side window.

I didn't expect her to reply, so almost missed her whispering, 'I'm not strong. I'm just not weak.'

From: Alice To **alice.to@police.gov.uk**
To: Gabriella Martin **gabriella.martin@mit.gov.uk**
Date: **12 October, 16:50**
Subject: **Apologies**

Gabe,

I apologise if I made you feel uncomfortable last night. That was not my intention. Maddy has explained that you're a private person and wouldn't want to talk about anything personal to yourself or Juliet. She also told me that if you'd known it was a girls' night, you probably wouldn't have come.

You need not worry I'll make the same mistake again.

Alice

Gabe

Karl didn't greet us at the gates like he had done every other time we'd driven onto the Dunlow Estate. We rang the buzzer and he let us in remotely.

'No friendly welcome for us anymore.' Juliet jabbed at her phone. She'd roused herself from reflections about Jordan's family as we'd swapped cramped houses for gaping expanses of green. Now we were hemmed in by trees.

My insides twinged as I drove past Karl's squat cottage. We would march down and confront him if Leo didn't give us satisfactory answers. That made me uneasy. Something told me Karl was a sad man, one I didn't want to harass.

The gravel drive wound towards the manor. Dark clouds glowered overhead, robbing the day of the last of its light. If the trees had been in full bloom, the scant sun would have been blocked out. I didn't know how the Dunlows were comfortable surrounded by such rampant greenery.

At the house, I pulled my Vauxhall Astra up near a sleek black BMW. Securing our coats around our necks, we climbed out of the car and strode over to the imposing front door.

The bell rang in the depths of the manor. Lavender sitting in pots either side of the door swayed in the wind, giving off a soft, clean scent. Juliet gazed out over the extensive grounds, the rolling lawns giving way to close-packed trees.

I watched Leo walk down the stairs through one of the glass panels to the sides of the front door. He stumbled when he saw me, then hurried over.

'Hello, Leo,' I said, as he opened the door. 'We have a few more questions to ask you about Melanie's death. Can we come in?'

'Yeah. Of course.' His voice was breathy. He swung the door wide and ushered us into the entrance hall.

Dunlow appeared at the top of the stairs. His face was set in its perpetual frown as he sauntered down towards us. After work, he'd discarded his jacket and his shirt sleeves were rolled up to his elbows. He looked formal next to Leo's jumper and jeans.

'Detectives,' Dunlow said. 'What's going on?'

He stood beside his son, leaving half-a-metre's distance between them. Leo was taller, lanky like his brother. If Leo and Terence were greyhounds, Dunlow was a Rottweiler.

'We have a few more questions to ask your son about the murder of Melanie Pirt.' Juliet forced Dunlow to look at her. She was taller than him too. 'Is there somewhere private we can chat?'

'Does it have to be private?' Dunlow asked.

'No.' Juliet unbuttoned her coat. 'You're perfectly welcome to sit in.'

The noise Dunlow made could only be described as a low growl. He walked away, leading us to the sitting room we'd talked in before. No tour of the grand manor for us. Juliet and I sat on the firm sofa and I got out my notepad. Leo sat in a chair opposite but Dunlow stayed standing, leaning an elbow on the marble mantle encasing the wide fireplace. Rain speckled the windows, distorting the view of the dark forest outside.

'When we last met, you told us you didn't know Melanie and that you had no idea why she would have been on the estate.' I unfolded the printed text transcripts. 'We have evidence to suggest that might not be true.'

I passed Leo the messages between Melanie and My Lion. As his eyes ran down the page, a blotchy blush rose up his neck. He lowered the paper and swallowed, his eyes darting to his father.

Dunlow strode over and snatched the paper. He stood beside Leo, reading the exchange, then dropped it onto his son's lap.

'This tells you nothing.' Dunlow resumed his position at the unlit fire. 'Leo's name is nowhere on that drivel.'

'You're right, it's not,' I said. 'But we already know the phone number is registered under your name. It won't be too hard to find out how many others are, and to match them to yourself and other members of your family.' I looked away from Dunlow, whose eyes would have bored holes straight through me if sheer hatred could be converted to force. 'You could save us the trouble and tell us whether or not you're My Lion.'

Leo's fingers coasted over the transcript. 'It's my number. They're messages from me.'

'Christ almighty,' Dunlow hissed.

'Okay, Leo. Let's go back to the start.' I ignored his father's barely contained rage. 'How did you know Melanie?'

'Do we need a solicitor?' Dunlow interrupted.

Leo swung his head to stare at him. 'I didn't kill Melanie, Dad.'

'That's not what I'm bloody well saying,' Dunlow bit back. 'These people might think you did.'

'That's not what we're suggesting at all.' It wasn't quite a lie. Believing Leo had a hand in Melanie's death and believing he pulled the trigger were two separate things. 'For now, we just want to establish Leo's relationship with Melanie and an accurate timeline of his movements on the night she died.'

Dunlow glared at me but allowed his son to speak.

'I didn't know her very well. We'd been meeting up for a couple of months to practise her singing,' Leo said. 'She hadn't come to the estate before.'

'But she wanted to on the night she died?' I asked.

'Yeah.' Leo licked his lips, his eyes darting to his father. 'I didn't go to meet her.'

'You didn't?' I made a note. 'What happened?'

'I decided it wasn't a good idea.'

I narrowed my eyes. 'But you didn't message Melanie to tell her you'd changed your mind?'

'I called her. She got mad. I guess she was already here and didn't want to have had a wasted trip.'

I twirled my pencil. That did make vague sense with the messages sent after her death. We'd have to check the phone records, see if there was a call between the two numbers. 'How did you feel about Melanie?'

Leo's patchy blush deepened. 'I thought she was nice.'

That was quite different from Jordan's assessment of the feelings between Melanie and her secret admirer.

Juliet sat forward. 'I don't believe you, Leo.' Apparently, she'd decided to retain my status as the good cop.

Dunlow bristled. 'My son is not a liar.'

'I'm sorry I didn't tell you before,' Leo said. 'I didn't want to get in trouble.'

'That's okay, Leo,' I said, as Juliet sat back. Dunlow mirrored her movement, leaning on the mantle again. 'You liked Melanie?'

Leo looked at me, then his father. 'As a friend, yeah.'

'Then why did you leave her out there alone?'

Leo closed his eyes in a prolonged blink. 'I didn't go meet her, but I had no idea what was going to happen.'

'So, you arranged to meet Melanie but then changed your mind. That's the truth?' I asked. 'You didn't see her that night?'

A gust of wind threw rain against the windows. Leo flinched, then nodded.

'Do you have any more questions for my son?' Dunlow stepped forward.

I glanced at Juliet, and we stood together. 'Thank you for telling us the truth, Leo,' I said.

He didn't look up as Dunlow escorted us from the room. We walked across the polished floor, our footsteps echoing in the tall entrance way. Dunlow held the front door open and shut it after us without a word. Gravel crunched underfoot as we rushed to the car, rain lashing our coats.

Juliet shook out her hair once we'd slammed the doors shut. 'Do you believe him?'

'Leo's new story does make some sense.' I wrinkled my nose as I started the car. 'But no, I don't believe him. I don't know exactly what he did that night, but he's hiding something. With Dunlow in the room, there was no way Leo was going to tell the truth.'

Juliet looked at the manor. 'Do you believe Jordan? That Leo was obsessed with Melanie? That he killed her?'

I turned the car and began the long drive towards the estate gates. 'Leo doesn't seem like a murderer to me, and there was no evidence on Melanie's phone of an obsessive relationship. I don't think Leo's telling the truth, but I don't see him as a stalker or a killer.'

'But why does he keep lying?'

'Could be as simple as not wanting to get bollocked for having a girl over. Dunlow seems like an incredibly unpleasant man. I wouldn't want to incur his wrath.'

Lights shone from the grimy windows of Karl's cottage. The gates opened before we came to a stop before them.

'There's not much point talking to Karl tonight.' Juliet pulled her phone out of her pocket. 'Until we unravel the lies and figure out who Leo is trying to protect, we don't have anything to throw at him.'

I nodded, secretly relieved we wouldn't interrupt the grounds-keeper's evening. 'Hopefully the forensics from Melanie's body will help.'

Juliet tutted. 'Whenever they come through.'

Ollie. Sent 19:42.

Late is fine, but you owe me breakfast in the morning
xxx

Gabe

Rain drummed on the window, but our office and the floor outside were quiet. Juliet sat across from me at her desk, her face turned colourless by the white glow of her computer screen.

'I can't stay for much longer.' I glanced at my phone. 'I've got a date.'

'Very nice,' Juliet said absently. 'Are you going to insist I leave with you?'

I threw details of my personal life at Juliet occasionally in the hope she'd bite and we could form a more conventional friendship. No luck today. I'd have to tell Maddy about Ollie.

'If you'll let me.'

Juliet didn't look up. 'Fine. Give me a minute.'

I shut down my computer and swivelled from side to side while Juliet continued to type. My eyes drifted over to the wall of evidence. It was almost completely full. It had been this cluttered during cases before, but not without a more concrete picture forming.

Melanie was in the middle. The selfie I'd taken from her bedroom overlapped with pictures from the forest and pathologist. Lines of messages between her and the two boys ran down to the floor. Leo was pinned on her right, Jordan on her left. So different but essentially the same. Two enamoured young men, but did either of them kill Melanie?

Karl was pinned next to Leo, the article about his family the only thing standing against him now we knew he definitely wasn't My Lion. He could be hiding nothing more than a sad past, or there might be something sinister lurking behind his locked cottage door that we'd miss if we didn't delve deeper.

The older son, Terence, was relegated to a corner of the board. His alibi was awaiting corroboration, but enough people had told us he was away when Melanie died for us to be reasonably sure he wasn't involved. Seeing no more of him wouldn't be a problem. I didn't enjoy spending time with his type; rich, confident men who expected women to laugh at their jokes and admire their easy beauty.

I preferred someone real, with enough scars of their own that they could begin to understand mine. Tattoos might have to make do. I hadn't known Ollie for long, but I suspected he didn't have anything deep and dark hiding in his past. There was no caginess to him, nothing he'd struggled to hide in the few conversations we'd had. But he seemed kind, like he would hold damaged things carefully. Maybe being with someone whole would be better than trying to merge my cracked edges with someone else's.

Juliet coughed, jolting my thoughts away from Ollie. I must like him more than the other people I'd slept with since moving here, for him to intrude while I was at work. I should have clocked that already. There weren't many people I met for a second time.

Dunlow was pinned beside Jordan. I mimicked the expression on his sour face. He should have been above the others, like he was in life. A horrific crime had been committed on his land but he remained untouched, floating over it all.

I pressed my fingers into my bottom lip. I didn't like Dunlow, but that didn't make him any more of a suspect. And just because I didn't think Leo or Jordan could have murdered Melanie, it didn't mean they hadn't. We had to work with the evidence. Intuition could only take us so far.

'Done.' Juliet swung her chair around. 'I've emailed forensics. Our case is being slowed down by the other one, but they know who their killers are. I don't understand the delay.'

She never would. A whole fleet of Krystals could be killed and Juliet would retain her tunnel vision. Still, I understood her frustration. In a case with far too many suspects and no easy answers, conclusive DNA evidence would be a massive boon.

The murder of a young, pretty child gained far too much publicity to be anything other than a priority. The forensics team would be going over the mountain of evidence gathered with their usual attention to detail, making certain nothing would undermine Paul's case against the parents. With the press prowling, everything had to be perfect and swift.

We needed those results though, and if anyone could write a demanding email, it was Juliet. Until we knew who Melanie had sex with and until we got evidence from the dog and gun casings, we couldn't build a case against any of our suspects. Leo, Jordan, Karl, Dunlow – they could all keep lying to us and we'd have no idea who was telling the truth.

I flicked off the lights as we walked out of our office, plunging the faces on the wall into darkness.

Day 4

Friday, 13 October

WHO COULD DO THAT TO AN INNOCENT GIRL? –
COMMUNITY ROCKED BY DISCOVERY OF BODY BY BINS...

Scroll.

MUM AND DAD WERE KNOWN TO SOCIAL SERVICES – WHY
WASN'T MORE DONE TO SAVE KRYSTAL BARRETT?...

Scroll.

POLICE FAIL TO FIND THE KILLERS – ARE OUR ESSENTIAL
SERVICES TOO STRETCHED TO PROTECT THE MOST
VULNERABLE...

Scroll.

Gabe

The café was busy; children fought with sticky fingers over mounds of waffles, and couples flirted around steaming coffees. A lone man in an oversized wool hat squinted at his laptop, crumbs abandoned on a plate at his elbow.

Ollie sat across from me, his light brown hair damp from our shared shower. His tan skin, exposed from the shoulder down after he'd stripped off his jacket, was patterned with mismatched tattoos. He'd explained a few of them to me last night, until we'd gotten distracted.

He ran a hand through his tousled hair. I'd assumed he spent an age making it look like he'd just stumbled out of bed, but his effortless look really was effortless. He'd chatted the whole walk here, extolling the virtues of the café and deliberating between their many breakfast options, but had been quiet since the waitress took our order.

'I want to know more about you,' he blurted out.

I only had a second to blink at him before the waitress reappeared beside our table. I bit the inside of my cheeks as she served our coffees and rushed away. Conjuring a smile, I tried not to think about all the things I didn't want to share. It wasn't like Ollie was going to demand I tell him everything after spending two nights together, he just wanted to know some things. I could do that.

'I propose we do it like this, since I get the feeling you're not so good at opening up.' He widened his eyes, giving me a chance to interject. 'We ask questions, but the rule is we both have to answer.'

That was doable. I nodded, curling my fingers around my mug. The heat from the contents seeped into my chilled flesh. I could always lie if Ollie veered close to something painful. It would spell the end though, before this thing had really begun. I didn't want that.

'Let's start off easy.' Ollie wiggled in his chair, his white top shifting across his toned chest. 'I feel like this is something I should know already, but what's your job?'

There was a reason he didn't know. When I met people from dating apps, I wasn't interested in talking. I needed them to quiet the noise in my head for a while, and words were no use.

'I'm a detective sergeant in the Major Investigations Team.'

'What?' Pinkness spread across his cheeks. He buried his face in his hands. 'That makes what I do even worse.'

'What do you do?' I smiled at the top of his head. 'You have to answer. It's in the rules.'

He lowered his hands and mock glared at me. 'I'm a model.'

'That's not so bad.' I took a sip of coffee.

'It's stupid and frivolous.' He pouted. 'You're off doing something noble, bringing bad guys to justice, and every day I'm prancing around in designer underwear.'

'I'd pay to see that.' His lips twitched upwards. 'My turn to ask now?'

'Yes, please. Move us away from my embarrassing lack of a proper job.'

I looked across the heaving restaurant, rubbing my fingers on my mug. 'What's your favourite colour?'

Ollie rolled his eyes, his cheeks flushed. It made him look younger. I wanted to reach out, feel the heat under his skin, but I kept my hands clasped around my drink. He seemed to like me, but that could change.

'Red, you?'

'Blue. Soft, like when the day is fresh and new.'

'Good answer,' Ollie said, all his ill humour dissipated. 'How did you come to live here?'

'Work. I was in the Met before, north London. I always wanted to be a detective and when the chance came to work down here with Juliet, I jumped at it.'

'Sub-question.' Ollie held up a finger. 'Who is Juliet?'

I searched for the right words. 'Juliet is the detective inspector I work with. She's incredibly clever. I've learnt so much working with her. How to read people, how to find information everyone else has overlooked. She's ruthless and works harder than anyone else and, despite her coldness and her distance, she cares. I know she does.'

I was slightly breathless at the end of my speech. Ollie beamed at me. 'She sounds great. I'd love to meet her someday.'

'You might,' I said, my heart skipping for a myriad of reasons. Juliet would never want to meet him so it was a moot point, but this man, his ankles tangling lazily with mine, wanted to meet the important people in my life. Maybe he could even become one of them.

The waitress came over with two heaped plates before I could get too ahead of myself. Eggs and avocado on toast for me, a stack of pancakes for Ollie. He dribbled maple syrup liberally over the top.

'How about you?' I picked up my knife and fork.

'I moved here for work too.' Ollie turned the syrup at an angle, trying to close it without getting stickiness on the outside. 'I was modelling in London but the rent was so expensive, everything was, and even though I was bartending as well I couldn't keep up. I started looking elsewhere about a year ago and an agent down here offered me representation.' He cut his pancakes into bitesize triangles. 'It's not what I want to do forever, but it works for now.'

His foot travelled up and down the back of my calf. I shook my head. A simple touch shouldn't have such power over me.

'Your question,' he reminded me.

'What about your parents?' I asked, stumbling to the edge of dangerous territory. I couldn't help myself. I knew the fire would burn but held my hand close to the flames. 'Where do they live? What do they do?'

'Cornwall.' Ollie speared soft dough on his fork and held it aloft. 'My dad's a farmer and Mum practically runs the village where I grew up. I go back a few times a year, when I can afford it. You?'

'They live in north London. Barnet. I lived with them until I moved here.' I pushed my eggs around on top of my bread, dislodging a fan of avocado.

'What do they do?' Ollie asked, food pressed into one cheek. That should have been unattractive, but it made him look like a lopsided hamster.

'My mum's a carer at a home for disabled kids. Dad's a carpenter.'

'Do you visit much?'

'I've not been back since I moved here.' I poked my fork into an egg yolk. 'My dad got mad when I told them I was moving. We haven't spoken since.'

It had been eight months since I'd fallen into my mum's soft warmth, eaten her food, relaxed in her mismatched kitchen and watched her bake. Eight months since I'd sat under my dad's cold gaze, his reproach clouding the air between us. Turns out there was a big difference between plain silence because neither of you has anything to say and someone refusing to speak to you.

'That's tough,' Ollie said. He offered me a small smile before selecting another triangle of pancake.

'Does all of that count as your question?' I loaded up my fork.

'No.' Ollie sucked maple syrup from his thumb. He moved his foot up my leg again and asked, 'Do you have any siblings?'

I pulled my feet under my chair and set my knife and fork down.

'I had a brother. Barnabas.' I pushed my teeth together, hard. I didn't want to lie. 'He died when I was young.'

'Oh, Gabe.' Ollie reached across the table to lay his hand over my clenched fist. 'I'm so sorry.'

'It was a long time ago.' The warmth of his palm settled into my knuckles. I extended my fingers and twined them through his.

My phone pinged. I extracted it from my pocket and read a message from Juliet. Non-specific, but demanding I get to the station as soon as possible.

I grimaced. 'I need to go to work.'

Ollie pulled out his wallet and threw a couple of notes onto the table. 'You got drinks last night, let me get this.'

'Thank you.' I stood and put on my coat.

Ollie grabbed my hand as we wound our way across the café. 'I have a sister,' he said. 'She's a colossal arsehole.'

My laugh was more like a bark, startling the waitress as we passed through the door. Briny air beat over our faces as we walked down the street, but at least the rain had stopped in the night.

At the corner, Ollie pressed his lips to mine. 'Have a good day of detecting.'

Call connected at 9:15.

'Juliet?'

'I just got your message. Sorry I couldn't call any sooner.'

'You didn't check your messages all day yesterday? While you have a case?'

'What do you want, Keith?'

'What is it you're working on at the moment? The little girl?'

'No, it's not.'

'But that's at your station, right?'

'Where's this going, Keith?'

'A young girl is murdered, and that doesn't even make you think for a second that you want to spend time with our daughters?'

'I don't know anything about that case.'

'That doesn't matter. You know it's happening. You know the girl is seven, so close to Marie and Flick.'

'I don't pay attention to any case but my own.'

'You don't pay attention to anything but the case, Juliet. We don't exist.'

'Look, Keith. It's not my fault I'm missing so much of their child-hoods.'

'You made your choice.'

'No, Keith, you made a choice. I can't do this again. I've explained this to you too many times.'

'What do you mean?'

'I have to go.'

'I thought that little girl dying would give you a wake-up call. I thought this time it would get through.'

'Don't do this, Keith.'

'What? What am I doing, Juliet? You have two beautiful daughters, and you're missing everything.'

'That's enough. I need to get back to work.'

'Are you coming home this weekend?'

'I don't think it's likely.'

'I guess once the case is finished, we'll be blessed with your time again.'

From: Smriti Brady **mrsbrady@gmail.co.uk**
To: Juliet Stern **juliet.stern@mit.gov.uk**
CC: Gabriella Martin **gabriella.martin@mit.gov.uk**
Date: **13 October, 10:02**
Subject: **Terence Dunlow**

Dear Juliet,

Sorry I haven't replied sooner. My husband and I are on honeymoon.

Teddy wasn't at our wedding. He RSVPed 'yes', but he didn't come.

I didn't think much of it on the day – there were so many guests and one person can slip through the net. I don't know Teddy very well, he's a friend of my husband, but I would have remembered seeing him.

I've contacted some friends, just to make sure, and they didn't see him either. Teddy booked a room in the hotel we had our reception in. I asked and they said he didn't check in.

I hope this is helpful and that Teddy is alright,

Smriti

Gabe

'Maybe we should ask for a key?' Juliet said, as the estate gates slid open.

'Dunlow would love that.'

We'd waited in a lay-by until he left in his sleek BMW. We'd seen the influence he had over Leo. It wasn't unreasonable to assume Dunlow would exert the same control over his older son.

The wheels crunched on the gravel drive. The windows of Karl's cottage were dark. He must have let us in remotely again.

The forest dripped with moisture, fat drops of rain falling on the windscreen at irregular intervals. The gun used to kill Melanie could be hidden somewhere in the fading greenery surrounding us. The rain last night could have washed away vital DNA and mangled any prints. What a perfect solution for one of the men pinned to the wall in our office.

The manor came into view, the brickwork soaked to a darker shade of beige. As we climbed out of the car, the gravel made a dull squelch. I pulled my collar up against the gusting wind and Juliet's hair danced around her face as we walked to the house. She lifted the door knocker.

'You up for taking the lead in here?'

I nodded, keeping a frown off my face. I considered myself in charge unless we decided otherwise. Juliet had said this was my case. But then, maybe her question had nothing to do with that. People responded better to one or the other of us. I wasn't exactly sure who Terence would more readily open up to.

Juliet lifted the knocker again and I moved from foot to foot. The man walking down the staircase, his auburn hair tangled, looked much less put together than when we'd met him in the forest.

'Hello? The detectives, right?' Terence said as he opened the door, revealing eyes crusted with sleep and a face crisscrossed with indentations. His T-shirt was faded by too many washes, his checked trousers baggy around his long legs.

'Detective Sergeant Gabe Martin and Detective Inspector Juliet Stern,' I filled in the blanks. 'Can we come in for a chat?'

Terence held the door wide. Our shoes left puddles on the hardwood floor as he led us through to a kitchen at the back of the manor. The view was no different here, long lawns giving way to tall trees. Terence gestured at some stools but Juliet and I remained standing on one side of a marble kitchen island.

'Dad's not here.' Terence rummaged in a top cupboard. 'Leo's at school as well. Drink?'

'Nothing for us,' I said.

Juliet watched Terence's back with narrowed eyes, her hands curled on the clean worktop. I pulled out my notepad.

'Suit yourself.' Terence pushed a pod into a silver coffee maker and it started up with a smooth purr. He slotted a cup into the front.

'We have a few questions for you,' I said.

'For me?' His face creased in posh boy confusion. We might think we wanted to talk to him, but we must have made a mistake. He wasn't the kind of man who got in serious trouble with the law.

The stream of coffee ended with a gurgle. He grabbed the cup before coming to stand across the island from us, his movements unhurried.

'What do you need to ask me?' He took a sip of his drink.

'We know you weren't at a wedding on the night Melanie Pirt was murdered,' I said.

Juliet pulled her hands back. She might have assumed I would pad out the reason we'd come. That would have been my usual tack, but there was something about Terence that made me want to ruffle his sleek feathers. He was too untouchable, too protected by his wealth and good looks from the gritty realities of life.

'Shit.' He set down his drink with too much force. Coffee spilled over the side and formed a brown pond around the cup. Terence didn't seem to notice. He rubbed his hands over his face, then pressed his palms into his cheeks. His mouth formed a momentary pout before he dropped his hands to the counter.

'It's not what you think.'

'What is it then?' I asked.

'I was away, but not at the wedding.' Terence puffed air out of the side of his mouth. 'I was with a friend.'

'Who?' I jotted down a note.

Terence stared at my pencil. 'Do I have to tell you?'

'We can't trust your alibi unless we have someone else to back it up,' Juliet stated.

'Christ.' Terence looked over at one of the long windows. 'His name's Benedict Hogan. He's an old school friend. I went to his house on the morning of the 8th and I didn't leave until I came home on the 10th.'

'What were you doing with Mr Hogan?' I asked.

'I'd rather not say.' Terence rubbed at his hair. 'It's not illegal or anything, just I'd rather not tell you. But I was there, Benny will confirm that.'

'Why did you tell us you were at a wedding?' I rapped my pencil on my pad. Terence was in theory swapping one alibi for another, but that didn't change the fact that suspects in this case had a bad habit of lying to us.

'I didn't actually tell you that.' Terence shrugged. 'That's what my dad told you.'

'Why did you lie to him?' I asked.

'Because that's what I do.' Terence stared at me, his lips pulled down. He looked a million miles from the untouchable, smarmy posho I'd assumed he was through and through. 'My dad loves Leo and me, but it's on his terms. We do things his way, or we're out on our ear.'

'And your dad wouldn't like you staying with a friend?'

'No, he wouldn't.'

Teddy noticed the puddle around his cup. He grabbed some kitchen roll and mopped up the mess. I tapped my pencil. No matter how legal whatever Terence was up to with Mr Hogan was, it was something his father would disapprove of, something Terence didn't want him to find out about. That didn't narrow the field much. Dunlow didn't seem the type to discriminate over what brought him displeasure.

'Did you know Melanie Pirt?' I asked, leaving Terence's activities with Mr Hogan for now.

Terence shook his head, locks of hair falling across his lined forehead. 'I'd not heard of her until all of this happened.'

'Why should we believe you?' Juliet spread her hands flat on the island. 'You lied to your father about where you were and let us believe that lie. Why should we trust your next alibi, especially since you won't tell us what you were up to?'

'I wasn't up to anything.' Terence scrunched the coffee-stained paper in his hand. 'I never lied, not really, and I've told you the truth now. I wasn't here, and I had nothing to do with what happened. You're wasting your time questioning me.' He threw the kitchen roll down onto the island. 'You shouldn't be talking to me or Leo or Dad. You should be arresting Karl.'

'Why would we arrest Karl?' I asked, my eyebrows lowering.

Terence looked between us, some of his swagger returning. He stood straighter, puffing out his chest.

'You don't know?' He shook his head. 'He has guns in that squalid little cottage.'

I glanced at Juliet. That was a good reason for Karl to avoid letting us into his home. We'd head down to see him next, regardless of my qualms about disturbing his peace.

Triumph flooded Terence's face. 'Bet he didn't tell you about those, did he? Any more questions for me?'

'Not for now,' I said, my smile tight.

Terence rounded the island and led us to the front door, his steps light. He watched us walk to the car.

'Don't believe a thing that idiot tells you about me,' he shouted.

From: Madison Campbell
madison.campbell@mitadmin.gov.uk
To: Juliet Stern **juliet.stern@mit.gov.uk**, Gabriella Martin **gabriella.martin@mit.gov.uk**
Date: **13 October, 10:59**
Subject: **Weekend**

Juliet and Gabe,

I would like to remind you that I do not work weekends. I don't get paid overtime and I don't work from home, so any emails sent to me after 5 p.m. today will be attended to after 9 a.m. on Monday morning.

Don't work too hard,

Maddy

Gabe

My knuckles throbbed after I knocked on the cottage door. I rubbed them as locks clicked behind the thick wood. Muted light filtered out of the smudged windows.

Karl pulled the door open. His wild hair was trapped under a fraying yellow bobble hat and he looked reduced without his long, green coat on. An orange-and-brown knitted jumper revealed narrow shoulders.

'Karl, could we come in for a minute?' I asked.

He looked between Juliet and me but pulled the door wide. It opened straight into his living room. A dining table was squashed under one window and sagging sofas aimed towards a blackened fireplace.

Two long shotguns crossed on the wall above. Dirty windows didn't let in much light, but the naked overhead bulb showed the guns were caked in dust.

'Are these the only guns you have?' I walked around a sofa to get a closer look at them. From this vantage, I could see into Karl's bedroom. A single mattress rested on the floor, the sheets on top rumpled.

'Yeah.' Karl swallowed, his Adam's apple bobbing in his long throat. 'They were here when I moved in. I didn't think it was important to tell you.'

Turns out, it wasn't. There was no way these guns had been fired recently, probably not for many years. I walked over to Juliet, shaking my head.

'I didn't mean to cause a problem.'

'You didn't,' I reassured Karl. Terence sent us down here. Had he known exactly what we'd find, but wanted us out of his kitchen as quickly as possible? 'Sorry to have intruded on you.'

Karl followed us to the front door. He stood watching as we climbed into our car. He fiddled with his phone and the gates swung open.

'That was pointless,' Juliet said as we passed through. 'Those guns couldn't have been used to kill Melanie.'

I pulled out into the lane. 'Do you think Terence knew that?'

'You think he sent us down there on purpose?'

'Maybe. He didn't like us asking questions and poking into his personal life, so he sent us on a wild goose chase. Or maybe he knows more than he's letting on.' I swerved into a lay-by to let a tractor pass. 'Even if his friend says they were together, what were they doing? What's not illegal but something he's desperate to keep hidden from his dad?'

'An affair?'

I huffed as the tractor trundled by. 'Dunlow seems the type to veer towards homophobia, but that isn't the only option. Could be Terence was gambling, or even indulging in some kind of drug that isn't strictly illegal. I can't see Dunlow being happy about their wealth being squandered or used frivolously.'

'Do you think Terence was involved in Melanie's murder?' Juliet's phone rested on one knee.

Terence was his father's son; believed himself untouchable whether or not he'd had a hand in Melanie's death. I didn't know if secrecy was important enough that he would end someone's life. It depended on whether Terence saw Melanie as a person or not. His treatment of Karl, throwing him under the bus and no doubt treating him as lesser because he worked for them, suggested he didn't think twice about how his actions affected other people.

'I don't know, but he was the only one with an alibi, which we've found out is a lie, and he has a new one but won't tell us anything. He's definitely hiding something.' I pulled into the road, biting my lip. 'How far would he go to keep his secret hidden? Maybe Melanie discovered something, and the only way to keep her quiet was to have her killed.'

From: David Rees **david.rees@forensics.gov.uk**
To: Juliet Stern **juliet.stern@mit.gov.uk**, Gabriella Martin **gabriella.martin@mit.gov.uk**
Date: **13 October, 11:47**
Subject: **Operation Chalice – Forensic summary**

Stern and Martin,

I've received reports from members of my team, the forensic vet, and the National Forensic Firearms lab on a number of pertinent materials found on the grounds of the Dunlow Estate. I've taken the liberty of summarising these findings, but the full reports are attached to this email.

REPORT ON:

#6 to #9 THREE GUN CASINGS found on Dunlow Estate near body of victim

#10 to #12 THREE BULLETS extracted from a tree on Dunlow Estate

#13 to #14 BOOT PRINTS by gun casings on Dunlow Estate

#19 to #26 ASSORTED GUNS taken from outbuilding on Dunlow Estate

#167 to #172 BODY OF DOG found on Dunlow Estate, **SURROUNDING DEBRIS** and **BULLET**

The **THREE GUN CASINGS** were dusted for prints but none were found and wiped for DNA samples but none were found. The **GUN CASINGS** were from a long nose hunting rifle.

The **THREE BULLETS** match the **CASINGS**. They were covered in blood and no prints could be taken. As we have not yet had the DNA sampling back from the body of **MELANIE PIRT**, we have not been able to confirm that the DNA taken was from her.

Impressions were taken of the **BOOT PRINTS** and the surrounding area swept for DNA samples but none were found. The boots were well used and we were unable to identify a brand. **TIMOTHY DUNLOW** allowed our team access to all boots on the premises, including those stored in the barn and the pair owned by **KARL BISS**, and none were a match. The size of the boots is men's UK 11.

ASSORTED GUNS taken from the Dunlow Estate were all hunting rifles. All were consistent with the gun used to kill **MELANIE PIRT**. All were dusted for prints and were a positive match for **TIMOTHY DUNLOW** and **TERENCE DUNLOW**. None of them had been fired recently. One rack was empty, but **TIMOTHY DUNLOW** said this gun had been sent away for cleaning.

DEBRIS was removed from the **BODY OF THE DOG** and was a positive match for **KARL BISS** in the areas he indicated that he had moved the **DEBRIS**. There were no other DNA samples in the **DEBRIS**.

The **DOG** had been shot once through the skull. The **BULLET** matched those extracted from the tree but we were unable to locate any casings and there were no matching boot prints around the **BODY OF THE DOG**. The ground was heavily disturbed. DNA samples taken from the **BODY OF THE DOG** matched those from **KARL BISS**, **LEONARD DUNLOW**, **TERENCE DUNLOW** and **TIMOTHY DUNLOW** (in order of most to least). The **DOG'S MOUTH** contained blood, which has been sent for testing. Until the results are back from the DNA samples taken from the body of **MELANIE PIRT**, we cannot be sure it is a match.

I hope this is helpful,

Rees

Gabe

'Is any of this helpful?' I asked.

Juliet stepped back from the wall of evidence, David's report pinned above Melanie's selfie. 'Not right now.'

I leant my elbows on the desk and pushed my fingers into my hair. 'When are we getting the results from Melanie's body?'

'I don't know.' Juliet huffed as she sat down. 'I've been hassling anyone I can think of, but they all come back with the same line. "There is a high priority case that's taking precedence." And you know they're going to be hopeless over the weekend.'

I dug my nails into my scalp. I shouldn't feel mad that not everyone had Juliet's messed up work-life balance and if there was more evidence to build a case against Krystal's parents, I was glad of it. 'We know the murderer has size 11 feet.'

'Like every one of our suspects?'

I released my hair and stood up. 'This case is ridiculous.' I walked over to the wall of evidence. Lime green twine wrapped around so many of the pins that it was hard to work out the connections. 'Let's talk it out.'

Juliet's chair squeaked as she came to stand beside me. 'Start at the beginning. What were Melanie's movements that day?'

'She went to school,' I recited information sprawled across the wall. 'She was unhappy because of the way Jordan had treated her and the messages he was sending. She made plans with Leo, lied to Ida about where she was going, and took a bus to the Dunlow Estate. That's when her timeline becomes unclear.'

'If we believe Leo, then at this point he called Melanie,' Juliet took over. 'There's a record of a call on her phone. He says he told Melanie he didn't want to meet up anymore.' Juliet stared at the notes I'd taken during our second interview with Leo. 'Despite this rebuff, Melanie then entered the estate, stayed in the forest for hours or met up with someone else, and was shot near midnight.'

'Or Leo did meet up with Melanie and they had sex.' I pointed at the question mark I'd stuck next to his changed statement. 'But then what happened? He flew into a rage and killed her? Jordan crept onto the estate, grabbed a gun, and chased her through the forest with an unknown dog? Terence, annoyed Melanie knew something about him, returned home secretly and killed her? Or asked someone else to do it?'

Juliet shook her head. 'Too much speculation. Let's stick to what we know.'

'Fine.' I walked closer to the board to look at the map of the Dunlow Estate. 'We were able to track Melanie's flight from the dog and her killer, and she ran this way.' I traced her route away from the manor. 'So presumably she met someone at or near the house and was running towards the road.'

'She then climbed a tree and was shot three times in the back,' Juliet added. 'She fell out of the tree, perhaps already dead, and was mauled by the dog.'

'Let's think about our suspects.' I took a breath. 'Leo lied to us. He'd been meeting up with Melanie for months before she was killed. He says he arranged to meet her but changed his mind. No one can confirm or deny that he was in the den above the garage when Melanie was murdered.'

'What do you think of him?' Juliet sat on the edge of her desk.

'I don't think it was him.' I looked at the photo of Leo in his smart school uniform and thick glasses. 'His shock when we told him someone had been killed seemed genuine, and the messages he sent Melanie afterwards suggest he didn't know what was going on.'

'You don't think he's a good enough liar?'

I shook my head. 'We've seen him lie. He couldn't fake shock like that.'

'Right. So we don't think it's likely Leo has told us everything, but we don't think he killed Melanie.' Juliet nodded at Terence's picture. 'What about the brother?'

'Another liar. He told everyone he was at a wedding, but he was somewhere different doing who knows what.'

'I've been pestering Benedict Hogan, but even if he confirms Terence was with him, we still have no idea what they were doing together.'

'He's got a secret.' I walked over to the other side of the board. 'What would he do to keep it from his father?'

'Terence's DNA was all over the guns. It wasn't just Dunlow using them.'

'But according to the report, none of the guns were used to murder Melanie.' I pointed at the picture of a younger Karl. 'Then we've got the groundskeeper. He reported the bodies, which would be a monumentally stupid move since he could have kept them hidden for a long time if he'd wanted too.'

'Unless he knew we wouldn't find anything incriminating on either body,' Juliet said.

I grimaced. 'I don't see him as a killer. What motive would he have had to murder her?'

Juliet dipped her head to the side, her eyes on the other side of the wall. 'You said we don't know how far Terence would go to protect his privacy. Maybe he was away that night but he asked his brother to lure Melanie onto the grounds and had Karl prepped to kill her.'

'That's a stretch.' I perched on the desk next to her. 'The messages sent to Leo indicate that it was Melanie's idea to come onto the estate.'

'How do we know the seed wasn't planted by Leo during one of their singing sessions?' Juliet asked. 'Terence, Leo and Karl all benefit from being close to Dunlow. What if Terence's secret is so explosive that it would expel them all from Dunlow's good graces? Sacrificing one life would seem like a fair trade to maintain the comfort of three.'

I pressed my lips together. It could be true. It at least fit with the impression of Terence I'd gotten so far.

Despite the many connections across the wall, so much was missing. Juliet's theory wove into all the gaps, pulled together motives and opportunities. It didn't matter that it didn't feel quite right, that such a neat connection between many of the suspects struck me as wrong. We just needed evidence to support it, and we could catch them all.

'Let's not forget Jordan.' I gestured over at his picture. 'How is he involved in all of this?'

'He has a history of violence towards the victim, and we know how often that leads to fatality.' Juliet's face was expressionless. 'He lied to us too, about the beatings. His alibi is as terrible as the rest, but do you really think he could have left that creaky house without his parents noticing? Every movement upstairs was obvious downstairs.'

'You're right.' I walked to my seat and thumped down. 'There's also the question of how he would have got hold of a gun. The store was locked and the only missing gun is accounted for.' I wiggled my mouse, hoping an email had arrived in the last five minutes that would clear all of this up. No such luck.

'We haven't mentioned Dunlow.' Juliet leant on her desk, staring at the wall of evidence.

'He's the same as the others. He has no alibi and is totally unconcerned about it.'

Juliet grabbed our mugs. 'I'm going to make coffee.'

'Before you go.' I tipped my head to the side. 'Do we have enough to ask for a warrant to search the Dunlow Estate? We have to do something.'

Juliet raised an eyebrow. 'You know what, I reckon we do.'

'It's not likely one of them was stupid enough to hide the gun under their bed or leave blood-stained boots in the attic, but we might find something.'

'And we'll piss off Dunlow,' Juliet said as she walked out of the office. 'Give him something to actually frown about.'

FORM 22A – FORMAL REQUEST FOR WARRANT: PERMISSION TO SEARCH A PRIVATE RESIDENCE

REQUESTING OFFICERS:

Detective Inspector Juliet Stern and Detective Sergeant Gabriella Martin

CASE NUMBER:

10098755

CASE DESCRIPTION:

Murder of Melanie Pirt on the grounds of the Dunlow Estate in the New Forest on 9 October.

REQUESTED SEARCH AREA:

Manor house and all outbuildings on the Dunlow Estate, including groundskeeper's cottage.

REASON FOR WARRANT REQUEST:

All residents of the Dunlow Estate (Karl Biss, Leonard Dunlow, Terence Dunlow and Timothy Dunlow) are currently without alibis for the period of time estimated for the murder of Melanie Pirt. After several rounds of questioning, there is a motive for each of them to have been directly or indirectly involved with the murder of Melanie Pirt. The murder weapon has not been recovered, nor has any clothing worn by the murderer. A preliminary search, permission given by Timothy Dunlow, of one of the outhouses on the Dunlow Estate uncovered a number of guns similar to the one used to kill Melanie Pirt. All the residents of the Dunlow Estate are high priority suspects in this murder investigation and we believe a search of the premises will uncover vital evidence.

Unknown Number. Sent 13:02.

You've got your money. Now fuck off.

Gabe

Chatter died as Juliet and I walked into the briefing room. Uniformed officers sank into seats around square tables, Alice To among them. I tried not to change my smile as our eyes met, but she quickly looked at the officer beside her. David and his forensic team lazed against the walls, dressed in thin jumpers and leggings that helped them keep cool in the white bodysuits they donned daily.

I logged onto a battered laptop in the corner of the room and Juliet moved to one side as a map of the Dunlow Estate projected onto the screen behind her. This was the first time we'd had any significant staffing allocation for this case, so we'd decided Juliet should take the reins temporarily. It wasn't that anyone would be disrespectful to me, but if you wanted a job done with a minimum of fuss then it made sense to put the highest-ranking officer at the wheel.

'On 9th October at around eight p.m. Melanie Pirt entered the Dunlow Estate in the New Forest, we believe via a broken section of wall,' Juliet said. 'She'd arranged to meet with Leonard Dunlow, but he says he reconsidered and did not meet her. Four hours later, she ran through the forest from the direction of the house, climbed a tree, and was shot three times. She fell to the ground and was mauled by a dog. This animal was also shot.'

On the screen, Melanie's flight path zigzagged through an overhead shot of trees. The site of the shooting was marked with a red dot. I clicked onto the next slide, which showed the bullets and gun casings pulled from the bodies. As I'd put the presentation together, I'd chosen not to include a photo of Melanie's dead body. It wasn't something the team needed to see.

'We have not yet recovered the murder weapon,' Juliet continued. 'The residents of the Dunlow Estate have given differing accounts of the night of the murder and, as of yet, we have no corroborated alibi for any of them.'

I clicked again and four faces filled the screen. Dunlow, his two sons, and Karl. Odds were, one of these men killed Melanie. Hopefully, the search would reveal something that pointed conclusively to one of them. If that happened, I'd swallow any lingering instincts leading another way. Not that my gut was pointing towards anyone, just away from too many of our suspects.

'We have a warrant to search the estate buildings,' Juliet said, while I brought up the map again. This time the buildings were highlighted. 'We'll work through the manor first, which I imagine will take most of the afternoon. After that, we'll head to the garage and rooms above then sweep out into the barn and other outbuildings. We'll finish with the groundskeeper's cottage at the entrance to the estate. I want any notebooks, unwashed clothing, and anything that looks like it was hidden away brought in for examination. Any questions?'

Alice raised her hand, her gaze firmly fixed on Juliet. 'Have the residents been informed of our intention to search the property, ma'am?'

'No.' Juliet folded her arms. 'We believe that Timothy Dunlow, the estate owner, will be unhappy about the search but neither he nor his youngest son, Leonard, should be home when we first arrive. We don't think Mr Dunlow will be any trouble when he does come home, but he may need assurance that we have a warrant and are carrying out our lawful duty.'

David didn't raise his hand. 'How come it's taken so long for you to request a search of the estate?'

Like everyone else, his eyes were on Juliet. Hidden from the others, her hands clenched into fists behind her folded arms.

'Initially, nothing suggested that any of the residents of the estate were linked to the murder,' Juliet answered, her tone mild. 'Only recently has new evidence punched holes through their shaky alibis and given us cause for the search.' She looked around the room. 'If there's nothing else, shall we head out?'

I logged off and stood beside her as everyone else left the room. Alice nodded as she walked by, her eyes carefully avoiding the space occupied by me. She was a woman of her word; there would be no more socialising with her in my future. It wasn't something that particularly saddened me, but I would have preferred a more cordial working relationship.

Juliet shook out her shoulders, her arms falling to her sides as David left the room. The last of the pack. 'Why does it always have to be him?'

'Because, unfortunately, he's the best.' I paused, sure Juliet wouldn't appreciate any meddling. 'I would offer to protect you, but I'm certain you can look after yourself.'

'It's nice to know you've got my back,' she said, and a rush of protectiveness swept through me despite her light tone. I didn't think she would ever ask for help, which meant I had to keep a close eye on her. 'If he finds something that closes this case, I'll forgive him.'

'Don't say anything you'll regret,' I warned. 'He's rather good at what he does.'

We had to hope Juliet would be doling out forgiveness David didn't deserve later today.

From: Ryan White **ryan.white@hmps.plo.gov.uk**
To: Juliet Stern **juliet.stern@mit.gov.uk**
CC: Gabriella Martin **gabriella.martin@mit.gov.uk**
Date: **13 October, 15:42**
Subject: **Legal Visit**

Hello Juliet,

Sorry for the delay in replying to your email. Unfortunately, the earliest we can have you in is 11 a.m. on the 17 October as Mr Biss has been injured in an incident with another prisoner. Please let me know if this works for you as soon as possible and I'll make all the necessary arrangements.

As you know, Mr Biss is under no obligation to talk to you and is able to end the visit at any time if he chooses. He has said a solicitor is unnecessary, but he can request one at any time. Hopefully, he will be fully cooperative with your investigation.

Ryan White

Police Liaison Officer

Gabe

Dunlow arrived home as we finished searching the main house. I stepped out of the front door and he strode into my personal space.

'What the hell is going on?' he spat, his face a map of blotchy reds.

The blue lights on top of one of the cars flashed. Dunlow whipped his head around. Alice leant against her car door, a taser hanging lazily from one hand.

Dunlow took a step back. 'Show me the bloody warrant.'

He snatched it from my hand. While he read, I dipped my head at Alice. I hadn't needed saving but didn't relish the idea of facing up to a man much taller and broader than myself.

Leo emerged from the black BMW his dad had stormed out of. His eyes darted between me and uniformed officers chatting beside another car.

'We're ready to go over to the garage now.' Juliet exited the house, followed by David and his team.

'This is a disgrace.' Dunlow threw the warrant at me.

'We're done with the main house. You may want to stay there for the rest of the search.' I folded the paper I'd caught with my fingertips and slotted it into my pocket.

I left my hand there. Dunlow didn't need to see he'd rattled me. He was fully aware of how he cut through the rest of the world, and he had to know how standing over a smaller person would make them feel. I wondered when he'd stopped being able to do that to his sons and had to resort to other forms of intimidation instead.

Dunlow sneered. 'And let you rifle through the rest of our things alone? Leave them in a goddamn mess when you're done? Not bloody likely.'

'I assure you, Mr Dunlow, our searches are carried out with the utmost care.' David pulled down the hood of his white suit and his ginger hair sprung free in a staticky jumble. 'Every item taken is carefully logged and will be returned as it was found.'

Dunlow narrowed his eyes. 'Even so, I'll observe the next portion.'

'Off you go,' Juliet said to the forensic team.

David and the rest of the white-suited group led the way over to the garage. They started downstairs, checking expensive four-by-fours and shiny BMWs. Only after they'd swept through did Juliet and I run our hands around the linings of spotless boots and take a look at the keys hanging on the wall. When I enquired about the missing keys, Dunlow told me in clipped sentences that he and his sons had some elsewhere.

'The spare for my BMW was lost months ago.' He flicked his hand at one of the empty hooks. 'Need another sent over.'

Upstairs in the den, we disturbed Terence. He'd let us into the main house earlier but hadn't accompanied us on our search. He heaved himself up from a beanbag and stood next to his father and brother in the doorway.

The room was huge, spanning the length of the garage below, but was set into the eaves. The sloping ceilings limited the amount of usable space. Terence and Leo had shoved as much clutter into the long room as possible. There were two desks, a couple of sofa beds, a mini fridge humming in one corner, and a TV with various gaming equipment trailing across the floor.

Their rooms in the manor were nothing like this. I glanced over at Dunlow. His mouth twitched, his upper lip curling in distaste. He might have allowed his sons this space, but he didn't enjoy being confronted by it.

Leo's eyes switched between his father and one of the messy desks.

'Have you looked at this?' I asked David as I walked over.

He nodded, distracted by bundling a duvet into an oversized evidence bag.

I shuffled through the papers and books on the desk. All academic, much more advanced than anything I'd studied at school. The drawers held more of the same, but I found a laptop power cable coiled in the bottom one. I pawed through the drawers and the stuff on top of the desk.

'Any idea where the computer is?' I asked the family gathered in the doorway.

Both sons whipped their heads back and forth. Their brown eyes didn't leave the desk. Terrible liars.

I pulled out the chair and crawled underneath. The floor was littered with sweet wrappers and a wonky pair of glasses. I knocked on the wooden backing of the desk and scooted out.

The desk wasn't flush with the sloping wall. There was a triangle of dark space behind it. I grabbed a dusty lamp and aimed it into the recess.

'David, can I borrow you for a minute?' I looked around. Terence clenched his jaw while Leo watched my progress with wide eyes.

'Something back there?' David got down onto his knees and reached a gloved hand behind the desk. 'Ah.' He straightened, pulling an expensive looking laptop out of the gap.

'Whose is that?' I turned to the Dunlows.

Leo swallowed. 'Mine.'

'Must have fallen,' his father said.

'Right.' I looked at the desk. No way the laptop fell. It had been hidden, and badly at that.

'We're done here.' David slipped the laptop into a clear bag. 'We'll head out to the gun store and barn, then over to the cottage?'

'I don't need to see any more of this,' Dunlow announced. 'Leo, come to the house. You, stay with them.'

Leo and Dunlow disappeared, leaving Terence to dodge out of the way as the forensic team filed past, their arms full of bags. His neck pulled taut. It didn't take a genius to figure out he was being punished. Perhaps it was for letting us onto the property, but there could be more to it. Only one person was alerted to our search and had time to hide anything incriminating. Maybe Dunlow was annoyed Terence had done a bad job.

Terence stood outside the gun store with me while the forensic team poked around inside. There was a locked cabinet, and we'd already checked the registration paperwork was in order. Juliet stood in the doorway, conferring with David. Her face stayed a controlled blank no matter how many times he spoke over or contradicted her.

'We haven't been able to get hold of Mr Hogan yet.' I kept my gaze on the stone and thatch building.

Terence snapped his head around. 'Benny will get back to you when he can. He's a busy man.'

I pursed my lips. 'If he confirms he was with you but won't tell us what you two were doing, that leaves us with a lot of unanswered questions.'

'Like what?' Terence asked, a line forming between his brows. He looked uncannily like his brother when worried, all his swagger swept away.

'Like, what lengths would you go to, to keep your terrible secret from coming out?' I didn't look directly at him but could see him fidgeting with the sleeve of his jacket. 'Or, even if you were away, who here might have helped get rid of someone who knew too much?'

'No,' Terence said. 'None of that's right.'

'Maybe you needed Melanie gone.' I shrugged, feigning relaxation. Even pushing a suspect this much made my heart race, but Terence was too wound up to see through my act. 'And maybe you asked Karl to do it. Leo lured her onto the estate and, while you were away, your secret was hushed up.'

Throwing Juliet's unsupported theory at Terence was risky, but it might pay off.

He rubbed his face with both hands. 'No, no, no. You've got it all wrong. Bloody hell.' He looked in the direction of the manor. 'I can't talk about this here; Dad could appear.'

'Juliet?' I called.

She stamped over in her sensible boots. 'Yes?'

'Terence has something he'd like to talk to us about.' I smiled sweetly at him.

He clenched his jaw. 'Not here. Come with me.'

Juliet fell into step beside me. 'Good work,' she whispered behind Terence's back.

I grinned, inordinately pleased with myself even as my heart returned to its normal rhythm. I didn't think it likely we'd solve Melanie's murder right now, but hopefully we could remove one or two people from the pool of suspects.

Terence led us along a twisting path through the forest to the back of the barn. Yips mixed with the tinny sound of a radio. Terence yanked open the back door. We were welcomed by a booming bark from the nearest stall, followed by Artie's head appearing at the top of his gate. I patted between his pointy ears and he vibrated with unsuppressed glee.

'Shut up, Artemis,' Terence snapped.

'I've told you not to come in that way,' Karl shouted, flicking off the radio. He spotted Juliet and me behind Terence and stilled.

'It's my barn,' Terence said over the occasional bark and whine. 'I'll do what I like.'

Karl put down a brush matted with fur. He folded his arms over his chest, disrupting the cheerful pattern of horses across the front of his thick green jumper.

Terence flinched at another loud bark from Artie. 'Let's go outside. We'll keep getting interrupted in here.'

'A forensic team will be down soon,' Juliet informed Karl as we walked out the main barn doors. 'Will the dogs be okay with that?'

'They'll be fine,' Terence answered.

It was that strange time of an autumn afternoon when the light outside had faded dramatically in the few moments we'd spent in the barn. Terence spun around and glared at Karl, his face half-hidden in shadow.

'The detectives think we worked together to kill the girl. They think I got you to do it to protect my secrets.'

'Oh.' Karl raised his eyebrows, seemingly unconcerned that he'd been implicated for murder. 'What did you tell them?'

'That it isn't bloody true,' Terence growled.

Karl cocked his head to one side. 'What else did you tell them?'

Terence's face flushed in uneven patches. 'Nothing.'

'Gentlemen,' Juliet interrupted. 'I'm afraid we need more than this. You're verging on obstruction of justice.'

'Let's start simple,' I suggested when neither man spoke. 'What's the nature of your relationship with one another?'

Terence scoffed. 'We have no relationship. He works for my dad, that's all.'

'That's not quite all,' Karl said. 'Sorry, Ted, but I'm not going to lie for you.'

'Don't call me Ted,' Terence snapped. 'You promised you wouldn't say anything.'

'We need the truth,' I interjected. 'Otherwise we'll have to draw our own conclusions.'

'Tell them.' Karl's face hardened. 'This is more important than your daddy getting in a snit with you.'

Terence's mouth opened and closed like a fish out of water. Karl didn't wait for him to compose himself.

'I know something about Terence. Something he doesn't want anyone to know.'

'What is it?' Juliet asked.

'You can't tell them,' Terence butted in, sweat building on his forehead. 'You promised.'

'It isn't anything serious.' Karl looked away. 'But it's something he thinks his dad would disown him for, and where would he be without all this?'

Terence hung his head. 'You can't tell them.'

'I've known about it for a while,' Karl carried on. 'I saw Terence, and I took a few photos. I told him about them and he asked me to destroy them, which I did.'

'Did you blackmail him?' Juliet demanded.

'No,' Terence said. 'It wasn't like that.'

'What was it like?' I asked, keeping my voice gentle.

'He wanted me gone and I needed money for that to happen,' Karl said. 'I didn't want to be treated like a lower class being anymore.'

'Terence didn't pay you to kill Melanie?' Juliet asked. 'Did she know his secret too?'

'Ted's careful.' Karl looked at the other man. I couldn't quite read the expression on his face. There was anger, mixed with something like pity or regret. 'Melanie couldn't have known, and he wouldn't have had her killed even if she did. Money is more his style.'

'Benedict will tell you.' Terence's chin trembled. 'I was with him the whole time, was barely out of his sight. I couldn't have orchestrated a murder. I didn't even know the girl existed before she died.'

'So that's it.' I looked between the two men. 'But you're still not going to tell us what you were doing while you were away?'

Karl stared at Terence. 'I did promise.'

'Thank you,' Terence breathed. He stood up straighter. 'Until you force me, arrest me or something, I'm not telling you anything.'

From: Juliet Stern **juliet.stern@mit.gov.uk**
To: Madison Campbell
madison.campbell@mitadmin.gov.uk
CC: Gabriella Martin **gabriella.martin@mit.gov.uk**
Date: **13 October, 19:18**
Subject: **Weekend**

Maddy,

We'll make sure there are lots of emails waiting for you on Monday.

Have a lovely weekend,

Juliet

Gabe

I sent the summary of our infuriating conversation with Terence and Karl to the printer. If we believed them, then they could be removed from the pool of suspects. Neither man knew Melanie or had a reason to kill her. But that damn secret. No matter what my personal hunches were, not knowing something about two possible murderers made my skin itch.

There was nothing we could do, for now. We couldn't arrest either of them and neither would talk without serious pressure. We had to hope they were telling the truth and that this secret was as irrelevant to Melanie's death as they said it was. Benedict Hogan was still unreachable. Since he didn't seem to have a job and lived alone, we were stuck repeatedly calling his mobile. If he didn't get back to us soon, Terence would have to suffer more intense questioning.

'I persuaded David to send the computers over to the IT team ahead of the rest of the evidence,' Juliet said, as she walked into our office. She'd wandered off after we arrived at the station. I'd hoped she was searching out dinner.

She sat and typed in her password. 'We recovered three in the end. Desktops from Terence's bedroom and Dunlow's study, plus the laptop that "fell" behind the desk in the den.'

'Brilliant.' I opened my top drawer, hoping I'd hidden a Twix in there.

'The IT team said they'll share the reports as they write them, which means the first few should be with us shortly.'

No Mars or Yorkie in sight. I shut the drawer and debated my options. Maybe Paul had brought in more bread to charcoal and wouldn't mind me stealing a couple of slices.

'The laptop from the garage is locked.' Juliet squinted as she read from her screen. 'Apparently it needs an update.'

I nodded absently. Despite Juliet's insistence that the team send over their findings as they uncovered them, it wasn't likely anything important would be thrown up tonight. Especially with the laptop whirring away.

We waited an hour, the volume of my stomach's protests gradually increasing. Juliet read out snippets of Dunlow's emails, his curt distain evident. Meanwhile, I learnt far more about managing art exhibits than I'd ever wanted to from the reports being sent over from Terence's computer.

'The team said Leonard's laptop update is at 18 per cent now.' I raised my eyebrows at the note at the end of the email. 'They're going to head home and continue tomorrow morning.'

The expected storm didn't materialise. Juliet stretched, her face untroubled. 'Let's take another look tomorrow then.'

'Are you suggesting we head home?' My stomach practically flipped over in relief.

Juliet rolled her eyes. 'It does happen, on occasion.'

'Once every eight months.' I hurriedly shut down my computer and grabbed my coat. 'Good to know.'

'Shut up, or I'll change my mind.'

Day 5

Saturday, 14 October

POLICE INSIST THEY DID NOT FAIL LITTLE KRYSTAL – YET
YEARS OF ABUSE WENT UNDETECTED...

Scroll.

HOW DID THEY HIDE HER? – EXCLUSIVE INTERVIEW WITH A
NEIGHBOUR WHO HAD NO IDEA KRYSTAL BARRETT
EXISTED...

Scroll.

FORGOTTEN. ABUSED. KILLED. – CAN WE CHANGE THE
STORY FOR OTHER AT RISK CHILDREN?...

Scroll.

Call connected at 9:02.

'Hello, Keith.'

'Juliet? I thought you were going to let me go to voicemail again.'

'I'm heading into work so I don't have long. What do you want?'

'Are you coming home this weekend at all? I want to know what to tell the girls.'

'I'm hoping to come home tonight.'

'Hoping?'

'It depends on how the case develops today.'

'That's not good enough.'

'Keith, I can't control this.'

'I don't want you letting them down again.'

'Don't tell them anything then. If I come, I come. If I don't, they won't know what they're missing.'

'Fine.'

'Hopefully, I'll see you later.'

'I'll keep everything crossed.'

Gabe

Juliet and I shuffled along a row of chairs. I hoped the stain on mine was old and dry. We'd dressed in black for the occasion; Juliet in a knee-length dress with her nails painted a deep red, me in one of my many jumpers and a pair of skinny chinos.

We'd chosen chairs two rows from the back. Those in front were already filled with sombrely dressed teens and clusters of older people. The air was filled with whispers, too fleeting to be captured. The building was nothing like Mum's church. The windows here were clear, not etched with biblical scenes, and the chairs marginally more comfortable than Mum's beloved pews.

Ida sat in the front row. Her face was covered with a thin black veil, her back hunched. Evie sat beside her. She wore a bulky grey jumper, her mouth pinched into a wrinkled line as she patted Ida's shoulder. She caught sight of Juliet and me and swiftly turned to the front, her brow furrowed.

Jordan sat surrounded by friends. They thrummed with suppressed energy, their normal boisterousness tamed out of respect. Jordan's hair was gelled flat and he looked older in an ill-fitting suit.

All whispering ceased as the minister walked up the centre aisle. He wore a creased grey suit, thinning strands of hair combed over the top of his freckled head. Coming to a stop at the front, he pointed a remote at a projector hanging from the ceiling. A picture of Melanie, her smile wide, filled the wall behind him.

'We are here today to celebrate the life of Melanie Pirt, who was so cruelly taken from us.' His amplified voice reverberated around the hall. 'Her grandmother, Ida, has picked some of Melanie's favourite songs for us to sing. Let's begin with *Amazing Grace*. Please stand.'

A shiver ran up my spine as the keyboard player pressed the first notes. She wasn't as talented as Leo, but through the verses Melanie's voice haunted me. Juliet seemed unaffected, the same reserved smile she'd erected as we stepped into the church playing around her mouth.

The back door opened as the song finished and everyone sat down. Leo slipped into the final row of seats on the other side of the aisle. He clutched an order of service, his mouth downturned. He flinched when he caught me watching him.

'Leo's here,' I whispered to Juliet.

Unabashed, she swivelled to look at him. He hunched in his chair, staring at the folded paper on his knee. I wondered if his reaction was purely because he'd been confronted with our presence when he'd expected to grieve in peace, or whether he was thinking of something we might have found on his laptop. We'd had a message from the IT team before we left the station this morning. The laptop was still updating. Juliet was worried someone had done a factory reset.

The minister spoke about Melanie's life in a generic way, noting her intelligence, beautiful singing voice, and loving family. When he prayed, he closed his eyes and reached one hand towards Ida. Her shoulders shook as she cried.

I swallowed. This wasn't the first funeral I'd been to since Barnabas's, but they were uncomfortably alike. We hadn't had a body to bury, and my parents had been broken by his death.

Juliet nudged me with her elbow and inclined her head towards Jordan. We weren't the only ones who'd spotted Leo. Jordan had twisted in his chair to glare at him. One of his friends whispered something in his ear and he turned back to the front, his jaw jutting.

Leo missed it all. Sitting alone, he bent his head towards his lap. During the last hymn he walked out of the church, his eyes brimming with tears.

'Thank you for coming,' the minister said. 'Ida would like to invite you all to the back hall, where she's laid on a spread of Melanie's favourite cakes. There's also tea and coffee, and pictures of Melanie.'

He sat down on Ida's unoccupied side, placing a soothing hand on her back. His and Evie's hands spread across the curved black fabric like uneven white spiders.

Jordan talked to his friends, their voices an ominous rumble. He stood but froze when he spotted Juliet and me. She waved at him with her fingers. Jordan said something in the liberally pierced ear of the boy beside him, and they hurried into the back hall.

'Wonder what he was plotting?' Juliet smoothed her dress as she stood.

'We might have saved Leo from some unwanted attention.'

We edged sideways towards the centre aisle. Ida stood as we walked over.

'Thank you for coming.' She cupped my hands in hers. 'It's good you could be here.'

Juliet nodded, hands clasped behind her back. Evie looped her arm through Ida's and guided her to the back room ahead of us.

It was cosy. Plants grew in mismatched pots on windowsills and bright posters, exhorting the benefits of giving your life to Jesus, dotted the walls. Worn sofas stood at odd angles, interspersed with the same mass–produced chairs from the main hall.

We beelined towards the photo display, eschewing the decimated table of cakes. Conversation rose, the hushed atmosphere of the memorial shrugged off. Jordan lounged with his friends in one corner, their paper plates piled high with baked goods.

'Do you find it strange that Melanie didn't seem to have any friends?' I asked. Apart from Jordan and his cronies, there were no other young people at her memorial.

'Classic abuser trick,' Juliet said, examining the photo display. 'Isolate the victim, then even if they cry out for help there's no one to hear them.'

An incredibly grim take on Melanie's friendlessness, but no doubt accurate.

The photo display was put together with care, pictures of Melanie decorated with flowers and the inspirational quotes from her bedroom wall. In one photo, a toddler stood holding the hand of a young woman. In another, a child sat reading a book. Melanie grew older, posing and smiling with Ida.

'When can we leave?' Juliet whispered, smiling blandly at the groups dotted around the hall. She hadn't come to anything like this before, preferred detachment in her cases. She'd only tagged along today because she was going mad with no new evidence to pick over.

'Look at this,' I said. Melanie, at around five years old, stood proudly in a fluffy dress, her feet encased in ballet shoes. A young woman stood beside her, their smiles radiant.

Juliet squinted at the woman. Her hair was pinned under a green hat that matched her boxy coat.

'Recognise those buttons?' I asked.

Juliet's eyes widened, then her mouth quirked downwards. 'It wasn't important then. I'd hoped it would be from the murderer's jacket, something significant.'

I sealed my lips. I'd had similar hopes but wouldn't have expressed them in that same way. The button wasn't going to crack open our case, but that didn't mean it wasn't important or significant. It meant enough to Melanie that she'd carried it with her always.

Evie walked over, brushing cake crumbs from her hands. Her wispy hair escaped from a low bun, the white strands curling around her sunken cheeks.

'How's the case going?' she asked without preamble.

'It's moving along as expected,' I said, glad Evie focused on me and didn't notice the face Juliet pulled at my bending the truth. 'How have you been?'

'Fine,' Evie batted away my question and nodded at Jordan. 'Have you talked to him yet?'

'We have, but I'm afraid we can't tell you more than that.'

'Make sure you take him seriously,' she chided. 'He might be young, but that doesn't mean he's not capable.'

She spun around and hurried over to the table, her twisted hands moving quickly to rearrange the remnants of cake.

Juliet tapped her shoe. 'Time to leave?'

'Yeah.'

I waved at Ida as we slipped back into the main hall. She sat on a low sofa, a plate of untouched cake on her knee. I rubbed my face as I followed Juliet. There were many reasons to want to find Melanie's killer, but one of the strongest was to give some modicum of peace to her loved ones. They deserved closure.

Not knowing wore away at a person. I wouldn't let that happen to Ida.

A TRANSCRIPT OF DOCUMENTS TAKEN FROM A LAPTOP BELONGING TO LEONARD DUNLOW

FILE DATED 28 SEPTEMBER:

Love is meant to be light,
To be filled with air,
But then I see you and you cry,
And tell me how he pulled your hair.
Is it love that makes me feel this mad?
Is it love that makes me want to do something bad?

FILE DATED 4 OCTOBER:

Why would you be with him,
When you could be with me?
Don't you see how much I love you,
So much I could bleed?

FILE DATED 7 OCTOBER:

People get what they deserve,
And you deserve more than this.
I will fight for you, my love,
And I will give you justice.

FILE DATED 11 OCTOBER:

We had one perfect moment,
Maybe that's all perfect love could have.

Keith. Sent 11:45.

The girls are so excited to see you later xx

Gabe

Someone had tried to wipe the laptop. They'd done a bad job.

The report from the IT team was waiting after the memorial. All they'd had to do to restore the files was click 'yes' on a notification. Since returning to the office, Juliet and I had sat side-by-side reading. Slowly, Jordan's theory that Leo was dangerously obsessed with Melanie had become much less far-fetched.

I sat back. 'We need to talk to Leo.'

'Now.' Juliet stood up and dragged her chair around to her desk. 'While he's vulnerable and sad.'

I didn't relish pouncing on Leo when he was mourning, but this was the moment he was most likely to trip up and his lies unravel around him. We needed to close this case.

I pulled my coat over my shoulders and grabbed a pair of cuffs from my drawers. As a detective, I didn't do much arresting anymore, but it didn't hurt to be ready. If Leo confessed, I wanted him in an interview room before his father interfered.

Juliet and I marched across the main floor. Paul made finger guns as we passed his office. It was obvious, especially in a slower case like Melanie's, when a breakthrough occurred. Despite our slight pariah status, the whole floor would get a kick out of this. When two cases were floundering, one moving forward felt like a victory for everyone.

We entered the lift and Juliet jabbed the button for the ground floor. She drummed her manicured nails on the handrail while the electronic screen above the door recorded our progress downwards. I tried not to get too ahead of myself, but what had been found on Leo's laptop felt like a definite move in the right direction. If he confessed, then we would be waiting for the DNA results from Melanie's body to confirm what we already knew, rather than pinning all our hopes on them.

The doors rumbled open and Juliet swept out. The glass entrance of the station showed a quiet street. Two gulls squabbled over the remains of a baguette.

'Gabe? Juliet?' Alice called from beside the reception desk. 'Jordan Haines is here.'

'What?' Juliet scrunched up her face. 'Why?'

Alice licked her lips as she walked over, her dark brown eyes darting between us. 'He was picked up by officers called to a fight between him and Leonard Dunlow. Apparently, it was over by the time they got there, but Leonard was hit by a car as well. They brought Jordan here and took Leonard to the hospital. It wasn't much more than a knock, but the paramedics had to be sure. I thought you'd want to know.'

'Thank you.' Apparently Jordan had only waited until we were out of sight to pursue Leo.

Alice folded her arms over her thick stab-proof vest. 'He's in one of the informal interview rooms. Number three.'

She walked back to the reception desk. That hadn't been a friendly encounter but I had hope for our working relationship yet. Alice might be sulking, but at least she wasn't petty.

Juliet huffed. 'We're wasting time here. Leo will be even more susceptible now.'

'He's not going anywhere.' Leo wouldn't get out of hospital in a hurry, even if he wasn't too badly injured. 'Let's see what Jordan has to say for himself first.'

Juliet nodded stiffly, and I led the way over to a similar room to the one we'd spoken to Jordan in before. An altered young man waited for us. Jordan's face was red, his eyes streaming. His short hair was mussed and his smart tie had disappeared. He twisted torn strips of tissue between bruised fingers. Someone had bandaged his knuckles, but spots of blood soaked through.

A uniformed officer, Alice's partner from the forest, patted him on the back. He stood as we entered the room but I gestured for him to stay. It was best if we had a witness. He perched on the angular sofa beside Jordan.

We sat opposite. Jordan swiped at his tears as I pulled out my notepad, the cuffs in my pocket clinking. I checked the name of the uniformed officer. James Knowles.

'Jordan?' Juliet hovered on the edge of our sofa, one leg crossed over the other. 'What's happened?'

More tears eked down his face, dribbling to his chin before he brushed them away. When he didn't answer, Juliet turned to me, her eyes wide. I made a calming motion. She folded her arms and tapped her foot against the floor.

'Jordan, could you please tell us what happened with Leo today?' I asked.

'He shouldn't have been there,' Jordan choked out. 'He murdered Mel and then he came to her funeral. It's not right.'

Jordan hadn't been thinking about his own strange position at the funeral then, mourning the girl he'd habitually beaten. Too busy turning his rage on someone else.

'We're in charge of finding Melanie's killer. Just because you think Leo had something to do with Melanie's death, that doesn't give you the right to beat him up.'

I ignored Juliet shifting beside me. She might want to run off to question Leo now it was clear Jordan had attacked him for no other reason than that he needed someone to blame, but I wasn't leaving until we'd impressed the importance of not taking the law into his own hands. Jordan needed to learn his fists weren't the only way to solve a problem.

Jordan glared at me, but his defiance flickered and died. 'I know. I know that. But I lost her, and it hurts. I can't make it right.'

'Beating anyone in any situation isn't going to make it better,' Juliet said, her voice harsh.

Jordan flinched and James offered him another tissue. 'Can I say, ma'am? I know Jordan wasn't right to hit the other lad, but he did stay with him after the car hit him.'

'It wasn't a car,' Jordan grumbled. 'It was a van.'

'What do you remember about it?' I asked, pencil ready in my hand even as Juliet jiggled her knee.

For once, Jordan's eyes weren't hard but wide and unsure. 'I didn't mean for him to get badly hurt. I just didn't want him to get away with this.' He sniffed. 'We were proper into it, my mates were shouting, and the van came out of nowhere and hit him.'

'What colour was it?' I asked.

'White.' Jordan's voice was steady, sure. 'One of those hire ones. And I got a look at the driver.' He wiped the back of his hand under his nose. 'Won't help much though. They were wearing a balaclava.'

Juliet stiffened. Jordan hadn't told us anything we wouldn't have been able to find in CCTV footage, but often the driver was out of focus. We might not have known they'd masked their face without his information. What was puzzling was whether they'd worn the balaclava specifically for the hit and run, or whether Leo had gotten caught in the middle of something else.

'Thank you, Jordan. That's helpful.' I spun my pencil. 'Can I ask again what you know about Melanie's relationship with the other boy she was seeing?' I wouldn't confirm it was Leo. Jordan attacked Leo when he suspected he was seeing Melanie; he didn't need to know the truth.

Jordan shrugged. 'I don't know anything, but I'm sure it was that posho. Mel was using him to make me jealous. It's not her fault he got the wrong idea and went mad when she set him straight.'

'But you have no evidence of this?' Juliet asked.

Jordan shook his head. 'No, but I know it was him.'

'From now on, please trust we are doing everything we can to find the person who killed Melanie.' I flipped my notepad closed. 'Doing things like this slows us down.'

More tears slid over Jordan's cheeks. Juliet and I stood, and James joined us at the door.

'His dad's on the way, ma'am,' he told us. 'I'll make sure this is processed, and we'll see if the other lad wants to press charges.'

'Thanks, James,' I said. Juliet dipped her head once and strode away.

Leo might not get the chance. If he confessed to Melanie's murder, then her boyfriend beating him before he was brought to justice would be brushed away by any jury. It wasn't like the injuries from his beating would be clearly distinct from those caused by the van.

I caught up with Juliet at the entrance to the station. No more distractions. It was time to talk to Leo. Time for the truth.

From: Juliet Stern **juliet.stern@mit.gov.uk**
To: Madison Campbell
madison.campbell@mitadmin.gov.uk
CC: Gabriella Martin **gabriella.martin@mit.gov.uk,**
Alice To **alice.to@police.gov.uk**
Date: **14 October, 13:30**
Subject: **Operation Chalice – CCTV of van and driver**

Maddy,

Please look into CCTV footage of Leonard Dunlow being hit by a van. Alice will be able to give you more information about the exact timing. A clear shot of the driver (without a balaclava) would be immensely helpful.

Please also contact hire companies and ask who rented vans today – if anyone from the case is flagged let me know.

Juliet

Call connected at 13:42.

'Hello, Dunlow Consultants. How can I help you?'

'Hello, could I please speak to Timothy Dunlow?'

'Can I ask what this is regarding?'

'I'm a nurse at Southampton General Hospital. We have his son here, Leonard.'

'One moment please.'

BEEP. BEEP. BEEP.

'What's happened to Leo?'

'Hello, is that Timothy Dunlow?'

'Yes, yes. What's happened to my son?'

'He's alright, Mr Dunlow. Please don't panic. My name is Consuelo, I'm a nurse at Southampton General Hospital. Leonard was admitted after he was in a fight with another boy and hit by a van.'

'Christ. Is he okay?'

'He's fine. He took a bit of a beating to his chest and stomach, but tests so far have shown no internal damage. He's got a cut on his cheek that needed stitches.'

'That doesn't sound fine to me. I'm on my way.'

AN ACCIDENT AND EMERGENCY TRIAGE FORM

DATE: 14 October
TIME: 14:16
NAME: Leonard Dunlow
AGE: 18

PRESENTING COMPLAINT: Assault and hit by van – torso pain and facial laceration

HISTORY OF PRESENTING COMPLAINT: Patient reports he was assaulted by a young man in the street at 13:00 on 14 October. He was beaten with fists and thrown to the ground. He was then kicked repeatedly in the chest, back and stomach. When he made an attempt to escape, he was hit by a van. Patient was self-mobile when paramedics arrived and treated at the scene. There did not seem to be any significant head injuries. The patient was breathing shallowly and guarding his chest.

ON EXAMINATION: The patient can stand unaided. There is blood on his face from a cut of about two inches on his right cheek. He is breathing shallowly and guarding his chest. The patient is alert and has multiple contusions across his chest and upper back. He has minor cuts and bruising on his knuckles.

PAST MEDICAL HISTORY: Anxiety

MEDICATION: Sertraline

SOCIAL AND FAMILY HISTORY: None

REPORT COMPLIED BY: Senior Staff Nurse Consuelo Day

Gabe

'His father is on his way,' Consuelo said as she led the way across the ward. 'He didn't sound happy.'

'That's about right,' Juliet muttered.

Leo had his eyes closed as we approached the bed. His head rested on white pillows, his russet hair fanning around his ears. A bruise bloomed under a dressing on his right cheek. Without his glasses, his face looked thinner, less defined. His hands, the knuckles covered in gauze, lay at his sides. His body was held taut, like stillness would prevent more pain.

His eyes snapped open, the whites made pink by burst blood vessels. He unfolded his glasses and slid them gingerly up his nose. The nurse left and I pulled the curtains shut while Juliet sat in the plastic chair beside the bed.

'Can you tell us what happened today, Leo?' I asked, standing at the foot of the bed.

Leo's gaze darted between us. 'I can't tell you much. Those guys jumped me, and then the van hit me when I was trying to get away.'

'We know you've been lying to us, Leo,' Juliet said, apparently satisfied we'd gotten all the information we needed about the hit and run. 'We've had a look at your laptop. We've seen the things you've been writing about Melanie. It's time to tell us the truth.'

I pulled my notepad out of my pocket as Leo's face crumpled. He tried to wipe away his tears but winced in pain, the movement playing on one of the sore spots on his body.

'I loved her,' he said. 'We met at a concert my school put on. I noticed her in the audience and messed up my solo because I could feel her watching. She found me after Dad finished yelling at me and said I was really good. She asked if I'd mind playing some songs with her so she could practise her singing. I would have done anything to spend time with her.'

Leo spoke differently when his father wasn't around, more expressive and emotional. If there was a time when he would tell us what happened the night Melanie died, it was now. I wasn't even mad Juliet had taken the reins without consultation. All I was concerned with were results.

I listened to the ward beyond the closed curtain. No rushing footfalls.

'We met up once a week, more if we could. I told Dad I was doing an extra orchestra session at school. Mel's voice was so beautiful. I liked her more and more but nothing was going to happen. She had a boyfriend.' Leo blinked rapidly. 'It was a couple of months before she told me what was going on. He hurt her.'

'We know,' Juliet said.

'Right.' Leo picked at the bandage on his hand. 'I told her to leave him but she wouldn't listen. It was getting worse and I hated how it made her feel. She was so sad, cried when we met up. Then one time, I don't know how, but I was hugging her and we started kissing. It was perfect.'

Their perfect moment.

'Is that what you meant in one of the poems we found on your laptop?' I asked.

Leo closed his eyes, pressing his lips together. 'Yes.'

'So you loved her.' Juliet leant closer. 'But when she begged to meet with you, you left her hanging?'

Tears escaped from under Leo's discoloured eyelids. He'd have shining black eyes by the end of the day. 'That's the biggest mistake of my life.'

Juliet's eyes narrowed. Something didn't feel right. I shifted my weight.

'Leo?' I said. His eyes fluttered open. 'What do you think happened that night?'

He bit his split lip, then winced. 'I don't know.'

'Has anyone been acting strangely since Melanie died?' I asked.

'Well.' Leo paused. 'I don't think so.'

'This is important, Leo,' Juliet jumped in. 'Have you noticed anything at all?'

Leo's lower lip trembled. 'You know Teddy wasn't around?'

'When Melanie died?' I clarified.

'Yeah. Well, since he got back, him and Karl have been a bit weird. They never got on, but it seemed like Karl was mad about something. I caught them arguing last night. I thought Karl was threatening Teddy, but he's not normally like that. And then, you know, Karl was gone this morning.'

My stomach turned over.

'Karl's gone?' Juliet asked.

'Yeah.' Leo sucked in his lip. 'Sorry, I assumed Dad would have told you.'

'He has not,' I said. 'Where has Karl gone?'

'We don't know. This morning the dogs were making a racket so me and Teddy went to check on them. After we fed them and let them out, we went over to check on Karl. His cottage was unlocked, and all his stuff's gone. He left a note.'

Juliet stared into the middle distance, no doubt pissed at me. The first case I'd taken the lead on, and I'd fucked it up by being too compassionate. I'd thought Karl was broken like me, but I conveniently forgot that broken people didn't always mend. Sometimes, they went on breaking and breaking until they broke someone else.

The curtain whipped back. Dunlow held the material tight in his fist, his nostrils flaring. Behind him, Consuelo cringed.

'I hope you're here to take my son's statement about the thug who beat him and pushed him in front of a car,' Dunlow ground out.

Juliet stood. 'Thank you, Leo. You've been most helpful.'

She walked away from the bed. I took a last look at Leo before I followed. He avoided his father's gaze, his fingers twisting in his lap. If the bandages on his hands were any indication, it hadn't been a one-way fight.

I caught up with Juliet halfway across the ward. 'I'm sorry,' I said before she could come at me. 'I totally fucked up.'

'What are you talking about?'

'I followed my gut too much. I didn't want to lean into Karl because of his past.'

'Chalk it up to experience.' Juliet pushed through a set of double doors to a wide corridor. 'Don't worry about it. All the evidence pointed more squarely towards Leo. This is the first time Karl's messed up. He nearly had me fooled with his act.'

I poked my tongue into my cheek. I couldn't shake the feeling that nothing Karl had said had been deliberately misleading. He'd kept

Terence's secret because he'd promised to and withheld his past to protect himself, but he hadn't outright lied.

I shook myself. That showed how wrong my gut could be. Why would an innocent man run?

'How fast can you get us to the estate?' Juliet's eyes were bright. 'If we're quick, we should be able to question Terence without his father interfering as well. I want to know what he has to say about his accomplice absconding.'

Call connected at 16:20.

'Hello?'

'Is that Terence?'

'Yes.'

'This is Detective Inspector Juliet Stern. I'm at the front gate. Could you come let us in?'

'I don't need to come down. I can let you in remotely.'

'We're going to go take a look at Karl's cottage, but we need to speak to you too. Meet us there.'

I didn't do anything but I know how this will end. You know about my dad so now you think you know me. I'm nothing like him. I'm not going to wait for you to decide I'm guilty when I'm not.

Gabe

Searching the cottage didn't take long. It looked abandoned from the outside, with no four-by-four parked snug alongside, and Karl had stripped the interior of his few personal items, leaving only the bulky furniture behind. His note was wedged under an empty vase on the dining table.

My chest felt tight as I reread it, squinting in the poor light cast by a naked bulb. The conclusion I'd leapt to as soon as Leo told us Karl had left was exactly what he'd been afraid of. Maybe the mistake I'd made wasn't trusting my gut too much, but not being open enough. If I'd told Karl I didn't see him as a serious suspect, he wouldn't have acted rashly and made himself one.

Gravel crunched outside and Terence ducked through the low wooden doorway. His hair was carefully styled, his coat probably worth more than I earned in a month.

'You've heard our groundskeeper has done a runner, then?'

Juliet walked out of Karl's bedroom. She'd been examining the books left on the shelves. 'Is that what you want us to think?'

Terence reared back. 'What?'

'Did you write this note?' Juliet pointed at it. 'Karl knew too much. Leo said you two argued last night. Maybe Karl was fed up of keeping your secret, and no amount of money you threw at him would work. There was only one way left to silence him. You killed him and faked his escape.'

Terence's mouth fell open. I kept my face blank. Juliet hadn't shared these suspicions with me. She probably didn't think it was true, but one way to get someone to talk was to throw a whole lot of muck at them. They'd clear it away without realising they were getting their hands dirty in the process.

'You don't honestly believe that?'

'You tell us the truth, and we'll know exactly what to believe,' Juliet said.

'Bloody hell.' Terence ran his hands through his hair, making it stick out at the sides. 'I can't talk in here. I can barely see you.'

He walked outside. Juliet winked at me before ducking through the wooden archway. I shook my head as I followed. I didn't enjoy playing with people like Juliet did. I couldn't ignore how it would impact them when they went on with their lives.

Terence led us over to my car. It was lighter outside despite the setting sun, the bags under Terence's eyes and the red skin around his bitten-down nails clear.

'I didn't have anything to do with Karl scarpering.' Terence planted his feet and sunk his hands into his coat pockets. 'We argued last night, but only because he was badgering me to tell you the truth and he wouldn't take no for a bloody answer.'

'Why do you think he ran?' I asked.

'You saw the note. I don't think Karl's a murderer. I don't like him but he's always very upright, a bit too honest. But apparently he's got a dark past. That was always going to stand against him.'

'Mr Hogan hasn't yet confirmed your alibi.' Juliet switched the conversation back to Terence. 'And you still won't tell us what you were doing.'

'Christ.' He looked skyward. 'Is it so important you know what I was doing? Isn't it enough to know I wasn't here?'

'You're being evasive,' Juliet said. 'That makes us think we're right, and that you had something to do with Melanie's death even though you were technically away when she was killed. Unless we know what you were doing, we'll assume the worst; that your secret is worth committing murder over. And why would you stop at Melanie? Karl was annoying you. The easy way to get rid of him was to kill him too.'

'Jesus.' The word was no more than misted breath over Terence's lips. He tore his hands from his pockets and dug the heels of his palms into his eyes. 'We were fucking, alright? I meet up with Benny a few times a year and we fuck.' He lowered his hands, the skin around his eyes pink. 'That's my big secret. That's it. I wouldn't kill anyone over it. I would just ask them not to tell my dad.'

My heart clutched uselessly inside my chest. Forcing someone to out themselves was never something I wanted to be involved in.

'So Karl saw you with Benedict? That's what he was threatening you with?' Juliet asked.

Terence rolled his eyes. 'He didn't threaten me. Or blackmail me. He took those photos because I wouldn't talk about it unless he had proof. He said he'd known for a while, God knows how, and he thought I should come out to Dad. But he doesn't know my father. I asked Karl to delete the photos and he did, but I didn't like him being here, knowing. I wanted him gone but he needed money, so I gave him some. End of story.'

'Would it be so terrible if your father found out about Benedict?' I asked. I'd been afraid to come out to my parents, everyone is, but more often it was becoming a positive experience. It had been for me. Mum fell over herself to reassure me that nothing had changed and Jesus still loved me, while Dad listened quietly from his chair and squeezed my hand.

'Yes.' A muscle in Terence's neck twitched. 'It would be.'

I felt an uptick of sympathy for him, despite the ways he helped me fight that impulse. Having to hide part of himself to be accepted by his remaining parent had to hurt.

'Melanie didn't know?' Juliet asked.

Terence shrugged. 'If she did, it would have been news to me. As I said, I wouldn't have killed her to ensure her silence anyway. If you could not tell my dad, I'd be much obliged.'

'We won't,' I said.

Terence examined me for a long moment. 'Thank you. I'm going to go deal with the dogs, since there's no one else to do it.'

He strode across the gravel driveway and into the forest, his shoulders slumped.

'Do you believe him?' Juliet asked.

'What he's said makes sense.' I unlocked the car. 'Dunlow doesn't seem particularly tolerant and Terence doesn't want to be disowned. He was hiding the truth because he doesn't want his dad to know he's with a man, not because he's a murderer.'

Juliet huffed and got into the car. I looked over at the cottage. If Terence's alibi was true, then he wasn't part of a plot to kill Melanie. That left Karl as our main suspect.

No matter how incriminating it was that he'd run away, thinking of him as a murderer didn't sit right. But if he wasn't the killer, who had shot Melanie between these silent trees?

'Detective Inspector Juliet Stern.'

    'What have you said to my sons?'

    'Sorry, who is this?'

    'Timothy Dunlow. I want to know what you've said to my boys.'

    'I'm sorry, Mr Dunlow. I can't discuss statements made by other individuals during a murder investigation.'

    'They're my sons.'

    'Yes, but they're both adults. If they don't choose to share their statements with you, there's nothing I can do about it.'

    'Christ almighty.'

    'Try to remain calm, Mr Dunlow.'

    'Calm? I am bloody calm. I want to know what you've said to my sons. Leo won't say a word to me, won't even press charges against the scumbag who beat him black and blue or whoever hit him with that van. Terence can't even look at me. I want to know what's going on right now.'

    'Mr Dunlow, I don't appreciate being spoken to in this way.'

    'I don't bloody care. Are you investigating them? Is that what this is all about? Are they suspects?'

    'Mr Dunlow, I suggest you call again once you've taken time to calm down.'

    'I don't need to calm down. Christ. My sons are being accused of murder. One of them has been hospitalised but is too afraid to talk about it.'

    'I'm sorry about Leo, but no one has been accused of murder yet.'

    'Well, I can tell you right bloody now; neither of my sons did it. So you can keep your nose out of our business. Leave my family alone.'

Gabe

Juliet foisted her overnight bag onto her shoulder. 'You'll be alright on your own?'

I looked up from the half-written notes from our interviews with Jordan, Leo and Terence. 'The amount of times you've stayed late alone, I think I can handle it.'

Juliet nodded but didn't leave.

'I'm going to type this lot up, then I'm meeting someone,' I told her.

'I can stay if you need me to.'

'I don't,' I said. 'It's important you go home to your family whenever you can, so go. I'll call if anything comes up.'

'You'd better.'

Juliet walked out of the office. I listened to her heels crossing the outer workspace, then turned back to my computer.

I only had Terence's interview left to write up. As I typed, I couldn't stop thinking about Karl. He'd ruined any chance we'd remove him as a serious suspect by running away, but what reason would he have had to kill Melanie if Terence was telling the truth?

The only person on the estate who knew Melanie was Leo. He claimed to be madly in love with her. He insisted he hadn't met her.

None of it felt right.

I grabbed my mug. I wanted to finish transcribing and meet Ollie. For that, I needed caffeine.

A few people milled around the main workspace. Paul gave me a hopeful thumbs-up from his office then pulled a comical sad face when I responded with mine pointed down.

I stumbled to a halt in the doorway of the break room.

Alice slammed the fridge closed. 'Oh, hi, ma'am.'

'Thanks for letting us know about Jordan earlier.' I recovered from the shock of seeing her unexpectedly and flicked on the kettle. 'It was really helpful.'

'It's fine, ma'am,' she said coolly as she walked towards the door.

Enough. Too many people at the station looked down on me because I was young, petite, and female, or pitied me because they'd taken too deep a dive into my personnel file. I didn't need this too.

'Alice? Do you have a minute?'

She spun slowly on her heel. 'Yes, ma'am.'

'I hope there's no bad feeling between us about the other night.' I spoke to her over my shoulder while I reached for the instant coffee, creating a false sense of nonchalance. 'I appreciated you asking me out, but during a case I have to be in bed early to make sure I get my full eight hours.'

That was working the truth hard, but it wasn't quite a lie. I flicked Alice a smile as I walked to the fridge for milk. Indecision worked out over her face. I'd definitely snubbed her, no matter what I said, but there was no point in a junior officer holding a grudge against someone more senior, not if she ever wanted me to put in a good word. Forgiveness worked in both our favour.

'It's fine,' she said eventually. 'I know what it's like.'

I dropped my spoon into the sink, where it joined a dozen others, and grabbed my coffee. I leant against the counter. 'I have a job for you, if you're up for it.'

'Depends on the job, ma'am,' Alice said, finally dropping the snide undertones from the honorific. The corners of her mouth tweaked upwards as she sipped disgustingly weak tea.

'One of our suspects has done a runner.' I winced internally. That was what had happened, and Alice didn't need to hear my complicated reasons for wishing Karl would find a way to vanish and not be found. 'If I email the missing persons poster over to you, will you pop it up around town?'

Alice grinned. 'Anything that gets me away from watching endless CCTV footage of empty warehouse car parks is fine by me.'

'So long as you're not neglecting your other work, you'll get to at least stretch your legs.'

I left the break room with a genuine smile on my face. Unresolved tension was something I didn't want to deal with at work, and no one could complain I hadn't done my utmost to find Karl if I made sure posters were stuck up around town. No one had to know I hoped he was too long gone for them to have any impact.

From: Gabriella Martin **gabriella.martin@mit.gov.uk**
To: Alice To **alice.to@police.gov.uk**
Date: **14 October, 18:18**
Subject: **Missing persons poster**

Alice,

Here's the missing persons poster. Please spread it far and wide.

Thanks,

Gabe

MISSING PERSON – KARL BISS

Police are appealing for any information regarding the disappearance of KARL BISS on 14 October. If you saw KARL after this date, please call your local police station and quote case number 10098755.

Karl is approx. 6'4 tall, 28 years old. He was last seen wearing a long green coat and jeans.

Police ask that members of the public do not approach KARL.

Gabe

Towers of barrels and cardboard boxes lined the walls and encroached on the middle space of the warehouse. My bare feet made faint slapping sounds as I walked across the cold floor. I held one hand over my nose to block the overwhelming chemical smell, my breath misting between my fingers.

'Gabe?'

My left arm throbbed where the bad man had grabbed me, but it felt better now. I didn't want to scream anymore. My stomach was a more pressing concern. It was tied in knots with thirst and hunger, demanding action. I'd crept from our hiding place after we'd tried eating the bitter tasting moss growing between the metal walls and the floor. It made our stomachs hurt more than when they were empty.

'Gabe?'

I crept around a pile of wrapped boxes with strange symbols printed on the side and froze. The bad man stood beside a barrel, his arms folded over his chest. They weren't as muscly as Dad's arms, but the bad man was strong. My elbow twinged like his fingers were closed around it again. I inched backward and my heel caught on one of the boxes. The paper crunched. The bad man turned. I ran.

'Wake up.'

The thump of the bad man's boots rang around the wide space. I ran as fast as I could without reawakening the howling pain in my arm. I should have stayed hidden, should have waited until it was dark, should have chewed on my tongue and waited for a grown up to find us. Someone kind. I tripped and fell to the floor. I screamed when my arm slammed into the concrete.

'Gabe, come on. Wake up.'

The bad man grabbed me by my ankles and dragged me across the floor. I shouted and twisted, cradling my arm. My vision went black, then white. I was sick over the rough concrete. The bad man pulled me to the barrel, but dropped my legs when cries echoed through the warehouse. I curled into myself, careful of my arm, and only saw shadows as a body hurled itself at the bad man. I closed my eyes, and sat bolt upright in bed.

My back prickled with sweat. I bowed my head, sucking ragged breaths into my lungs. My head pealed with alarm bells, demanding that I run, get help, do something. Years too late.

I flinched when a hand coasted across my damp skin. Ready to punch and scream, I turned, but it was just Ollie. I blinked at his concerned frown, remembering when and where I was.

'I couldn't wake you,' he said.

I shook my head. Nothing ever could.

Bile rose in my throat but I counted deep breaths in and out and forced it down. I breathed until the adrenaline was spent and my arms broke out in goose pimples. I ran my fingers from wrist to elbow. The break had healed years ago. The doctors said the bone had sheered cleanly in two, that once re-melded my arm would be as good as new, but I knew exactly where the hidden scar was.

I flopped onto the bed, kicking to loosen the duvet cocooning my legs. Ollie propped himself on one elbow but I closed my eyes, welcoming the darkness.

'What was that?' He gently pushed hair from my forehead.

I didn't ask him to stop, even though his soft touch grated against my nerves. It was meant to be soothing. I'd scared him.

'A nightmare.'

Ollie lay down and placed his hand on my sternum. That felt good, the warm pressure grounding me to the here and now.

'I've never had a nightmare like that,' he murmured.

Calling it a dream wasn't accurate. A hyper-realistic flashback. Memories I wished would stay buried. They were usually awakened by cases involving children, but I thought I'd kept distant enough from Krystal's case to avoid this. I should have known Alice's comment about warehouse footage would trip the monsters waiting in the dark recesses of my brain.

Ollie's breaths deepened. His hand went limp, so I placed mine on top to keep it in place. I didn't look forward to the inevitable conversation we'd have once Ollie had slept with me enough and realised how often I was trapped in terrible dreams.

I was glad he was here. Waking up from reliving my last memory of my brother was hardest when I was alone. It was too similar to when I'd woken in that warehouse, with no need to fear the bad man anymore. He was long gone.

He'd gotten what he came for.

You Think you're unTouchable. ThaT's whaT she ThoughT.
I'm going To make you hurT worse Than she ever did.

Day 6

Sunday, 15 October

Call connected at 4:22.

'999, what's your emergency?'
 'Fire. I need the fire brigade.'

   SLAM.

'Hold for one moment while I put you through.'
 PLEASE HOLD. PLEASE HOLD. PLEASE HOLD.
 'Hello, this is fire and rescue. What's your emergency?'
 'There's a fire. A fire in my house.'

   SLAM.

'What's your address, please?'
 'Dunlow Manor, on the Dunlow Estate. Near Black Hill farm in the New Forest.'

   SLAM. SLAM.

'There's a response team on their way. What's your name, please?'
 'Timothy. Timothy Dunlow.'
 'How big is the fire, Mr Dunlow?'
 'Bloody huge. I didn't notice it until it was too far gone.'

   SLAM.

'Have you left the building?'
 'I'm closing the doors. I don't want it spreading.'

   SLAM.

'It's much more important that you get yourself out of the building and away to a safe distance. Is there anyone else in the building?'
 'My sons. They were here. I sent them out straight away.'

SLAM.

'Please join them, Mr Dunlow. The response team is minutes away.'

CRASH.

'Mr Dunlow? Are you alright? Timothy?'
    'Yes, I'm fine. Something fell. Gave me a bloody shock. I'm leaving now.'
    'The team will be with you soon. Would you like me to stay on the line with you until they arrive?'
    'That won't be necessary.'

Gabe

I sipped my hazelnut latte. Ollie and I had returned to the same café for breakfast. Families clustered around tables stacked with bowls of fruit and sugary treats.

I needed the caffeine. After my familiar nightmare I'd lain awake for hours, comforted by Ollie's gentle breathing. At least Juliet wouldn't be at the station today so no one would mock me for staring vacantly into space.

Ollie tipped another sachet of sugar into his mocha, his little finger pointing. The sun broke through the clouds and lit up the blond streaks in his hair. All natural, he'd assured me. The waitress came over with our breakfasts. I bit into my almond croissant while Ollie concentrated on cutting his waffles into even triangles, each perfectly bite sized. Something warm spread inside my ribcage as I watched him.

'I need to talk to you.' Ollie set down his knife and fork either side of his disassembled meal.

I slipped my hands under the table and wiped my instantly clammy palms on my trousers. Witnessing one of my nightmares usually put people off, but I'd hoped Ollie was made of sterner stuff.

He sucked on his bottom lip, searching for the right words. I should put him out of his misery, tell him I'd heard this too many times for anything he said to be original, but I didn't want this to end even a second before it had to.

I should have known something was wrong. This morning, he'd stared at me for long moments between each lingering kiss. He was uncharacteristically quiet as we showered together, and had insisted we come out for breakfast somewhere he knew from experience would be busy. He couldn't know I wouldn't make a scene, too used to partners darting in and out of my life to protest.

'What is it?' I might not help him over the finish line, but waiting was excruciating. I edged my nails into the sides of my thighs.

'I don't know what this thing is.' He waved a hand over the table. 'I don't need to, not really.'

'Okay.'

Ollie pressed his palms together in a long steeple. 'I know we haven't been seeing each other for long, and I don't know how you feel about me, not really, but the more time I spend with you, the more I like you, and not talking about that was making me nervous.'

'You're telling me you like me?' I clarified, the vice-like grip of my fingers bruising my legs.

Ollie grinned. 'Yeah. I really do.'

I loosened my hold on my thighs and breathed out, shaky like I'd been running for miles. 'I like you too.'

'That's good.' Ollie picked up his fork and speared a triangle of waffle.

It wasn't quite as simple as that. 'I want to be honest with you. I haven't had many relationships, no serious ones, and I don't know if I'll be much good at it. I'm always busy at work and I'm not great at talking about how I feel and there's stuff from my past—'

'Hey.' Ollie reached across the table to catch one of my flailing hands. He linked his fingers through mine, skimming over my knuckles. 'I'm all for honesty, but we can cross these bridges when we come to them, yeah?' He let go, leaving my skin tingling. 'Anyway, I'm great at talking about my feelings and shit, so I can teach you.'

I took a bite of my pastry, mulling over his words. I wasn't sure it would be quite so simple as skipping across a bridge together when my issues surfaced, but I didn't mind leaving them for now.

'I'd like to be exclusive.' Even when Barnabas was alive, I hadn't been good at sharing.

Ollie chewed around a grin. 'I'd like that too. Do you want to be my girlfriend?'

I scrunched up my nose and he laughed, light and carefree. I wanted to make him laugh all the time, let the sound seep into my bones.

My phone buzzed, then kept on buzzing. I flipped it over.

'It's the station calling.' I stood up. 'I need to take this.'

I hurried out of the café. Ollie carried on eating, a smile playing around his lips. I wanted what he was offering, but it was too easy to make promises at the start of a relationship. I wouldn't hold him to them. I'd keep him for as long as I could, until something I did or said wedged itself between us.

I answered the call. 'This is Detective Sergeant Gabe Martin.'

'Morning, ma'am. There's been a fire at Dunlow Manor.'

CHILD KILLERS STILL ON THE RUN – KRYSTAL BARRETT'S
PARENTS HAVE NOT BEEN FOUND...

Scroll.

THE MAKING OF A KILLER COUPLE – WHAT TURNS LOVERS
INTO ACCOMPLICES...

Scroll.

WHO IS FIGHTING FOR KRYSTAL? – POLICE UNABLE TO
FIND HER KILLERS AND BRING HER JUSTICE...

Scroll.

Gabe

I drove through the open gates and up the long drive to Dunlow Manor. The sun peeked from behind grey clouds, weak and without warmth. Emerging from the forest, the lawn at the front of the house had been churned by thick wheels. Great grooves tore through the smooth surface. Pools of water gathered in the imprints of heavy boots and tyres across the uneven driveway. A cordon wrapped around the house, the blue-and-white plastic flapping in the breeze.

One fire engine remained. A firefighter aimed a hose towards the house, a steady stream of water soaking what remained of the right side. Crooked beams jutted into empty space, collapsed ceiling carvings mingled with charred sofas and damp papers. Over it all, the spray of water created fleeting rainbows.

I'd been pissed about cutting breakfast short, since the information from the station had been infuriatingly vague. A fire could mean a kitchen needed repainting. Or it could mean this.

I parked near the garage and walked over to Dunlow and his sons. They stood a safe distance from their half-destroyed home. Dunlow's soot-stained face was carved into an angry snarl, one of his hands bandaged and held in a sling. Terence had his arm around Leo, who shivered under a reflective blanket.

'Good morning.' I cringed at myself but powered on, pulling my notepad out of my pocket. 'Can you tell me what happened here?'

'The fire started early this morning. The boys were in their rooms.' Dunlow's flinty eyes tracked my pencil. 'I couldn't sleep. I was making a coffee when I heard crackling and went through to the drawing room. There was a fire. It looked like it started over by the window, but it had spread too far and I couldn't fight it. I shouted for the boys to get out and called the fire brigade.'

Terence nodded, but I couldn't be sure Leo was listening. He huddled close to his brother, watching the jet of water. His glasses sat lopsided on his nose, his hair mussed.

'Was there anything in the room that could have caused the fire?' I asked. 'Candles, cigarettes, any open flames?'

'We don't light candles and none of us smoke.' Dunlow's face was stony. 'I'd had a fire the evening before, but it was extinguished hours before this started.'

Terence shuffled, jostling Leo. 'I do occasionally have a cigarette.' He avoided his father's piercing stare. 'I smoked last night, but down near the barn. I didn't bring it up to the house.'

'Thank you for being honest.'

He blushed in the same uneven way as his brother.

'Did you notice anything strange last night?' I asked. 'Anyone on the estate who shouldn't have been?'

'I thought someone was hanging around, but I didn't see them.' Dunlow tutted. 'We occasionally get people wandering onto the estate because they feel entitled to come onto any land they choose, private or not.'

What a hardship, occasionally sharing all this space with curious ramblers. I glanced over at the manor. 'Do you need help finding somewhere to stay?'

'We'll manage,' Dunlow said.

'Great.' I flipped my notepad shut. 'Give me a call if you think of anything. We'll be in contact when we know more.'

'There was this.' Leo's eyes were unfocused as he handed me a piece of paper, the blanket across his shoulders crinkling. 'It was posted through the door last night.'

I scanned the note, then pulled an evidence bag from my pocket and slipped it inside. Dunlow glared the whole time, too dignified to peek but clearly outraged his son had kept this from him.

I tucked the note away without giving him a chance to peruse it. He was already prejudiced against other suspects in this case, I didn't need to give him further reason.

'Thank you, Leo.'

The young man didn't look at me before I crunched across the gravel towards the fire engine. A firefighter jumped down from the cabin as I approached. He'd abandoned his fluorescent jacket but didn't seem cold in a tight-fitting T-shirt. His corded arm muscles were streaked with black, the skin underneath a soft brown.

'Detective Sergeant Gabe Martin,' I said, offering my hand.

'Matt Lam. I'm the forensic officer.' He gripped my knuckles firmly in his large hand.

'There was a murder on the grounds a few nights ago. I was called out just in case the fire is related in any way.' The other firefighter continued hosing the ruined side of the house. 'Are you almost done?'

'Nearly.' Matt smiled, revealing a gap between his top teeth. 'With old places like this, we drench them down. A lot of the wood is dry and we don't want it catching again. I won't be able to do a proper examination until the area has cooled for twenty-four hours.'

'Any idea how the fire started?'

'Some.' Matt led me around to the side of the house. He was a good foot and a half taller than me. I resisted jogging to keep up. 'According to Mr Dunlow, the fire started near this window. I had a quick look around when things quietened down.'

We stopped under a blown-out window. Shards of broken glass mingled with gravel.

'You see these?' Matt pointed near the wall.

Crinkled stubs of cigarettes shone through the damp shadows. My heart sank. Only one other smoker associated with this case, apart from Terence, would have been capable of wandering the estate at night. Together with the note, Jordan was going to find it incredibly difficult to explain his way out of an arson charge.

'We think maybe someone was here, watching Mr Dunlow.' Matt scratched his head, thick fingers disappearing into his sweaty, black locks. 'Strange thing is, we haven't been able to find a butt in the room yet. Mr Dunlow was sure the fire started over near the window, but if it was caused by a stub then we would have found some evidence, even if it had burnt up. Most of the damage in this room was around the fireplace. The blaze spread to other rooms from there.'

I raised my eyebrows as I whipped out my notepad. We'd need to talk to Jordan, figure out if he was lurking near the manor, but maybe the fire was an unlucky coincidence. I hoped so. Jordan might have hit his girlfriend and be a hard man in training, but heading to prison right on the cusp of adulthood wouldn't straighten him out.

I walked over to the lawn, searching the once perfect grass for footprints. There were none. Only churned up grass and soil.

'Thank you.' I turned to Matt. 'There's nothing I can do here, so I'm going to head off.'

He held out his hand again. I fumbled my notepad into my pocket and took it, unused to tactile colleagues. Maybe it was a fire service thing.

'Let me know if there's anything else I can help with.' He held my hand to his hot palm for a beat and let go, his dark brown eyes intense. 'Here's my card, if you need me.'

I looked over at him once I'd climbed into my car. I wished Juliet was here. She could have given a second opinion on whether I'd been flirted with. Not that it mattered, since I'd asked Ollie to be exclusive. But still.

I fiddled with Matt's card. He stood beside the fire engine, his arm flexing as he leant against the door. Behind his well-built frame, water streamed into the dark hulk of the ruined manor.

Call connected at 10:10.

'Gabe, what's up?'

'Hi, Juliet. Sorry to ring you at home.'

'What's wrong?'

'There's been a fire up at the Dunlow Estate. Half the manor was destroyed.'

'Shit.'

'I talked to Dunlow and he thinks someone was lurking around last night, and that the fire was started by a cigarette thrown in through the window. The firefighter I spoke to wasn't so sure, but it needs to be followed up. There was also a threatening note put through the door.'

'Any idea who sent it?'

'Jordan has to be in the frame. I've checked, and the handwriting doesn't match Karl's.'

'Okay, so we need to talk to Jordan. I can be back in about an hour.'

'You don't need to come back for that.'

'I'm coming. I'll text you the details of my train and you can pick me up from the station.'

Gabe

Juliet led the way through the weeds to Jordan's front door. She'd thrown on a blazer over her jeans and flowery blouse, but it didn't dampen the humanising effect of her casual clothes.

She pressed the doorbell while I twisted the binding of my notepad, trying to squash down the guilt squirming in my belly. Juliet would have rushed back no matter what I'd said. The only way to stop her abandoning her family would have been to withhold information, and that would not have gone well.

'Stop it,' she murmured.

I dropped my hands to my sides. 'What?'

'Feeling guilty.'

The door opened, revealing a rail-thin man. His coppery hair was swept off his forehead, his pointy nose prominent. Full sleeve tattoos covered his once pale arms, his narrow face the only place not invaded by ink.

'Mr Haines?' Juliet checked. 'I'm Detective Inspector Juliet Stern and this is Detective Sergeant Gabe Martin.'

'That was quick.' His voice was as unusually high as Jordan's. 'We were told not to expect you for hours. Call me Andy.'

A line bisected Juliet's forehead as we were ushered inside. 'We're here to ask Jordan about a fire on the Dunlow Estate.'

'Oh.' Andy's face clouded. 'You're not here because he's missing?'

We walked into the cramped living room and Jordan's dad settled into the armchair near the French doors. Juliet and I sat on the sofa. She stared out at the patch of neglected lawn.

'Jordan's missing?' I flipped open my notepad.

'Yeah. He didn't come home last night.' Andy rubbed at his chin, his elbow a sharp point through his shirt. 'Sometimes he comes home late and forgets to text to say he's staying out, but he didn't come home before we went to bed. We called around his mates. None of them has seen him and he hadn't said anything to them about what he was doing. We waited until this morning and called the police.'

Upstairs, a floorboard creaked.

'We know Jordan was at the memorial for Melanie Pirt yesterday morning, and later he was in an altercation with another boy,' I said. 'You have no idea what he did after that?'

Andy ran a hand over his slicked-back hair. 'I picked him up from the police station, but he scarpered when we stopped at some traffic lights.'

'You have no idea where he went?' I asked. Jordan must have been desperate to escape. Did he want to go to the estate, or could he not bear to be in close proximity with his father any longer?

'He doesn't tell me much these days.'

Andy stopped speaking as Jordan's mum appeared in the doorway, her hair piled into a messy bun on top of her head. She started when she saw Juliet and me. The skin of her face reddened, except for a misshapen purple bruise across her left cheek and forehead.

Juliet stood, roused from her staring match with a dandelion outside, but Jordan's mum shied away. She scurried out of the room, her progress upstairs marked by uneven creaks. Juliet sat down, breathing through flared nostrils.

'I hope your wife's okay?' I broke the thick silence.

Andy shrugged. 'She's fine. She fell down the stairs last night, bumped her head.'

Juliet's hands fisted in her lap. Such an obvious lie, but we couldn't pursue a charge of domestic abuse without a strong witness or inclination from the victim. We had neither.

'To confirm, you've not seen Jordan since you picked him up from the station yesterday?' I asked.

'That's right.' Andy's voice was cool. 'And he's in trouble now, right?'

'As Juliet said, we'd like to ask Jordan about a fire on the Dunlow Estate. We don't know whether Jordan was involved, but could you give us a call when he comes home?'

'But he's missing,' Andy said. 'What if he's got nothing to do with it?'

'Officers will be around later today to discuss opening a missing person's case.' I tapped my pencil. 'Could we please have a sample of Jordan's handwriting?'

'What for?' Jordan's father wasn't a kind man, but he had some protective instincts towards his son.

'We forgot to get one the other day.' I pressed my thumb into the side of my notepad rather than look away from Andy's piercing eyes. 'It's standard procedure.'

He stared at me for a second, then bent to search through the papers under the coffee table. I tried not to make my sigh of relief too obvious. If Jordan was missing, we needed to get a sample of his handwriting from his home. Coming back with a warrant would have caused an unnecessary delay.

'Here.' Andy passed me a dog-eared magazine. 'Jordan and his mum were doing the crossword together the other day.'

I kept my face expressionless as I scanned the clues, the distinctive capitalisation of every T bouncing off the page. I rose from the sofa and Juliet followed suit. 'Thank you for this. We'll make sure someone is sent around to start a missing person's case as soon as possible.'

Andy led the way to the front door. He watched us walk to the car, his unwavering gaze causing prickles across the back of my neck. Once the door snapped shut, I glanced at the house. Jordan's mum stood at an upstairs window. She jumped and disappeared, like someone inside had shouted her name.

I climbed into the car and turned the key in the ignition. Juliet stared at Jordan's house until I pulled away.

'Did you notice how she held herself?' She mimicked cradling her arm. 'There was more damage done to that woman than we could see.'

I indicated at the end of the road. I hadn't been as watchful as Juliet, more focused on getting answers from Jordan's dad.

'The handwriting is a match?' Juliet leant into the head rest, closing her eyes. 'Do you think Jordan started the fire?'

'He might have,' I said. 'Someone was lurking outside the manor before the fire started. Jordan's absence and his tendency towards hurting people won't help his case if he had nothing to do with it.'

'If he wasn't there, who was?' Juliet mused. 'What were the Dunlows like when you talked to them?'

'Same as usual.' I swept across a mini roundabout. 'Dunlow treated me like I was scum. The boys were scared.'

'Do you think any of them started the fire?'

I wrinkled my nose. 'Why would they? We've already searched the house.'

'But maybe we didn't find everything.' Juliet opened her eyes. 'You said the fire might have originated around the fireplace? Maybe someone was burning evidence and it got out of hand.'

'Or maybe someone wanted to distract us?' I bit my lip. 'The sooner Jordan turns up the better. The Dunlows aren't going to give anything away.'

I was beginning to think they were all much better liars than I'd given them credit for. Or their lies were so many and varied that it was hard to spot the truth between them.

At least Jordan was an open book. He might bluster and lash out, but it was all done honestly. Despite Leo's claims that he loved Melanie, he hadn't broken down in the way Jordan did on hearing she'd died. Leo wasn't spiralling in grief. There was a stillness to him that reminded me of his father. He was untouchable, by us and by the death of someone he'd loved.

Call connected at 14:32.

'Hello?'

'Hi, Keith. It's me.'

'Hello, Juliet.'

'How are the girls?'

'You know how they are. Oh, wait, no, you don't, because you're never the one left with them when a parent runs away.'

'What have you said to them?'

'You'd know that if you were here.'

'Keith, I had to come back.'

'Did you? Or did you choose your job over us again?'

'I had to come back. Can I talk to them?'

'I don't think so.'

'You're going to refuse to let me speak to my daughters?'

'If you insist, I'll pass the phone over. But I've just settled them. I can't see how talking to the person who abandons them on a regular basis is going to help.'

'Fine.'

'And you don't even fight for them.'

'I can't do this now, Keith. I'll talk to you soon.'

'Great. We can start arguing about next weekend.'

'I look forward to it.'

Gabe

Juliet put down her phone and stood up. 'Jordan's here.'

'What?' I'd been reading an article by Matt Lam about housefires caused by cigarettes. If anyone could spot the signs of one, it was him. A headshot at the top of the article didn't do him justice.

Juliet pulled on her blazer. Maybe she didn't have clothes stored here; she'd stayed in jeans since we'd gotten to the station.

'He and his mum have been taken through to interview room one,' she said, straightening her collar. She tugged a copy of the threatening note from the evidence wall and slotted it into a file. 'They came into the station to give a witness statement.'

I jumped up and brushed biscuit crumbs from my trousers. 'A witness statement? Not to confess a crime?'

Juliet quirked her eyebrows. 'Exactly.'

We walked through the crowded main floor and took the lift down to reception. The street outside the glass entrance was already switching to twilight. Juliet marched towards the wide corridor of interview rooms but paused outside the first door.

'How do you want to play this?'

I took a deep breath. 'I reckon we both jump in as needed. Jordan's a funny one; he needs a bit of pushing and soothing. We can do both.'

Juliet gave me a small smile. 'We work well together.'

I'd thought that many times, yet part of me wondered whether Juliet wouldn't be happier working alone. She hadn't literally said she wanted me around, but this was the next best thing.

Juliet pushed open the door to the interview room and walked around to the far side of the metal table. Jordan and his mum sat opposite. Jordan stared down at his hands, his clothes dirty and torn. The smell of smoke filled the room. His mum's back was straight in the plastic chair and her bruised face set like a statue.

Juliet reached a hand over the table. 'I need to apologise. We didn't ask your name before.'

Jordan's mum stared at Juliet's hand, but slowly lifted her arm. 'It's Terrie.'

'Thank you, Terrie.' Juliet whipped her hand back to her side. 'You've been offered a solicitor?'

'We don't need it,' she said. Jordan's head remained bowed.

Juliet pressed the button to record.

'Interview commencing at 4:55 p.m. on 15th October regarding a fire on the Dunlow Estate in the New Forest,' I said. 'Interviewee is Jordan Haines, a seventeen-year-old minor accompanied by his mother, Terrie Haines. They have declined legal representation. Interview conducted by Detective Inspector Juliet Stern and myself, Detective Sergeant Gabriella Martin. Jordan, you are not under arrest and are free to leave at any time.'

I found a clean page in my notebook, resisting the grimace my full name always evoked. 'Jordan, can you please tell us your movements since you left the station yesterday?'

He shuffled in his seat. Terrie rested a hand on his arm and he sat up. His face was as dirty as his clothes, his eyes puffy and rimmed with red.

'I ran off from my dad's car and I caught a bus over to the Dunlow Estate.' His voice was brittle.

'How did you get onto the estate?' Juliet asked.

Jordan swallowed. 'I climbed the wall. It's crumbling, so it was easy to get over.'

'What did you do once you were on the estate?' I asked.

'I followed the paths through the forest.' Jordan rubbed his hands together, the skin a mixture of clay-like white and charcoal black. 'I knew which direction to go to find the house. It started getting dark, but then I saw lights.'

I made a note. Melanie's killer knew their way around the estate, knew how to find a gun and the dog and where to hide evidence. Jordan hadn't admitted to all of this, but he was comfortable following the twisting paths through the forest at least.

'Why did you go to the estate?' Juliet asked.

'I was going crazy. Nothing was happening about Mel, no one was being punished.' Jordan's partially shaved eyebrows pulled together. 'I was angry.'

'What were you planning to do?' I asked.

Jordan looked up, eyes wide. 'Not start a fire. I was just going to scare Leo. I wouldn't have done anything serious.'

His definition of something serious and ours were most likely quite different. I flipped to a fresh page in my notepad. 'Tell us what you did after you saw the lights at the manor.'

'I followed them. I could see in but those poshos couldn't see me. I watched them have dinner together. They didn't talk much, but Leo was safe. His brother said something when their dad left the room and Leo laughed. I wanted to hurt him.'

'What did you do?' Juliet asked.

Jordan scowled at her. 'Nothing. Leo went off upstairs. So did his brother. Only the dad was left downstairs, reading.'

'You did nothing?' I asked. 'You made no attempt to make contact with any member of the Dunlow family?'

Jordan licked his cracked lips. 'No.'

'Please explain this.' Juliet flipped open the file and spun the copy of the note to face Jordan.

His mouth moved uselessly, denials and lies building on his tongue.

'We know it's your handwriting.' I headed off any blustering before it could begin. 'When did you put the note through the door?'

Jordan's eyes flicked to his motionless mum. 'Way before the fire started.'

'When?' Juliet demanded.

'I'd seen Leo leave the dining room. I followed him around the house, had already written the note days ago. He was in the hallway alone, so I posted it through the door. Then I ran off to the other side of the house.'

Juliet turned the note towards us. '"You think you're untouchable",' she read. '"I'm going to make you hurt."'

'Can you see why this would make us suspicious about your involvement in the fire?' I asked. Juliet had avoided the sections of the note that referred to Melanie, so I held back my renewed suspicions about Jordan's involvement in her death. I didn't want to derail him from giving us a full account of his movements last night.

'I didn't have anything to do with it, I swear.' Jordan licked his ashy lips. 'I just wanted to scare him.'

'You posted a threatening note. What did you do after that?' Juliet prompted.

Jordan's jaw quivered. His fingers worked furiously at the laces of his hoodie, leaving smudges of black on the grey material. 'I didn't mean to start a fire. I didn't mean to do anything.'

'It's alright, Jordan,' I said. 'Just tell us what happened next.'

He sniffed. 'I'd been smoking the whole time, dropping the ends around the house. I hoped Leo would get in trouble for it, or it would freak him out because he'd know someone had been outside. I sat out by where the old man was reading most of the night. The window was the only light, and that place was freaky in the dark. I kept thinking I heard someone outside, gravel crunching and stuff, but everyone else was inside the house. I was going to wait until morning to find my way out of there. I must have dozed off, because the next thing I knew there was loads of shouting and smoke.'

'Had one of your cigarettes started the fire?' Juliet asked.

A tear leaked out of the corner of Jordan's eye. 'I don't think so, but I don't know. I fell asleep with one lit. I guess it could have caught on something, and the fire spread inside.'

I frowned. 'Can I check? You didn't throw a lit cigarette into the house?'

'What?' Jordan reared back in his seat. 'No, I wouldn't do that. I was angry, but I didn't want to burn the house down. I couldn't have, anyway. The windows were closed.'

'All your cigarettes butts are outside the manor?' Juliet asked.

'Yeah.' Jordan looked between us. 'I swear I didn't mean for this to happen.'

If Jordan was telling the truth, then he hadn't started the fire. But that meant Dunlow had either made up the fire spreading from a cigarette butt or he was mistaken. He didn't seem the type to get confused.

'What did you do when you saw the fire?' Juliet asked.

'I panicked.' Jordan rubbed at his face with a frayed sleeve. 'I knew that if one of the poshos saw me, they'd assume I'd caused it, but I couldn't move. I wanted to hurt Leo, but I didn't want him to burn to death. I was freaking out until the window exploded. After that, I ran off to the edge of the woods. I checked they were all out before I went any further. Then I followed a path away from there. There was smoke everywhere, but I found that barn where they keep their dogs. I figured no one else was going to go there, so I hid until it got light.'

'You didn't mind the dogs?' I asked, trying to keep the anticipation out of my voice.

'I love dogs, would have one if Dad let me.' Jordan shot a startled look at his mum, but she didn't react. 'They were all freaking out so I gave them a fuss. There was a big friendly one that I let out. He kept me warm.'

The most noticeable thing about Jordan's appearance was the mud and ash staining his clothes, but I spotted a few brown hairs. The exact shade of Artie's fur.

I'd have to wait until we were alone to ask Juliet if Jordan had incriminated himself far more during this interview than in any other. Desperate to prove he hadn't started the fire, he was letting things slip.

His shock when we told him Melanie was dead might not have been because he didn't know. It could have been because he was devastated we'd found her so soon.

'You left the estate when it got light?' Juliet asked. 'Where did you go then?'

Jordan darted a look at his mum. She sat rigid, her face a blank mask.

'I didn't want to go home. Dad would be there, and I didn't want to talk to him. He wouldn't listen if I tried to explain what had happened.'

A flicker of emotion crossed his mum's face, there and gone before I could name it.

'So where did you go?' Juliet asked.

Jordan jerked his shoulders up. 'I hid out around the place.'

'Why did you go home this afternoon?' I asked.

'I was hungry. I thought I'd be able to sneak in while Dad was out.'

Juliet pinched her mouth to one side. 'What happened when you went home?'

'Only Mum was there. She told me you'd come looking for me. She said I had to tell you what happened.'

He reached over and placed a grubby hand on top of his mum's knotted fingers. She blinked at him, her eyes filling with tears.

This didn't make sense. Why would Jordan have come in to the station if he'd started the fire? If he hadn't, who did? And did his slip-ups today mean that discounting him as Melanie's killer had been a big mistake?

You have one new voicemail. Voicemail left today at 5:10 p.m.

'Benny, where the bloody hell are you? You can't have missed my messages, and the police said they've tried to get in touch too. I don't know if you're mad at me for leaving early, but this is bigger than that. I need you to clear my name but more than that, I need you. My house fucking well burnt down last night. Someone's been murdered on the estate grounds and Leo's been beaten up. Everything's going wrong. I know I'm a shit but please call me. I can't go through all of this alone.'

Gabe

Juliet stood facing the wall of evidence, blazer discarded on her desk. 'What did you make of that?'

'I'm not sure Jordan had anything to do with the fire.' I started with the easiest conclusion. 'The firefighter doesn't think a cigarette butt started it.'

'I agree.' Juliet didn't look away from the wall.

'Other things he said gave me pause.' I flicked through my notes. 'Jordan's clearly more comfortable moving around the estate than we thought, and he has an affinity for dogs.'

Juliet glanced over her shoulder. 'I'm glad you clocked that too.'

'Melanie's murderer knew their way around the forest and wasn't attacked by a violent dog. Jordan fits at least that part of the picture.'

Juliet flicked through various bits of evidence on the wall, her loose blouse flowing around her arms. My earlier guilt returned.

'Juliet? I'm sorry for calling you back.'

She let go of the notes from our first interview with Jordan. 'It's fine. Keith was being difficult. I didn't mind leaving.'

This was the closest Juliet had ever come to revealing something about her home life, and I wasn't sure what she wanted from me. Word around the station was that Juliet's husband was a nice guy and that their strange living arrangement was the result of Juliet's dedication to her work. There was no hint of anything else.

She snatched up her bag and blazer. 'We need that fucking forensic report.'

She stormed out. I didn't know if she was going to harass whoever was working forensics on a Sunday evening or if she was going home, but I'd missed my chance to offer any kind of comfort. It might be better to leave it. Juliet was like a stray cat; if I overwhelmed her, she would run away and never come back.

I took her place in front of the wall of evidence, scanning the pictures and statements. With no word from Benedict Hogan, we couldn't put Terence in the clear. And Jordan had edged his way into the serious suspect category as well. That made me uneasy. He'd made huge mistakes, but I wasn't sure shooting his girlfriend was one of them.

If only Karl hadn't run away. He was a firm suspect as well, but I didn't want him to be. I could understand his reasoning. He'd carved out a peaceful, history-free space for himself and when it was threatened, he'd fled. It was a defence mechanism, but it had backfired. It made him look more guilty than staying and riding out the storm would have done.

I leant on my desk, staring at Leo and his father's photos. It would be satisfying to pin this on Dunlow, but I didn't think it was likely. He still floated above this mess, although half his ancestral home burning down had to have stolen away some of his detachment.

Leo had lied and lied again, but I didn't think he was a killer. He hadn't yet told us the whole story of that night, probably because he didn't want to get in trouble with his father rather than that he'd killed Melanie.

But someone had. Someone chased her into the forest, shot her three times, and left her to be mauled by a dog.

I sighed and gathered up my things. Hanging around here wouldn't help. Hopefully, Juliet would have some luck with the DNA results. We needed them. If we knew who had sex with Melanie or got any unusual DNA from her body, then we might be able to catch her killer.

'Hi, Mum?'

   'Hello, darling.'

   'Is everything okay?'

   'Yes. Why wouldn't it be?'

   'You don't normally call this late.'

   'I wanted to check in. You normally work the weekends during a big case. I remember how you used to pace around the kitchen.'

   'You're right. I've just gotten home.'

   'That's a long day for a Sunday.'

   'Yeah. This case is the gift that keeps giving. You sure you're okay?'

   'Yes, darling. I only called because I miss you.'

   'Oh. I miss you too.'

   'And your dad misses you.'

   'Does he?'

   'Of course he does.'

   'He's got a funny way of showing it.'

   'I know, I know.'

   'Sorry, it's not your fault. Being away is even harder because he's not speaking to me.'

   'He's a silly man. I love him, but he doesn't always make the best decisions.'

   'I love him too.'

   'You're a good girl, Gabriella.'

   'Ah, you'll be happy. I interviewed a suspect today and had to state my full name for the recording.'

   'You're such a ninny. Who wouldn't love your name?'

   'It's ridiculous. I can only assume you were high on pain meds when you named us.'

   'I picked beautiful names for my children. I won't hear a word against them. Anyway, I know you can't tell me anything about the case you're working on, so what have you been up to outside of work?'

   'I've, um, started seeing someone.'

'Oh, Gabriella. How lovely. What's he like?'

'Kind. And it is a he, by the way.'

'Oh, well. Yes. What does he do?'

'He's a model.'

'Oh my. Handsome then?'

'Very.'

'Will we get to meet him?'

'Maybe, probably. It's early days.'

'It's so nice to hear you're seeing someone, putting yourself out there.'

'Yeah. How's the food bank going?'

'You remembered!'

'Course I did.'

'It's great. I'm getting to know the families. They have such a hard time of it.'

'I bet.'

'Have you found yourself a church down there yet?'

'Um, not yet.'

'I know you don't think much of it all, but it's a good place to find friends, have a community.'

'I guess. I have to go. My dinner's almost ready. Love you, Mum.'

'I love you, Gabriella.'

'I'm going now.'

'Goodbye, Gabriella.'

'Bye, Mother.'

From: Alice To **alice.to@police.gov.uk**
To: Paul Willis **paul.willis@mit.gov.uk**
Date: **15 October, 20:37**
Subject: **Operation Toucan: Warehouse CCTV**

Sir,

I've found something – the clip is attached. They appear five seconds in, watch the door in the bottom right corner.

Alice

Day 7

Monday, 16 October

BREAKING NEWS: FIRE AT THE DUNLOW ESTATE

The Dunlow family had to move out of their ancestral home in the north-east of the New Forest following a fire in the manor early on Sunday morning. Several rooms have been heavily burned and many more have smoke damage.

The quick thinking of the estate owner, Timothy Dunlow, slowed the spread of the fire. Before vacating the property, he closed many of the doors.

None of the Dunlow family were seriously harmed, although Timothy Dunlow did sprain his wrist when leaving the property.

The property is grade one listed, so repairs will be costly. It is unlikely the family will stay on the estate while work is in progress.

This fire comes after the shooting of a local school girl, Melanie Pirt, on the grounds of the estate on 9 October. Questions are being raised as to whether these two events are linked. The detectives leading the case declined to comment.

FULL FORENSIC ASSESSMENT

REPORT ON:

DNA SAMPLES taken from the body of **MELANIE PIRT** and her **CLOTHING.**

DNA SAMPLES were taken from **MELANIE PIRT'S HAIR, MOUTH, HANDS, GENITALS** and **CLOTHES.** Samples of **BLOOD** were also taken.

Using **BLOOD SAMPLES**, we are able to estimate the time of death as between 22:00 and 23:59 on 9 October. **MELANIE'S BLOOD** showed no alcohol or drugs in her system at the time of death.

We can confirm that the **DOG** shot on the Dunlow Estate was the same animal involved in the attack on **MELANIE PIRT. SAMPLES OF BLOOD** taken from its **MOUTH** were a positive match for **MELANIE PIRT.**

Many of the samples taken from **MELANIE PIRT** provided positive matches for **DNA SAMPLES** collected in conjunction with this case. The results are listed below:

HAIR sample: **POSITIVE MATCH** for **LEONARD DUNLOW**

MOUTH sample: **POSITIVE MATCH** for **LEONARD DUNLOW**

HAND sample: **POSITIVE MATCH** for **LEONARD DUNLOW**

GENITAL sample: **POSTIVE MATCH** for **LEONARD DUNLOW**

MELANIE PIRT had unprotected sex 1 to 2 hours before her death. There was no sign of undue force.

MELANIE PIRT'S CLOTHES were a **POSITIVE MATCH** for **LEONARD DUNLOW.** There were small amounts of material that provided positive matches for **TERENCE DUNLOW, JORDAN HAINES, KARL BISS** and **TIMOTHY DUNLOW** (in order from most to least). These were small enough to be incidental and may not have been picked up via direct contact.

REPORT COMPILED BY DEREK HOPKINS AND DAVID REES

Gabe

'Of course they're staying here,' Juliet said, tucking her scarf into her coat.

Wind whipped our hair around as we walked across a car park packed with vehicles more in keeping with Dunlow's BMW than my Vauxhall Astra. Implausibly clean windows shone above the entrance to the Southampton Harbour Hotel.

The front doors opened automatically as we approached, the movement unhurried. Comfortable heat enveloped us as we walked inside.

Juliet shook her head and was as immaculate as ever as we approached the reception desk. I ran my fingers through my cropped hair, willing it to behave. We waited while the receptionist finished a call, her voice set to a low tone of apology.

Someone with good taste had arranged what I presumed were original works of abstract art behind the gleaming white reception desk, had chosen the smooth cream wallpaper and picked out the light wood for the floors. A polished marble staircase wound upwards. The tapping of Juliet's heel didn't travel well, the sound dampened by high ceilings. The spacious reception seemed larger due to windows looking out over the harbour.

The receptionist smiled as she put down the phone, her white-blonde hair waving neatly. Hers was the kind of carefully curated look that would have had Maddy groaning with envy. She always complained about how difficult it was to make her hair anything other than a frizzy jumble.

The smile froze on the receptionist's face when I set my ID on the counter.

'We need the room number for Leonard Dunlow,' I said. 'There's no need to tell him we're here.'

The receptionist tucked her hair behind her ears. 'He's in one of the Deluxe Marina View suites. Number two.' Her eyes flicked across her computer screen. 'His father and brother are in three and four. They're on the fourth floor. Do you need someone to show you the way?'

'That won't be necessary,' Juliet said, turning towards the lifts.

I thanked the receptionist before following. The silver doors of the lift opened, revealing smudge-free mirrors. Classical music played as the doors closed soundlessly.

'What are the odds we'll get Leo out of here without Dunlow interfering?' Juliet checked her coat pockets as we ascended. Clinking from her left revealed where she'd secreted her cuffs.

'Almost none.' My stomach swooped as the lift came to a gentle stop and the doors glided open.

The walls on this floor were a mixture of wooden panelling and more cream wallpaper. The hallway was silent as we walked to suite two, no sounds pervading from the surrounding rooms. This was nothing like the Travelodge I'd stayed in for a few nights when I moved down here.

Juliet knocked on the door, one heel twisting on the spotless floor. I took a deep breath and composed myself. We were here to take Leo to the station with minimal fuss, where he would finally tell the truth.

I still wasn't sure he was Melanie's murderer, but he was certainly a chronic liar.

Leo opened the door, the glossed wood whispering over soft carpet. He wore the same wide-eyed doe look as when we'd first met him, innocence personified in a spotless white top and light blue jeans. He hadn't planned on going to school today. Apparently, losing a home was enough to warrant a break from the norm in Dunlow's eyes.

'Leonard Dunlow, you are under arrest for the murder of Melanie Pirt.' Juliet stepped forward and placed a hand on his arm. 'You do not have to say anything. But, it may harm your defence if you do not mention when questioned something which you may later rely on in court. Anything you do say may be given in evidence. Do you understand?'

Leo's face was almost as pale as the dressing on his cheek as he nodded. 'Let me put my shoes on.'

He pulled trainers from under a highly polished desk, his movements sure as he sat on the queen-size bed to lace them up. He must have known this day was coming. There was no way we wouldn't find the DNA he'd left all over Melanie.

I glanced around the suite. French doors led out onto a private balcony, the tops of masts visible but the majority of the view dominated by undulating water. I'd never slept so close to the sea. The hissing of waves would be unrelenting.

A door beside the deeply quilted bed banged open as Leo stood up. Dunlow strode in. He placed himself in front of his son, his chest heaving beneath a pressed grey suit.

'Whatever the hell you're doing here, I suggest you leave.' He pointed a finger at Juliet. 'My son has nothing more to tell you.'

'Your son is under arrest for murder,' Juliet said, unmoved by Dunlow's bluster. 'If you won't get out of our way, then we'll have to arrest you for obstruction of justice.'

Dunlow's eyes narrowed to slits. I breathed slowly, glad of Juliet's steady presence. I tried not to show intimidation in the face of men like Dunlow, but I was a small woman. Something inside me screamed to recoil. We'd come here without backup, sure Dunlow wouldn't make a scene in such a public place. But hotel rooms became private spaces for the people staying in them.

Dunlow flinched when Leo placed a hand on his shoulder.

'I have to go, Dad. It'll be okay.'

Dunlow gripped his son's arm. 'Don't tell them anything until I've sorted a solicitor.'

Leo nodded. He eased past his father, the older man's hand falling to his side.

'Call me when you get there,' Dunlow commanded. 'Make sure they let you talk to me as soon as you arrive.'

Terence appeared at the inner door in his pyjamas. 'What's going on?'

Juliet placed her hand under Leo's elbow. 'We're taking Leo to the station. We have some questions for him about the murder of Melanie Pirt.'

Leo allowed himself to be propelled out into the corridor and along towards the lift. Dunlow's face was contorted with rage as I left the room, a blotchy mix of reds and whites. The connecting door snapped shut.

Terence was wise. Best to hide away when a storm came, and Dunlow's bad moods would be as destructive and threatening as a hurricane.

Ollie. Sent 9:10.

> Hey, girlfriend. I'd love to see you again soon –
> maybe even for dinner this time? xx

Call connected at 10:36.

'Timothy Dunlow.'

'Hey, Dad.'

'Why didn't you call as soon as you got there?'

'I couldn't. Sorry. There was paperwork to do and they took my fingerprints. But they made sure I called you at the first possible time.'

'What's happening now?'

'I think I'm going in a cell for a bit, while I wait for the solicitor.'

'Gerard is on the way. He'll be there within the hour.'

'Okay. I feel—'

'Is one of them with you now?'

'A police officer? Yeah.'

'Don't let them see any weakness. Don't let them see anything.'

'Okay, Dad.'

'And don't tell them anything. Don't let them trip you up. Any question you're not sure how to answer, you look to Gerard first.'

'I will.'

'You haven't done anything wrong. They won't be able to charge you.'

'I know. Thank you, Dad.'

'For what?'

'Believing in me.'

'The biggest mistake you made was letting that girl onto the estate, but nothing that happened after has anything to do with you.'

*FORM 30D – FORMAL REQUEST FOR SURVEILLANCE OF A
COMMERCIAL PROPERTY*

REQUESTING OFFICERS:

Detective Inspector Paul Willis

CASE NUMBER:

10098756

CASE DESCRIPTION:

Murder of Krystal Barrett on the Northwood Housing Estate in
Southampton on 10 October.

REQUESTED SURVEILLANCE AREA:

A condemned warehouse on the Liners' Industrial Estate – see the
attached map of the area.

REASON FOR WARRANT REQUEST:

We have evidence that Justin and Sonia Barrett are hiding in this
warehouse to avoid arrest. CCTV shows both individuals entering
the property two days ago. We would like 24-hour surveillance on the
warehouse to ascertain if they are still in the vicinity and whether they
are armed. We have conclusive proof Justin and Sonia Barrett abused
and murdered their seven-year-old daughter, Krystal Barrett.

Gabe

'We're ready for you.' The aged solicitor held open the door to the interview room. He was exactly who I'd have pictured giving the Dunlows legal advice. He might be older and thinner, but he was cut from the same cloth as his moneyed employer.

Juliet and I pushed away from the wall. We'd waited in the corridor for over an hour while Leo conferred with his legal representative. Neither of us had suggested going up to the office.

I followed Juliet into the room and settled in the chair opposite Leo. She opened a file of evidence while I pressed the record button.

'Interview commencing at 11:20 a.m. on 16th October. Interviewee is Leonard Dunlow and his solicitor, Gerard Hargrave, is present. They have been given time prior to this interview to consult. Leonard Dunlow has been arrested in conjunction with the murder of Melanie Pirt on the Dunlow Estate in the New Forest on 9th October. This interview is being conducted by myself, Detective Sergeant Gabriella Martin, and Detective Inspector Juliet Stern.'

As I finished my spiel, Juliet passed me a piece of paper. I slid it across the table towards Leo, my hand steady. Adrenaline fizzed in my gut, but I'd practised calming breathing while we waited.

'This was your original statement, made on 10th October,' I said. 'You claimed you didn't know Melanie.'

Leo skimmed the words. Juliet placed another piece of paper next to the first.

'This is your second statement, where you admitted you knew Melanie. You said you didn't go to meet her.' Juliet slid a final statement across the table as I continued. 'And your third statement, amending your relationship with Melanie. You were in love with her but maintained that when she came to the estate you didn't meet with her.'

I placed a fourth piece of paper, detailing the forensics from Melanie's body, beside the first three. 'We have DNA evidence that proves you've lied again. Now, Leo, it's time for you to tell us the truth.'

'I'm sorry I lied, but I promise I didn't kill Mel.'

'We'd be much more inclined to believe you if you tell us what actually happened on 9th October,' Juliet said.

Leo pushed his glasses up his nose. He didn't look at his solicitor but Hargrave took a deep breath, his brow furrowed. This was why they'd taken so long to confer; there was some kind of disagreement between them. We could work with that.

'Everything I told you was true, apart from the bit where I didn't go to meet Mel. I did meet her,' Leo said. 'She was desperate. I'd told her what my dad was like about girls, so I knew she was only asking to come over because something bad had happened. I met her at the bus stop. I thought I would be able to talk to her there and send her home, but she was so upset. She started crying as soon as she saw me. She told me how her ex wouldn't leave her alone and kept sending her horrible messages. I didn't want to make her go away, so I snuck her onto the estate.'

'You didn't go through the gates?' I asked.

Leo shook his head. 'Parts of the boundary walls are falling down. We climbed over, then followed one of the paths through the forest. I took her to the den over the garage. I thought Dad wouldn't notice us there.' He gulped. 'I don't know how it happened, but we were talking and then kissing. We ended up having sex.'

Red patches formed on Leo's neck, but he forged on. 'It was amazing. I'd never had sex before, and Mel was so kind and lovely. But I didn't handle it well afterwards. I told her she couldn't stay. I wanted to be there for her, but I couldn't risk Dad finding out I'd had a girl over. He would go mad.'

I made a note. 'What happened then, Leo?'

'She was upset. I needed her to leave but I didn't want her to think I was using her. I didn't know what to say as she got dressed. She left.' He pressed his lips together. 'I let her go.'

'You didn't follow?' I asked.

Leo glanced at his solicitor, who studiously ignored him. 'I fell asleep.'

'You didn't hear anything that happened during the night?' I pushed.

'I wish I'd gone after her.' Leo's chin quivered. 'I could have made sure she got off the estate safely.'

Leo had lied before, but never well. It may have been pathetic that he fell asleep when Melanie left, rather than chasing after her, but it had a ring of truth to it. If this was the first time he'd had sex, he wouldn't have expected the energy drop that came after.

Juliet tapped Leo's previous statements. 'Why did you lie before?'

'It wasn't my idea.'

'Whose idea was it?' I asked, even though I could take a good guess.

Leo scrunched his nose. 'My dad's.'

Juliet raised her eyebrows. This was the first time Dunlow had done anything other than be an arrogant prick. He wasn't floating above this anymore.

'How did your dad know Melanie was there?' I asked.

Leo shuffled in his chair while Hargrave drummed his fingers on the table. That meant something to the younger man. Leo straightened and shook his head.

'I have to tell them the truth,' he muttered. 'It's not going to get Dad in trouble.'

The look of distaste on Hargrave's face was familiar from time we'd spent in Dunlow's presence. Maybe they went to the same school, had learnt together how to make people feel like insignificant worms.

'Leo?' I prompted.

'I don't know how Dad knew, but he stormed into the den as soon as Mel left. He was shouting all kinds of stuff.' He paused. 'He cares about me. He doesn't want me to mess up my education or anything, that's all.'

'What was he saying?' Juliet asked.

Leo cringed. 'Just that I couldn't have girls over and I should know better.'

I gripped my pencil. I bet Dunlow had a lot more to say than that. 'Did he say anything about Melanie specifically?'

More uneven patches of blood worked their way across Leo's face. 'I don't remember.'

There we go. Lying again. It was obvious now.

Juliet sighed. 'What happened after your dad left?'

'The last thing he said was to not go after Mel. He told me to go to sleep,' Leo said in a rush, happy to move away from whatever vile things his father said that night. 'I was going to wait until he was in the house to go after her, but I fell asleep. I woke up the next morning.'

His voice caught at the end of his speech. This was the most emotion we'd seen from Leo. Perhaps he'd been keeping the truth so carefully locked inside that he couldn't let out his guilt or sadness either. Or maybe it was what his dad expected of him. It was believable that in the Dunlow household men did not cry.

'When did your dad tell you to lie?' Juliet asked.

Leo squinted one eye. 'When I got home from school. Dad told me the police were coming and that I was to tell you nothing. He said it would look bad if I told you I'd let Mel onto the estate.' He shrugged. 'Since you took my DNA, I've been waiting for you to come. I didn't know why it was taking so long.'

Juliet's nostrils flared. 'If you knew we'd get here in the end, why did you continue to lie? Your dad wasn't in the hospital. That would have been a good time to confess.'

Leo's eyes flicked between us. 'I know it was stupid, I'm sorry, but Dad told me to lie so I tried to. The only other time I'd broken one of his rules, Mel died. I didn't want to tempt fate like that again.'

Flawed logic, but a reason nonetheless. I started a new page in my notepad. 'Leo, do you have any idea who would have killed Melanie?'

'I don't know.' His nose wrinkled. 'Dad thinks it was Karl. He keeps going on about how an innocent person wouldn't have run away, but I think he's just mad about the dogs. We've had to take care of them, at least until we find somewhere for them, and he doesn't like doing all that stuff. I knew Karl better than Dad, and he was a nice guy. He wouldn't have killed Mel.'

'What did your dad do after he left the den that night?' Juliet asked.

Leo's eyes widened. 'He didn't go off and kill Mel, if that's what you're implying.'

Juliet held up her hands. 'I'm not implying anything. I'm simply asking what your dad did after he left the den. Did you see him walk into the house?'

Leo frowned down at the table and flinched when Hargrave coughed. Clearly, they'd already spoken about this. Their chat was full of disagreements.

Leo sat up straight. 'Right. I didn't see him walk into the house, okay? I fell asleep almost as soon as he left. But he wouldn't have gone and killed Mel. He didn't like me seeing her, but he had no reason to want her dead.'

It was interesting that everyone jumped so readily to Dunlow's defence, keen to assure us he wasn't a murderer. Juliet pressed her fingers together.

'I'm sorry, Leo, but I'm not sure I believe any of this,' she said. 'You've lied repeatedly, and I have no reason to assume you're not lying again. You admit you argued with Melanie before she died. What if this conversation with your dad is another fabrication, one he told you to add so that it wouldn't be crystal clear you were so upset with Melanie after she left that you followed her into the forest and killed her?'

Leo gaped at Juliet. If I didn't know exactly how her mind worked, I might have done the same. I was much more trusting of my gut than her. It told me Leo was telling the truth at last, but she would push and prod until she was sure.

'I'm not lying anymore, I swear.' Leo voice was hoarse. 'I didn't kill Mel. I loved her.'

'Have you got any evidence to support these accusations?' Hargrave asked, eyes half lidded with boredom.

Juliet smiled. 'We have Leo's DNA all over the victim. We know he had access to the kind of gun used to kill her. He has the right sized feet to have made an incredibly clear boot print at the scene. We know he was friendly with the dogs, and in close contact with the animal that mauled the victim. His father has a temper, and what could be more natural than a son sharing the same trait? And we found these on Leo's computer. They make for interesting reading.'

Juliet placed a copy of Leo's poems in the middle of the table.

Leo shook his head. 'I know it looks bad, but I don't know how to shoot. Ask my dad or Teddy, they'll tell you. I'm useless. And I don't know about the boot print, but I wasn't down there. If I had been, Lucy was more likely to attack me than Mel. She hated me, bit me the other day because I got too close. And I'm not like my dad, not like that. He's been worse since Mum died. It's grief talking most of the time when he gets cross.' He looked at his poems. 'No one was supposed to see these. They don't mean anything.'

'I'm sure.' Juliet crossed her arms. 'Has Melanie got what she deserves now?' she asked, referencing one of the poems.

249

'You don't have to answer that,' Hargrave cut in before Leo could open his mouth.

'And how about this one?' Juliet carried on, relentless. 'Had you had your perfect moment and couldn't bear to have it ruined?'

I'd made a connection to that poem before. In the hospital, I thought it meant the kiss Leo and Melanie had shared during a singing practice. I'd jumped to a conclusion, and enabled Leo to go on lying. I bit my tongue between my teeth.

'I loved Mel,' Leo protested. 'I wouldn't have hurt her.'

'Jordan, Melanie's boyfriend, thinks you were obsessed with her,' I said, desperate to add something of value. 'He said you were scaring her.'

'*I* was scaring Mel?' Leo's eyebrows rose. 'I wasn't the one beating her.'

'Jordan is adamant you had something to do with her death,' I pushed.

Leo raised a hand to the gauze on his cheek, covering Jordan's handiwork. He would probably carry a scar for the rest of his life.

'He's jealous,' Leo said. 'He doesn't know what mine and Mel's relationship was like.'

'Trouble is, Leo, the only other person who did know what your relationship was like is dead,' Juliet said.

Leo flinched but recovered quickly. 'That's not true. We met in the church hall at St Peter's. The vicar let us in, and sometimes he would hang around to listen to Mel sing. He can tell you everything between us was normal, that I was always nice and kind.'

I made a note. I wasn't sure if a vicar who only saw Melanie and Leo during practices was a great character witness, but he might have noticed anything nasty going on.

'Were you upset when Melanie left, after you had sex?' Juliet asked.

'I was sad. She said some horrible things, as she was leaving. That I was a loser, just like her ex. I didn't want the night to end like that.' Leo eyebrows gathered together. 'I was going to follow her, but then Dad burst in.'

'But after he left, you didn't go then?' Juliet tipped her head to one side.

'I told you. I was waiting for Dad to go into the house, but I fell asleep.'

'You fell asleep when the love of your life had walked out into the night alone?' Juliet asked.

Leo swallowed, tears gathering in his eyes. 'You think I don't regret that more than anything else I've ever done? If I'd stayed awake, Mel would be alive right now. I wouldn't even care if she was mad at me, I would have made sure she got home.' He let out a shuddering breath. 'I don't know what happened. One minute I was watching Dad, the next I woke up and it was morning and everything had gone wrong.'

He pulled off his glasses and covered his face with his hands. I used the quiet moment while Leo took several deep breaths to gather the pieces of paper on the table and pass them to Juliet. The solicitor's face screamed contempt. He could see through all of this. Leo was in deep trouble, but there were serious holes in our knowledge. We didn't have the murder weapon and if everyone confirmed Leo was as terrible at shooting as he claimed then our case against him would come tumbling down.

'Leo?' Juliet said. 'When were you bitten by the dog?'

He wiped his eyes and put his glasses back on. 'I told you, it was the day before all this happened.'

He rubbed at his arm. The bandage was gone.

'Are you sure, Leo?' Juliet asked. 'Or were you bitten by the dog after it was done with Melanie? Did it turn on you, and you had to shoot to stop it from really hurting you?'

Juliet had read the same DNA report as me about the dog. Only Melanie's blood was in its mouth when it died. But Leo didn't know that. Juliet was withholding information, hoping Leo would twist himself into knots and reveal something more.

'No,' Leo spluttered. 'That's not what happened. Lucy bit me when I let her out the day before. Karl told you.'

'But Karl's gone,' Juliet said. 'Your brother paid him a lot of money to disappear.'

She was counting on another gap in Leo's knowledge. The brothers seemed close, both cowering in Dunlow's shadow, but would Terence have trusted his younger brother with his secret?

Leo's skin was a curdled mix of whites and reds. 'Teddy did what? Why would he do that?'

'You tell us.' Juliet's voice had a harsh edge, like she was tiring of circling the truth.

'I know this doesn't look good. I should have gone after Mel and I never should have let her go out onto the estate on her own, but I have no idea why Karl left or why Teddy would have given him any money.' Leo sat up, his eyes brimming. 'I made one stupid mistake, and it's caused so much pain. That's the worst thing I've ever done; letting Mel go out alone to die.'

Tears fell from his chin and splashed onto his jeans. He buried his face in his hands, his shoulders shaking. His glasses clattered onto the desk.

Hargrave shifted in his seat. 'I think it's time we took a break.'

I pressed the button to stop the recording. Juliet straightened the papers and flipped the folder closed, before rising to her feet and walking out of the room.

I paused in the doorway. Hargrave rested a hand on Leo's heaving back. If I was looking for a display of emotion to prove Leo was cut up about Melanie's death, then here it was.

Call connected at 11:27.

'Hello, Reverend Geoff Mandle speaking. How may I help you?'

'Hello. I'm Detective Sergeant Gabe Martin. I was wondering if you had a moment to answer some questions about a case?'

'Of course. Anything I can do to help.'

'Thank you. I believe you oversee the church hall next to St Peter's church?'

'Yes, I'm handling all the bookings at the moment. Our church administrator is on maternity leave and the parish couldn't find anyone to replace her.'

'Did you ever meet Melanie Pirt?'

'Oh, yes. I was sad to hear about that poor girl. She was so polite whenever I saw her.'

'And Leonard Dunlow?'

'He was quiet, but he called to make sure the hall was free and he paid the room charge.'

'What was your impression of the two of them together?'

'They were infatuated with each other. That much was clear. They booked the hall to sing but most of the time when I popped in, they were talking. I thought it was only a matter of time before they started dating.'

'You had no inkling Leonard might want to hurt Melanie in any way?'

'Oh, heavens no. He was always so sweet to her; held open doors and encouraged her when she wasn't sure about her voice. Gosh. You don't think he was involved with what happened to her? I have to say, I really don't think he would have hurt her.'

'Okay. Thank you for your time.'

'That's alright. God bless.'

Gabe

Juliet walked into our office and threw a signed piece of paper on my desk. 'We have permission from Angela to keep Leo overnight. Hopefully that will make him more talkative. We can question him again in the morning.'

I glanced at our superintendent's signature. 'You think he'll say anything different?'

Juliet shrugged as she sat down. 'At every opportunity that boy has lied to us. You really think he's not doing it again?'

I bit my lip, remembering Leo's undeniably real tears. 'His confession seemed genuine to me.'

'You may not think he did it, but at the moment he's our best bet.' Juliet stabbed at her keyboard, losing herself in emails.

I pressed my thumbs together. Juliet was frustrated with the case, not annoyed at me, but I wondered if this investigation would have been more successful without my bumbling attempts to lead. All I'd done was let one suspect get away and continually trust my gut in wrong directions.

Or maybe not. We wouldn't know until we had all the evidence.

'I can't shake the feeling something isn't right,' I said. 'There's stuff missing, like the gun and the murderer's clothes, but I feel like something else is out of joint.'

Juliet looked away from her screen. 'I know what you mean, but we have to work with what we've got.' She tipped her head and rolled it from side to side, working out a kink in her neck. 'And what we've got is someone who keeps lying to us, who was obsessed with the victim, who had motive and opportunity, and no real alibi.'

'Yeah.'

I might not like it, but we had to rely on the evidence we did have. It all pointed towards Leo.

Juliet shoved her cup across to my desk. 'Go make coffee. A walk will clear your head.'

'You're so considerate.' I grabbed both of our mugs and stood up.

'I'm a martyr.' Juliet flashed a grin at me before turning back to her computer screen.

I nodded at various people as I crossed the outer office. Our job was to find out who murdered Melanie Pirt and bring that person to justice. My feelings were irrelevant. Leo had the best reason and chance to kill her, so I had to consider him a real suspect. No matter how much my insides screamed otherwise.

'Detective Inspector Juliet Stern.'

'Hello, hi. This is Laura James. I work at Dunlow Consultants, at reception. We've spoken before.'

'I remember. What can I help you with?'

'I saw something strange at lunch time. I thought I should call.'

'What was it?'

'I want to check, is this call being recorded?'

'No.'

'Can it be confidential? Can my name be kept out of this?'

'It can be.'

'Sorry. I'm worried Mr Dunlow will get rid of me if he finds out I told you anything, and I can't afford to lose my job.'

'I understand. We'll call this an anonymous tip. What did you see, Laura?'

'I was eating lunch in my car. I, um, don't eat in the staff room. There's a lot of people in there and I like a bit of time to myself. I was trying to find my phone in my bag when Mr Dunlow pulled in. He'd been out with a client in the morning. He parked up and went over to the industrial bins we share with the other businesses in the building, and he threw something in.'

'What was it?'

'I'm not sure. I waited until Mr Dunlow was gone and had a look, but the bins are big and I couldn't see much. It could be a scarf. It's right at the bottom of the bin though, and I would have had to climb in to see what it was.'

'Do you know if it's still there?'

'It should be. Mr Dunlow hasn't left the building since, and the rubbish was collected yesterday.'

'Did Mr Dunlow see you?'

'I don't think so. I hope not. He didn't look over, and I don't think he knows I eat lunch out there.'

'Okay. Thank you. We're going to come over and take a look in the bins. After, we'll come in to speak to Mr Dunlow, but I'll treat you like a stranger.'

'Thank you.'

'Thank you for calling this in, Laura. You made the right decision.'

From: Madison Campbell
madison.campbell@mitadmin.gov.uk
To: Juliet Stern **juliet.stern@mit.gov.uk,** Gabriella Martin **gabri-ella.martin@mit.gov.uk**
Date: **16 October, 12:56**
Subject: **Operation Chalice – Van**

Juliet and Gabe,

Just wanted to update you on CCTV for the van and the info I've gathered so far. The headline – I've had no joy.

I tracked the van before and after it hit Leonard Dunlow. It only shows up on cameras three minutes before and five minutes after, and at no point did the driver remove their balaclava. There is also no clear footage of the hit and run itself, so there's no way to tell if it was intentional or accidental.

I've tracked the number plate to Southampton Car Hire. Unfortunately, there seems to have been a mistake when it was hired. A temp was working that day and didn't take a copy of ID or fill in paperwork. They took the payment in cash. The car was returned on time, but there's a drop-off point with no staff involved and no CCTV.

Sorry I couldn't solve this one for you,

Maddy

Gabe

I crouched between bin bags, examining a dark blue scarf patterned with grey birds. It was wrapped around something.

'Take a picture before you touch it,' Juliet advised from outside the industrial bin.

I snapped photos from all angles. 'Happy?'

'Ridiculously so.' Juliet's mouth twitched. We'd had a short yet intense argument on the way here over who should retrieve whatever Dunlow had thrown away. The spare pair of trainers in the boot of my car swung it in Juliet's favour. 'The birds are swallows, by the way.'

'Fascinating.'

It didn't take long to unravel the scarf. It had been torn in half, the soft fabric interrupted by a ragged tear.

'Leather gloves.' I looked up at Juliet, her head visible over the lip of the bin. 'Do you think this scarf belonged to Melanie? Were these the gloves Dunlow was wearing when he killed her?'

Juliet passed me two evidence bags. 'We can't jump to conclusions. Dunlow was seen throwing these away, he wasn't seen shooting anyone.'

I placed the scarf and gloves into the bags while vibrating with restless energy. 'I'm not jumping to conclusions. Why would Dunlow get rid of these if they weren't incriminating?'

I passed her the evidence bags and vaulted out of the bin, then I pulled off my sullied gloves and slotted them into another bag. Juliet followed at a more leisurely pace while I jogged over to my car. She labelled the evidence bags, laying them flat on the roof of the car, while I changed into a clean pair of boots.

'What are you thinking?' she asked.

'That this could be what we need.' I slammed the boot shut on my trainers and the new evidence. 'Dunlow threw away a scarf that most likely belonged to Melanie. That has to mean something.'

Juliet drummed her fingers on the roof of the car. 'You think he could be the killer?'

'I don't know.' I sniffed my jumper, checking I didn't smell of bin. 'He's been a suspect all along, but there's never been a good reason to shine a spotlight on him. Now he's made a big mistake, and there has to be something in him going apeshit at Leo for having a girl over. Maybe he never went back to the house. Maybe he walked straight out and killed Melanie.'

More than any of the other theories we'd entertained, this felt right. We didn't have all the puzzle pieces yet, but a picture was forming. The rich estate owner, fiercely protective of his sons, wouldn't let anything damage their futures. What lengths would Dunlow go to, to protect his family from something he perceived as a threat?

Juliet wasn't moving. I wanted to race into Dunlow's office and throw a pair of cuffs on him, but I stayed put and clenched my fists.

'What are you thinking?' I asked.

'What does Dunlow care about the most? Family.' Juliet answered her own question. 'His son is arrested and suddenly he appears with new evidence. He disposes of it in a place he would be seen, when he had a whole forest where he could have gotten rid of it. Karl told us that if someone wanted to lose something in those trees, it would be all too easy.'

'You think Dunlow is incriminating himself to save Leo?' I asked. 'Does he care about his sons that much?'

Juliet shrugged but started walking towards the front of the building. 'You think it's a coincidence he dumped this when his receptionist was out here?'

'You said she didn't think he knew she was watching.'

Juliet sneered. 'Someone as controlling as Dunlow, you think he doesn't know how his staff spend their breaks? Look at how small this space is. How could he not have seen her?'

The car park wasn't huge, but that didn't mean this was as curated as Juliet claimed. 'He could have gotten scared. Maybe he was so wrapped up in getting rid of it, he didn't think.'

Juliet shook her head. 'Dunlow may be many things, but thought-less isn't one of them.'

She stopped outside Dunlow Consultants. The windows were polished to a high shine. Inside, flourishing plants broke up the waiting area. A receptionist sat behind a silver desk, her head lowered.

'This is potentially an exciting new lead,' Juliet said, one hand on the door. 'But we need to be careful. There are a lot of variables here and if Dunlow is the killer, he's not going to be easily pinned down.'

'I'll be careful,' I assured her. I might be convinced Dunlow had made his first mistake, but I wasn't going to arrest him immediately. No matter how good that would feel.

Juliet pushed open the door and walked over to the desk.

'Hello. I'm Detective Inspector Juliet Stern and this is Detective Sergeant Gabe Martin.' There was no one else in the room, but she carried out the charade that we'd had no prior contact with Laura. 'We need to ask Timothy Dunlow a few questions. Can we go through?'

Laura bent over her computer, her straight black hair half-obscuring her ruddy cheeks. She picked up a phone and pressed the red button at the top.

'Mr Dunlow, two detectives are here for—' She placed the phone on its holder. 'He'll be right down. Please take a seat.'

Juliet and I stepped away from the reception desk but didn't sit on one of the grey sofas. I didn't think Juliet was as keyed up as me, but neither of us would feel comfortable sitting still.

Dunlow strode out from a corridor behind the reception desk, a blue square peeking from the pocket of his tailored jacket. He completely disregarded Laura, glaring instead at Juliet and me.

'Are you releasing my son?'

'We have a few questions for you, Mr Dunlow,' I said. The door opened behind us and a man in jeans that probably cost more than my entire outfit walked over to the reception desk. 'Maybe it would be better if we stepped into your office.'

Dunlow led us along a short corridor and up a flight of stairs. His office looked out over the street, the view segmented by wooden blinds. Dunlow settled behind his wide desk. The spacious room had minimal furnishings, but they all screamed expense. Dunlow had never set foot in an Argos or IKEA, couldn't sympathise with the tricky decision between a comfier sofa but no dining table or the cheaper sofa and a separate space to eat meals. I'd gotten used to eating in front of the TV.

Juliet and I sat in chairs opposite his desk, the rigid backs designed to provide the utmost support.

'Is Leo being released?' Dunlow repeated, his habitual frown in place.

'That isn't what we're here about.' I moved on before he could ask again. Dunlow wasn't accustomed to being denied answers. I hoped he thought the same of us. 'This afternoon you were seen throwing something into one of the industrial bins at the back of this office. We searched them and found a pair of leather gloves wrapped in a scarf.'

Dunlow's face was blank. No flicker of guilt. Nothing.

'Did you attempt to dispose of evidence, Timothy?' Juliet asked.

He threaded his fingers together. 'I don't think I have to answer that question.'

'If you refuse to answer our questions, we will have to arrest you,' I said, keeping my voice even.

Dunlow tipped his head slightly, the lazy look in his eyes whispering he was untouchable. 'On what grounds?'

'For failing to give evidence in a criminal investigation,' Juliet jumped in. 'You told us you didn't know about Melanie Pirt and that you didn't go outside the night she was murdered.'

'We're wondering what else you might have lied about,' I said. 'If you fail to cooperate, we'll have to take you into the station.'

'But not for murder, no?' Dunlow didn't take his eyes off of me, calculation in his gaze. I didn't know what he was gambling on.

I looked at Juliet. Her frown mirrored his.

'What are you saying?' she asked. 'Do you want us to arrest you for murder?'

A smirk ghosted over Dunlow's lips, there and gone in heartbeat. 'Not at all. There's not nearly enough evidence for that, is there? And I imagine you've not got enough to hold my son for much longer. Especially with this new development.'

The nervous energy that had been coursing through me ever since Juliet got the call from Laura flipped my stomach. I might be wrong, Dunlow might just be a smug bastard who was trying to distract us and clear his son's name, but I believed he'd killed Melanie Pirt. He thought himself above the law, thought he could taunt us and not get caught.

I stood up. 'Timothy Dunlow, you are under arrest for the murder of Melanie Pirt. You do not have to say anything. But it may harm your defence if you do not mention when questioned something which you later rely on in court. Anything you do say may be given in evidence.'

Juliet rose and pulled a pair of cuffs from her pocket. 'Will these be necessary?'

For the first time, Dunlow looked ruffled. 'Christ, no.'

As he stood and rounded the desk, Juliet shot me a look. Her eyebrows sat high on her forehead. I didn't know if she was noting Dunlow's discomfort at being cuffed over being accused of murder, or silently passing judgement on what I'd done. Clearly, she'd thought arresting him was a possibility, otherwise she wouldn't have brought her cuffs. She would probably have waited for DNA results from the gloves and scarf before she made a move. But I didn't need the results. Dunlow was guilty of something, and I suspected it was everything.

Juliet led the way down the stairs and through the reception. As I walked through the front door, I heard a soft word.

'Hey?' Laura peered from behind the front desk, her chin length black hair framing her round face.

I held the door open. 'We're taking Mr Dunlow in for questioning.' I didn't have time to deal with curious co-workers. 'I'll be off.'

'He's been arrested?' Laura blinked striking blue eyes.

'I'm afraid so.' I dispelled thoughts about the softness of her skin. 'Unless you have anything to tell me, then I need to get going.'

She shook her head. 'I don't know anything about any of this.'

'Bye then.'

I'd have to question Ollie about finding other people attractive. Surely it was fine so long as I didn't act on it. He probably didn't expect basic relationship etiquette to be one of the bridges we'd cross together.

Juliet and Dunlow were waiting in the car. I stole glances at him in my rear-view mirror as I reversed out of the space. His expression remained the same. He believed he was untouchable.

Something hardened within me. We were going to get justice for Melanie. That was always something I wanted, but it was especially true in this twisted case. So many suspects, so many lies, and it all led to this. I was right about Dunlow, I could feel it.

But I couldn't ignore the twisting in my stomach, borne of Juliet's words before we'd stepped into the office building. Despite the arrest and accusations, I couldn't shake the feeling that Dunlow had gotten exactly what he wanted.

From: Juliet Stern **juliet.stern@mit.gov.uk**
To: David Rees **david.rees@forensics.gov.uk**
CC: Gabriella Martin **gabriella.martin@mit.gov.uk**
Date: **16 October, 14:19**
Subject: **Operation Chalice: URGENT – Results needed ASAP**

David,

I've just submitted a pair of gloves and a scarf for DNA testing. Please can you put these at the top of your priority list. We have two suspects in custody that these items relate to, and the result could be essential for bringing them to justice.

Juliet

Gabe

'I thought you would be more interested in the father,' Gerard Hargrave said, as we walked towards the interview room.

Leo stopped short. 'You've got Dad here?'

'Yes.' I glared at the solicitor. It was a conflict of interest for him to represent both father and son, but he'd found a way to make trouble. 'That's not important right now. We have a few more questions for you about the night Melanie was killed.'

'Not important?' Leo echoed, allowing himself to be shepherded into the interview room. He sat down heavily. 'How can that be true? I told you, Dad didn't have anything to do with what happened.'

I stared at Hargrave, trying to convey with the merest twitch of facial muscles that he was a twat who had made our job a whole lot harder. He settled in his chair, unconcerned.

My finger hovered over the button to begin recording. 'We need you to focus and answer our questions as carefully as possible. Can you do that for us, Leo?'

He bit his lip. 'I'll try.'

'Thank you.' I pressed the button.

'Second interview with Leonard Dunlow.' Juliet rattled off the information, her voice a gentle monotone.

My mind drifted to Dunlow. Such unaffected calm. Nothing like his son, who wore his lies plainly for everyone to see. We hoped that asking Leo about the gloves and scarf might give us something concrete to throw at his father before the DNA results came back. It wasn't likely Dunlow would crack under questioning, so we needed to smash him open.

'We have a couple more questions for you, Leo,' Juliet said.

I opened my notepad. 'After your father came to the den and spoke to you on the night Melanie was killed, you said you watched him walk in the direction of the house. Is that correct?'

Leo nodded. 'Yeah. I didn't stay awake long enough to see him go inside, but that was definitely the way he was headed.'

Hargrave didn't move, but disapproval radiated from him in waves. Dunlow was making his wishes known by proxy. But what did Hargrave expect Leo to say? He'd already confessed he hadn't seen his father go into the house, and it wasn't like we would let him change his mind now.

'Can you remember if your dad was wearing gloves that night?' I asked.

Leo's forehead creased with vertical lines. 'I don't know.'

'What do you remember him wearing?' Juliet nudged.

'It was a cold night, so he was in a coat.' Leo closed his eyes, the skin around them bruised from his encounter with Jordan. After a moment, he reopened them. 'I'm sorry. He was shouting and all I was thinking about was Mel and how tired I felt. I don't remember.'

'It's okay, Leo,' I reassured him, hoping my lies were not as obvious as his. 'The other thing we wanted to check was whether Melanie was wearing a scarf when she came to see you that evening.'

'Yeah, she was.' His face twisted into a sad smile. 'I'd given it to her a couple of weeks beforehand.'

'Can you describe it?' Juliet asked.

'I picked it really carefully.' Leo's voice thickened. 'It was navy, looked amazing on her. It had swooping grey swallows on it.'

A perfect description of the piece of scarf we'd found in the bins. I made a note, my handwriting messy with excitement. Whatever the DNA results said about those gloves, Dunlow having access to Melanie's scarf had to be incriminating.

'Do you remember if Melanie was wearing the scarf when she left?' Juliet sat forward, her eyes not leaving Leo for a second.

'I think so.' He wrinkled his nose. 'It's all a bit of a mess in my head, I've thought about it too many times. I wasn't paying much attention to what she wore as she left. She got dressed quickly and I was upset. I guess she could have left it, but I would have noticed it afterwards.'

'Could your dad have taken it?' I asked.

Leo looked between the two of us. 'Is this important? Have you found something?'

'It would help if you'd tell us whether your dad took the scarf,' Juliet said.

'Like I said, everything from that night is a muddle.' Leo grimaced. 'I guess he could have. He was shouting for a long time and I wasn't always looking at him. But I think I would have noticed him holding it.'

Not if he'd hidden it. I knew how useful a deep coat pocket was.

'Okay, Leo. That's all we need,' Juliet said.

I reached for the button to stop the recording, but Leo spoke before I pressed it.

'Do you think Dad did it? Is that what this is about?'

Juliet tapped one manicured fingernail on the table. 'We have some questions for your father, but at the moment we are no closer to discovering who killed Melanie.'

I hoped Juliet was saying that to reassure Leo, although that wasn't her style. The scarf and gloves had to mean we were closer to finding Melanie's killer.

'Dad wouldn't have done it,' Leo said. 'He's not always nice and he didn't like that I was with Mel, but he wouldn't have killed her. I told him I loved her.'

Leo's gaze was beseeching. He offered his words in the innocent belief they would clear his father's name.

Family was the most important thing to Timothy Dunlow. What would he have done to disentangle one of his sons from a relationship he considered unsuitable?

'Hello?'

'Hello, is that Terence?'

'Yes. Who's this?'

'It's Detective Sergeant Gabe Martin. I have a few questions for you.'

'Have you still got Leo?'

'Yes.'

'You know he would never have killed that girl, right? He can't even bear to come hunting with me and Dad. Even if he could, he's got such bad eyesight. He's a terrible shot.'

'I wanted to ask some questions about your father.'

'Dad? What about him?'

'Since we left with Leo this morning, what do you know about his movements?'

'His movements? Why do you want to know that?'

'It's important we know what your father did after we left with Leo this morning.'

'Fine. There isn't much to tell. He shouted in the hotel room for a while, then left for work.'

'Is that where he said he was going?'

'I don't remember. He might not have, but I assumed.'

'Did he say anything in particular after we left with Leo?'

'I don't remember the details. He was cross. His son had been wrongfully arrested. He was entitled to feel upset.'

'Thank you, Terence.'

'Can I say? Dad didn't tell me exactly where he was going this morning, but that doesn't mean anything. Of course work was where he would go. He didn't kill that girl.'

'You're very sure of who didn't kill Melanie, Terence. Any idea of who did?'

'It's not my job to figure that out, is it? It's yours. But I know my family and Dad wouldn't have done this. Neither would Leo.'

'You of all people should know the secrets family members keep from one another.'

'That's an entirely different matter.'

'Are you so sure who didn't kill Melanie because you did? Or at least orchestrated it? We haven't heard from Mr Hogan. Your alibi is weak.'

'It's not weak, because it's true. I don't know where the hell Benny is but as soon as he's able to, he'll confirm everything I've said to you. I'm sure my brother and father didn't kill Melanie because I know them. I might not know every bloody thing about them, just like they don't about me, but I know who they are. Leo and my dad are not murderers.'

From: Juliet Stern **juliet.stern@mit.gov.uk**
To: Laura Peters **peters@dunlowconsultants.co.uk**
Date: **16 October, 15:28**
Subject: **Dunlow's movements this morning**

Laura,

Please could you tell me Mr Dunlow's movements from the time he arrived at your office this morning, to the time he was escorted from the premises?

Thank you,

Detective Inspector Juliet Stern

Teddy. Sent 16:21.

Ben, I don't know where the hell you are or what you think you're playing at, but you need to call the police back. Keep ignoring me all you like, but stop being such a petty bastard. I'm a fucking suspect for murder without your word to back up mine.

Gabe

'Interview commencing at 4:40 p.m. on 16th October.' I looked up from the red light. 'Interviewee is Timothy Dunlow and his solicitor, Samuel Hull, is also in attendance. They have been given time to consult prior to this interview. The interview is being conducted by myself, Detective Sergeant Gabriella Martin, and Detective Inspector Juliet Stern. This interview is regarding the murder of Melanie Pirt on 9th October.'

I let the silence stretch as I found a clean page in my notepad, aware of Dunlow following my every movement. Juliet crossed her arms over her chest. We had no real strategy except throwing everything at him and seeing if something stuck. He wasn't the kind of man who could be intimidated or tricked.

'Mr Dunlow, can you please tell us your movements on the night Melanie Pirt was shot on your estate?' I began.

'I believe you already have a statement from my client,' Hull said. He was freakishly similar to Leo's solicitor. The same expensive glasses perched on his nose below the same receding hairline. Dunlow no doubt had a legion of these men, ready to jump to his aid at the merest click of his fingers.

'We do.' I extracted it from a thin folder of notes. 'We have a few points to clarify, and we thought it best to go back to the start together.'

Dunlow tore his heavy gaze from me for long enough to nod at his solicitor.

'On the night Melanie Pirt was murdered, I came home from work and cooked a meal for my son, Leo,' Dunlow recited in a bored drawl. 'We ate together at about seven p.m., then we went our separate ways.' He sat forward, draping his forearms across the table. 'That was my original statement, yes?'

'Yes.' I resisted the urge to sit back in my chair to increase the distance between us.

'It needs amendment.' Dunlow clasped his hands together. 'Leo has since told you what he got up to that evening. After our meal, I didn't go to bed. I sat working in my study. Before retiring, I looked out to the den over the garage, where Leo had gone after dinner, and I saw he was not alone. There was a girl with him, despite my no tolerance policy for female visitors on the estate.'

'What is the reason for this policy?' Juliet asked.

Dunlow glared at her. 'My son is studying for his A Levels. He doesn't need any distractions.'

'You saw Leo wasn't alone,' I said. 'Then what did you do?'

'I went over to the garage.' Dunlow turned to me. 'By the time I got there, the girl had left. I admit, I was harsh with Leo. I told him on no uncertain terms he was never to do anything like that again.'

'Can I backtrack for one moment?' I pressed my pencil into my pad. 'What were you wearing when you went over to the garage?'

'What was I wearing?' Each word dripped with disdain.

'It was a cold night,' Juliet said. 'Had you already changed into your pyjamas and dressing gown? Did you grab a coat?'

'I had not yet changed for bed,' growled Dunlow, as though personally offended Juliet dared refer to the clothes he slept in. 'I put on a coat, but I wasn't too concerned with the cold at the time.'

'No scarf? Gloves?' Juliet pushed.

'No scarf or gloves.'

'You didn't meet Melanie when you went over to the garage?' I returned to where I'd interrupted Dunlow's account.

'As I said, she had already left.'

'You didn't see her any closer than from the manor, through the window in the den?'

'That's correct.' Dunlow's eyes were like flint.

I flicked through my notepad. 'Leo said you arrived seconds after Melanie left, but you didn't see her?'

'It was dark.' The lines around Dunlow's mouth tightened. 'I also find it highly likely Leo is mistaken. He was tired and confused that night. I would have passed the girl on the steps up to the den, had we exited and entered in such quick succession. Leo must have misremembered.'

'So you definitely didn't see Melanie as she left the room?' I turned to the current page of my notepad. 'You had no idea who Leo had in the den?'

'None at all.'

'Yet you knew it was a girl?' I dipped my head to the side. 'Even though you saw her from such a distance?'

Dunlow clenched his jaw before answering. 'When I looked out of the window in the manor, I believed it was a girl, but I couldn't be sure. I knew Leo was not alone, and whether it was a friend or a girl, he should have been sleeping. Once I spoke to Leo, my suspicions were confirmed.'

That was an easy trap to wriggle out of. Hopefully Dunlow would struggle to extract himself from others.

'What did you say to Leo when you got up to the den?' Juliet asked.

'I reminded Leo that while he was living under my roof and going to a school I paid for, I expected him to conduct himself in a way that displayed his appreciation. I would not allow him to throw it all away.'

'How did Leo respond?' I asked.

'He was quiet, half-asleep even as we spoke. He spouted nonsense about loving the girl, but I told him that couldn't be true and that he wasn't to see her again.'

'Why couldn't he have loved Melanie?' Juliet asked.

Dunlow sneered. 'Who knows what real love is at eighteen?'

'How old were you when you met your wife?' I asked.

Dunlow gave me his deepest glare yet. 'We met when we were nineteen.'

'Is this relevant?' Hull jumped in.

'We need to get a whole picture of the family situation,' Juliet said. 'I understand Mrs Dunlow passed away several years ago. I'm sorry to hear that, but could you tell us the circumstances of her death?'

A vein in Dunlow's neck pulsed. 'My wife died four years, three months and six days ago. She had been ill for some time, cancer had spread throughout her body. Despite receiving the best possible care, it was too late.'

Dunlow was not a sympathetic figure, but hearing anyone talk about a significant loss was difficult. I reminded myself that the same man who remembered exactly when he'd lost his wife had likely shot a young woman three times and let a dog maul her.

'What was your wife like?' Juliet prodded.

'She was the single most brilliant person I have ever met.'

'And since your wife died, you've raised Leo and Terence alone?' Juliet asked.

'Yes.'

'Would you say the boys are your main priority?' she asked.

'Of course.'

'Children don't always know what's in their best interests.'

'Do you have a question?' Hull asked.

Juliet shook her head, her hair falling across her shoulders. 'No question. Just something to think about.'

'When you left the den, did you take anything with you?' I asked, steering away from antagonising Dunlow too much.

His eyes narrowed. 'Like a scarf?'

'Exactly.' I stared him down.

He looked away, but it wasn't the action of someone who couldn't bear to look me in the eye any longer. Dunlow simply didn't find the game worth playing.

'I didn't take anything from the den.'

'What did you do after you'd spoken with Leo?'

'I went back to the manor,' Dunlow spoke to the wall above my head. 'And I went to bed.'

'You didn't follow Melanie down into the grounds?' Juliet asked.

'No, I did not.'

Dunlow had no tells, was annoyed by everything. He'd had too long to figure this out and was far too practised at concealment. It would be a staple in a career built on establishing trust with companies before crushing them.

'You didn't hear anything during the night?' I asked.

'I slept right through. I didn't know anything had happened until Karl called me.'

'You weren't worried about a young woman wandering around your estate at night?' Juliet asked.

'No.' The word was final. 'She'd found her way in; she could find her own way out.'

'And you weren't concerned Leo would follow her?' I asked.

Dunlow's eyes narrowed. 'I'd told him not to.'

'Teenage sons are notoriously obedient,' Juliet said. 'Case in point; I believe you told him not to tell us anything and yet we now know everything Leo did that night.'

'Why did you tell your son to lie during a murder investigation?' I asked.

'I thought hearing about his silly little tryst would distract you,' Dunlow said. 'I thought you would catch the killer swiftly and my son would be unaffected by the investigation. We could then reveal he'd been seeing the girl, once he was beyond suspicion.'

Dunlow had told his son to lie to us for our own good. Right.

'A dog was involved in the attack.' I pulled two photos out of the file. The first showed Melanie's face, torn and bruised. Dunlow barely looked at it. The second was of the dog. His eyes lingered on the discoloured fur.

'Karl said Lucy was your dog,' I said.

'They're all my dogs.'

'He told us Lucy was your favourite,' I clarified.

Dunlow sniffed. 'She wasn't. They're all bred for hunting. I only use them for that.'

Artie's unstoppable enthusiasm flashed into my mind. He didn't seem particularly well suited to the life Dunlow had chosen for him.

'Why would Karl have thought Lucy was your favourite?' Juliet asked.

'I don't know,' Dunlow said. 'You'll have to ask him. Ah, but you can't, because he's run off.'

Triumph shone in his eyes. I plucked another couple of photos from the file. They showed the scarf and uncovered gloves in the bottom of the bin.

'Tell us about these,' I said.

'I found them this morning.' Dunlow slipped into a monotone, the only sign these words were rehearsed. 'Now Karl is gone, the boys and I are taking care of the dogs until I can find homes for them. I went over to the estate after meeting with a client this morning. I was taking a few of the dogs on a walk when I spotted the scarf and gloves in a tree. I pulled them out and realised what they were.' His eyes roved between us. 'I panicked, so I got rid of them.'

I'm not sure I'd ever heard a confession of heightened emotion performed with such detachment.

'You don't seem like a panic-prone man,' Juliet said.

Dunlow spread his hands. 'We're all capable, given the right application of pressure.'

'Why did you panic?' I asked.

'I thought the scarf probably belonged to the girl. Together with the gloves, which are an old pair of mine I'd lost long ago, that added up to something unfortunate.'

'So we'll find your DNA on the scarf and inside the gloves?' Juliet asked.

'Most likely you will,' Dunlow said.

Juliet pressed her lips together. 'We think it's probable these gloves were worn by the killer when they shot Melanie. Does it not concern you that your DNA could be all over them?'

Dunlow's frown was immovable. 'Those gloves were lost a long time ago. I don't know how they came to be in the forest, wrapped in that scarf.'

'Did you not think, since you're confident Leo didn't kill Melanie, that rather than throwing the gloves away, this was your chance to clear his name?' I asked.

'Like I said, I panicked.' Dunlow visibly calmed himself, taking a deep breath before continuing. 'There are several possibilities. The scarf could be nothing to do with that girl. Walkers often trespass on my land, one of them could have lost it. Similarly, I believe those are my old gloves, but they could be nothing to do with me. I didn't get a good look at them. This could all be a lot of fuss about nothing. If this was true, then handing in the scarf and gloves would have had no impact. Leo would still be your prime suspect.

'Or, the killer could have worn my gloves while shooting a young woman. I love my son, but I wasn't about to hand in something that incriminated me.'

I noted these different options. It sounded so plausible, that the gloves were either lost or used by someone else. But something inside of me chanted, *wrong wrong wrong*.

'Why did you dispose of the gloves and scarf in the bins at work?' I asked. 'Why not go somewhere random, or leave them in the forest?'

'I wasn't thinking clearly,' Dunlow said. 'I wanted to get rid of them and that seemed like the best place.'

'You didn't realise you were being watched?' Juliet asked.

'Obviously not.'

I tapped my pencil. Enough of this. Dunlow was going to deny and postulate until we had something undeniable to pin on him.

'This is your story,' I said. 'You had nothing to do with the death of Melanie Pirt. You didn't even know it was her in the den with Leo. You went straight back to the house after shouting at your son and went to bed. You slept all night and woke up to the news of the shooting. You found the scarf and gloves by chance and panicked. By sheer bad luck, you were seen dumping them. You're telling us you're an innocent man, caught up in some unfortunate circumstances?'

'That's right.' Dunlow's eyes bored into mine.

'I think you're lying,' I said.

'Do you have any proof?' Hull asked. I got the sense he would have liked to have added *young lady* to the end of his question.

'No, please,' Dunlow said, his mouth playing around a self-satisfied smile. 'I'd love to hear what the detective thinks.'

Juliet crossed one leg over the other, but I couldn't tell what the movement meant. Dunlow was lying, he was trying to get away with murder, and I was going to take this chance to let him know we were onto him.

'I think you knew Leo had a girl up in the den; either you'd suspected he'd been seeing someone for a while or you spotted Melanie through the window. I think you saw her leave, and you saw her cheap coat and her brown skin and couldn't bear to have your son associated with someone you wouldn't have picked for him. I think you worked yourself into a rage with Leo, then followed Melanie into the woods with your dog and your gun. I think you shot her so she wouldn't mess up your perfect life.'

Dunlow's eyes were alight with interest.

'You let this all play out, safe in a big pool of suspects,' I went on. 'You felt sure this couldn't be pinned on you, since you'd hidden away all the incriminating evidence, but then we arrested Leo. You couldn't have that. You waited until you knew you'd be watched and dumped the scarf and gloves, which I think you know won't point to your son at all.'

'Do you have any proof of any of this?' Hull asked, more nettled than his client.

'No, they don't.' Dunlow looked away from me for the first time in minutes, including Juliet in his dismissal. 'Because if they did, they would already have thrown it at me.'

'If your DNA's on those gloves, you're going to find it hard to talk your way out of that,' I said.

'I've already told you, those used to be my gloves. My DNA will most likely be on them.' He settled his weight in his chair. 'Now, shall I tell you what I think?'

'Please, enlighten us,' Juliet said, her voice cool. I wanted to emulate her, but fury bubbled through me. I could see the truth, but I didn't know if there was any way we would be able to gather enough evidence to pin this man down.

Dunlow knew something about those gloves. He must, otherwise he wouldn't have made sure we'd found them.

'The truth is, and don't dally or I'll make a complaint, that soon you'll have to release me and my son,' Dunlow said. 'You don't have enough evidence to charge either of us. Take Leo or I to court on the strength of what you think happened, and it will be thrown out within minutes. And I'm sure the investigation I'd insist upon afterwards would cause many problems for your department.'

He folded his arms. 'I didn't kill that girl, but even if I had, there are too many variables at play. Too many people can't account for their movements that night, and you have far too little concrete evidence to help you place blame.

'Maybe it was Leo.' Dunlow's frown grew deeper at the idea of even theoretically blaming his son, but he barrelled on. 'Maybe he was so enraged at that girl for running off that he killed her. Not likely though, given he was dead on his feet and is a poor shot. More likely it was Karl. He hasn't helped his case by running off. He has a tragic past, but isn't that the way with all killers?

'And what about that little shit who tried to burn down my house and beat my son? You're telling me someone with a proven record of violent actions isn't more of a suspect than me or Leo? That thug was driven half-mad by jealousy, so he got a gun like the ones I own and took one of the dogs. It's often the partner, I've heard, in cases like these.' Dunlow tugged at the cuffs of his jacket. 'Anyway, you have no idea who killed that poor girl. This investigation has been a mess from start to finish. You've even been questioning Terence, and he wasn't at home when it happened.'

I stayed still so I wouldn't betray the emotions roiling inside of me. This man truly believed himself above the law. He sat on record and accused others, discredited our investigation, and tried to parcel blame onto anyone but himself. We didn't have proof, not yet, but nothing Dunlow said would convince me he hadn't killed Melanie Pirt.

Dunlow chuckled. I flinched, rocking back from the table. The sound was utterly unexpected, like hearing an animal speak.

Juliet leant forward. 'What's so funny?'

'But maybe it was me,' Dunlow said, ignoring her and staring straight at me. 'Maybe I did everything you said. I guess we'll never know, will we?'

REPORT ON THE FIRE AT THE DUNLOW ESTATE

At 04:35 hrs on Sunday 15 October the Hampshire and Isle of Wight Fire and Rescue Service responded to and extinguished a structural fire at Dunlow Manor in the New Forest. Local police units were also in attendance.

The senior fire officer was informed by the senior police officer present that arson was considered a possibility. A request was made for a full Forensic Fire Service examination.

We evaluated the scene on the ground floor from exterior to interior, then from least damaged to most damaged areas. We worked first to establish the area of origin, then worked to determine with a reasonable degree of professional certainty the cause of the fire.

The heaviest fire activity was observed around the open fireplace in the living room, which was the most damaged area. A carpet adjacent to the fireplace provided combustible material needed to accelerate the fire. Burn marks on the wooden wall fittings indicated the fire took hold swiftly and reached high temperatures.

The fire then tracked to adjacent rooms on the ground floor. The majority of significant damage was caused to walls and ceilings above waist height, with several windows also broken by the sudden heat.

Cigarette butts were retrieved from the scene but there is no evidence they were dropped while lit or that they caused the fire. There were no cigarette butts found inside the property.

Due to the speed and nature of the fire much damage was caused, which will result in a need for a near total refurbishment. It was noted that one of the reasons for the speed and ferocity of the fire was the availability of combustible materials and non-fireproofed furniture. I recommend the owners receive Fire Prevention Advice when considering repair and refurbishment of the building.

This fire was determined to be accidental in nature and is now administratively closed.

REPORT COMPILED BY: Forensic Fire Brigade Officer Matt Lam.

Call connected at 17:52.

'Hello?'

'Hello, is that Jordan Haines?'

'Yeah, who's this?'

'It's Detective Inspector Juliet Stern.'

'Oh. What do you want?'

'I have an update on the investigation into the fire on the Dunlow Estate.'

'Do you need me to come in?'

'No, that isn't why I'm calling. I wanted to let you know you had nothing to do with the fire. It spread from the fireplace.'

'I didn't start it?'

'No, Jordan.'

'Shit. Sorry for swearing. I was just so freaked out.'

'I understand.'

'Thanks for letting me know.'

'You're in the clear for this, but you need to stay away from the Dunlows from now on.'

'Sure. I will.'

'I wanted to give you some advice as well.'

'What's that?'

'Stop following in your father's footsteps.'

'What are you talking about?'

'Don't play dumb, Jordan. I've seen your mum. I know what happens in your house.'

'You don't know anything.'

'I know far more than I wish to. And I know you don't want to be like your father. If I'm right, you should get help, Jordan. You might tell yourself it's over now, that you won't hurt another woman the way you hurt Melanie, but you're lying to yourself. Unless you work through your issues, you will continue hurting the people you love.'

'I didn't mean to hurt Mel.'

'I believe you. But the fact is, you did hurt her. A lot. And it's up to you to make sure that doesn't happen again.'

'I'll try, I promise.'

'There's a group that meets at the Methodist Hall on St James Road every Wednesday at seven p.m. They won't pry, but they could help both you and your mum.'

'I'll take her there.'

'Good.'

'Have you found Mel's killer yet?'

'That's a complicated question. We're following some strong lines of enquiry.'

'I hope you get them.'

'Me too. Look after yourself, Jordan.'

From: David Rees **david.rees@forensics.gov.uk**
To: Juliet Stern **juliet.stern@mit.gov.uk**
Date: **16 October, 18:19**
Subject: **Operation Chalice: URGENT – Results needed ASAP**

Stern,

I tend to make tests for murder enquiries a priority, but thank you for the reminder.

There were no prints on the gloves and it looks like they've been cleaned, but we did find traces of gunshot residue, along with some white powder. We've sent them both for testing.

We also found several traces of DNA on both the scarf and gloves.

The results should be ready tomorrow morning.

Rees.

Gabe

'Do you feel better?' Juliet looked up from the paperwork spread across her desk as I walked into our office.

'No.' I slumped into my chair and rested my face in my hands. 'There has to be something.'

I'd repeated this refrain since we'd walked out of the interview room. Juliet sent me on a walk around the block after I'd insisted we talk through all the evidence a fourth time.

There was nothing. Dunlow sat in his cell, smug and untouchable. He'd basically told us he'd murdered Melanie and we had no way of bringing him to justice. Jordan being cleared of any involvement in the fire at the estate was a small boon, but it hadn't removed him as a suspect in Melanie's murder. I needed everyone else gone if I wasn't going to take a blind shot at Dunlow.

'The DNA results will be in tomorrow morning.' Juliet's nails clacked on her keyboard. 'There's nothing we can do until we get those so I suggest we go home, get as much sleep as we can, and come back here bright and early tomorrow morning.'

I looked up, shame blistering through my chest. 'You can say it, you know.'

Juliet clicked her mouse, her eyes on her computer screen. 'Say what?'

'That I acted rashly.' I bunched my hands into fists. 'I messed up the case by bringing Dunlow in too soon.'

Juliet looked over our desks at me. 'I would have if you hadn't.'

Her words allowed a tiny lightening of the misery that had been dragging me down since Dunlow mocked us so brazenly. 'Really?'

'He's an arrogant shit.' Juliet clicked her mouse then stood up. 'He deserved to have a bit of dirt thrown at him.'

Juliet wouldn't lie to make me feel better. I grabbed my coat and followed her out of the office. The main work area was quiet, but Paul's office was lit, his head bowed over a stack of paper.

I felt better, knowing I hadn't brought Dunlow in too quickly, but I couldn't shake the restlessness. Juliet fiddled with her phone, completely unaffected.

'Doesn't it bother you?' I asked, as we walked into the lift. 'We know Dunlow did it, he knows we know, and there's nothing we can do it about it. Doesn't it make you mad?'

Juliet lowered her phone. 'What will drive you mad is if you can't let moments like this go. We can't win every time.'

I looked down at my feet. I didn't want to hang onto old cases, but this one was different. To know who the murderer was and have no way to pin him down was agony.

Until the DNA results came in, I wouldn't lose faith. Dunlow was smug, but he couldn't be a hundred per cent sure of what they would bring to light.

He had to make a mistake some time. I hoped he already had.

From: Laura Peters **peters@dunlowconsultants.co.uk**
To: Juliet Stern **juliet.stern@mit.gov.uk**
Date: **16 October, 19:11**
Subject: **Dunlow's movements this morning**

Dear Juliet,

Unfortunately, Mr Dunlow's schedule for today doesn't go into much detail. He didn't come into the office until midday, as he had been out with a client in the morning.

I can investigate further, but if possible I would like to avoid asking the client. Mr Dunlow would be unhappy if anyone else became aware of his arrest.

Thank you,

Laura

Gabe. Sent 20:46.

I need to see you x

Ollie. Sent 20:47.

Are you okay? xx

Gabe. Sent 20:47.

I've had the worst day at work. Can I see you? x

Ollie. Sent 20:49.

A small reminder – I'm not a booty call. I'm your
boyfriend. And as your boyfriend, I'm going to call
you after I've gotten out of the bath and we can talk
through your bad day xx

Gabe. Sent 20:50.

I don't really want to talk x

Ollie. Sent 20:52.

I know that, but I think you probably need to. Plus, I really like you and I don't just want to be someone you use to temporarily fuck your problems away. I have a shoot tomorrow, I need my beauty sleep. I can't meet up but I can talk xx

Gabe. Sent 20:55.

I like you too. A chat would be good x

Ollie. Sent 20:56.

Don't be afraid – I'll teach you how to express those pesky emotions. Now, leave me alone for ten minutes, I need to do a face mask xx

FORM 91A – FORMAL REQUEST FOR ARMED ASSIST-
ANCE

REQUESTING OFFICERS:

Detective Inspector Paul Willis

CASE NUMBER:

10098756

CASE DESCRIPTION:

Murder of Krystal Barrett on the Northwood Housing Estate in
Southampton on 10 October

REQUESTED ARMED RESPONSE TIME AND PLACE:

17 October – morning. Warehouse on the Liners Industrial Estate

REASON FOR WARRANT REQUEST:

We have gathered surveillance information and can confirm that Justin
and Sonia Barrett (both strong suspects for the murder of their seven-
year-old daughter, Krystal Barrett) are using a condemned warehouse
on the Liners Industrial Estate to avoid arrest. We believe they could
be armed and dangerous, so to ensure the safety of my team I'd like to
follow an armed response unit into the building.

Day 8

Tuesday, 17 October

Teddy. Sent 7:23.

Benny – I don't know if it's just me you're ignoring or the whole world but I've just seen this article. God knows how my dad is going to react. I didn't sleep with the guy or anything. I didn't want you to think that. If you could get back to me some time this century, I'd appreciate it.

Attached article from OMGFOMO.COM
Could everyone's favourite playboy/art curator be gay? Pictures taken as Terence Dunlow left a club last night show him in the arms of another man…
Click here to find out more!

FORENSIC REPORT ON:

#578 to #579 GLOVES found in an industrial bin used by Dunlow Consultants

#580 SCARF found in an industrial bin used by Dunlow Consultants

The examination confirms the **GLOVES** are made of leather. No fingerprints, full or partial, were found. Gunshot residue on the **GLOVES** was examined using a scanning electron microscope with x-ray analysis capability. Examination at high magnification showed particles consistent with the type of gun believed to have been used to shoot **MELANIE PIRT**.

DNA SAMPLES taken from inside the **GLOVES** and from various areas of the **SCARF** were tested for comparison against **DNA SAMPLES** taken from persons connected with this case. Many of the samples provided positive matches. The results are listed below:

GLOVES: POSITIVE MATCH for **TIMOTHY DUNLOW** and **KARL BISS** (in order from most to least).

SCARF: POSITIVE MATCH for **LEONARD DUNLOW, TIMOTHY DUNLOW** and **KARL BISS** (in order from most to least).

Traces of white powder found inside of the **GLOVES** were tested. This is latex residue.

REPORT COMPILED BY DAVID REES

Gabe

'No. This can't be right.' I stared at the report I'd been waiting for since I came into the station unusually early this morning. Juliet had arrived before me, her newly painted nails a perfect match for her lilac heels and navy suit.

Juliet's eyes narrowed. 'How could Dunlow have known we'd find this?'

I stood up, shaking out my hands. 'What's this saying? That Karl or Dunlow could have shot Melanie?' I raked my fingers through my hair. 'That's not right. Dunlow pretty much admitted to killing her. Even if Karl's DNA is all over the gloves and scarf, it has to be there simply because he lived on the estate.'

I'd run through various scenarios during a sleepless night after my calming chat with Ollie. I'd concluded Dunlow was cocky because he knew something we didn't. I hadn't imagined this.

'Juliet, what does this mean?' I turned away from Dunlow's mocking frown.

Juliet sat back in her chair. 'The evidence could be pointing towards either of them.'

The toast I'd stolen from Paul twisted in my stomach. 'You don't believe that? Karl might have run, but apart from that he's given us no reason to suspect he had anything to do with this.'

'I trust the evidence, and the evidence is saying Karl and Dunlow came into contact with gloves covered in gunshot residue.'

'What about what Dunlow said yesterday?'

Juliet shrugged. 'I guess he was playing with us or trying to throw us off his scent. At the moment, there's no way to know.'

I shook my head and turned back to the evidence wall. 'Dunlow's the killer. I can feel it. He knew we'd find mixed-up DNA on those gloves. I don't know how he got it there, but Dunlow did it.'

'We have two options,' Juliet said. 'You could be right, or Karl could have shot Melanie and tried to hide the gloves, then Dunlow really did find them and panic.'

'Stop being so cold.' I glared at Dunlow's shiny corporate photo. 'It's him. Can't you feel it?' The haughty distain, the taunting; it wasn't just arrogance. He'd killed someone and was certain he would get away with it.

'Gabe.' A warning note crept into Juliet's voice. 'We have to follow the evidence.'

'I'm not letting Dunlow go free while we pursue dead ends.' I balled my hands into fists. I couldn't believe the DNA results had let us down. I'd been sure they would point at Dunlow, not mire us even further between different suspects.

'That's not what I'm suggesting, but we have to keep our eyes on Karl and Dunlow.'

Hot rage exploded inside of me. I lifted my fist and smashed it into Dunlow's face.

'It's him.' I mashed my knuckles into the paper. 'It's him and I'm not going to let him get away with it.'

'Glad to hear it,' said a voice from the doorway.

I snatched my hand back. During my outburst, I'd forgotten our office wasn't a closed-off space.

David Rees leant against the door frame, his ginger eyebrows raised. His baggy grey jumper and habitual black leggings made his legs look extra sticklike. Trust the biggest prick we worked with to witness this.

'What do you want?' Juliet snapped.

Her back was rigid, her jaw set. That could have been due to David's sudden appearance or what I'd said. I'd turned on her because she didn't agree that Dunlow was a cold-hearted murderer.

'I wanted to talk to you about the results I sent through,' David said.

'Not necessary.' Juliet turned to her computer. 'They're crystal clear.'

I pressed my nails into my palms. That was a rebuke for David and me.

'Not quite,' he said.

I walked around to my desk. Wiggling my mouse, I woke my computer and brought up the results. As much as I didn't like what they said, it seemed straight forward.

'What do you mean?' I asked.

David rapped his knuckles on the door frame. 'It's the powder. Did you read the note about it?'

I scrolled down. I had read it, but it seemed unimportant after the glaringly wrong results above. 'What does it mean?'

'Latex powder is used as a covering on lots of things,' David explained. 'In this situation, I'd argue it was left over from a pair of plastic gloves.'

I frowned at the line of text on the screen. 'Someone wore plastic gloves inside the leather gloves?'

Juliet gasped, jumping up from her chair. 'We saw them in the barn. Do you remember?'

I scrunched my face. 'When exactly?'

Juliet rummaged through the notes pinned to the board around Karl's picture. 'Don't you remember me asking about the plastic gloves? Karl said something about having them for the dogs.'

The memory resurfaced, Juliet's disgusted cringe clear in my mind. I stood up as well. 'So Dunlow did kill Melanie.'

Juliet's mouth pressed into a thin line. 'We can't prove that.'

'But this is something, right?' I paced over to the wall. 'Dunlow would have known about the plastic gloves. He must have gone to get the dog and a gun, and spotted the leather gloves, then put them on over the top of the plastic ones. He probably only said he'd lost them because he knew he wouldn't get rid of all his DNA. He would have known they were Karl's. He was ready to frame Karl right from the start.'

I wished the groundskeeper was contactable. If we could ask him if he'd lost a pair of gloves recently, we would have more to trap Dunlow with.

Juliet stared at the wall. 'We've got no way to prove it. And if the latex gloves protect the killer's identity, who's to say Terence or Jordan didn't kill Melanie?'

'That's possible, but we can build on this.' I turned and grabbed my notepad. 'We know what to look for now. We need those plastic gloves. They're what will really incriminate Dunlow.'

'We already searched the whole property.' Juliet looked at the aerial map of the Dunlow Estate. 'We didn't find anything. What if he burned them?'

'He'll still have them.' I jabbed my pencil into the paper. 'Dunlow isn't the type to leave anything to chance. He's hidden them, and we need to wait until he slips up.'

'Unfortunately, time is something you don't have a great deal of,' Superintendent Angela Dobson said from behind David.

'Ma'am,' he said, hastily sidestepping out of her way.

Angela walked into our office, black cornrows making straight lines down her back. Her starched uniform was perfect, her belt cinched across her wide stomach. Juliet had no visible reaction to our superior's appearance, but I couldn't help compulsively tugging at the hem of my jumper, my eyes darting to the crumpled chocolate wrappers that hadn't quite made it into the bin.

'How's the case coming along?' Angela nodded at the cluttered wall of evidence. 'Have you found anything to charge Leonard or Timothy Dunlow with? If not, I need you to release them.'

The excitement that had filled me since David's latex explanation vanished. It was a step forward but wasn't nearly enough to charge Dunlow with murder. I could imagine his smug face if we brought this evidence before him; it was exactly what he'd expected us to find and he knew we couldn't do a thing with it.

'We have to let them go, ma'am,' Juliet said. 'We had some good leads, but they've not taken us anywhere.'

That was an unusually kind thing to say. More accurate would have been that we'd taken one shot in the dark after another, but this time I'd jumped ahead and arrested Dunlow too soon.

'Is anything likely to come up in the next few hours?' Angela asked, her dark brown cheeks rounding with a sympathetic wince.

We could ask Dunlow about the gloves, but that would exonerate rather than trap him. Better to leave him guessing what we'd found until we had more to throw at him. We could ask Terence and Jordan about the gloves, but I didn't want to tip them off on the small chance either of them was the killer. And there was no way to ask Karl about any of this.

We had a visit booked with Matthew Biss this afternoon. He wouldn't be any help with the gloves, but hopefully he would provide another thread so that the tapestry proclaiming Karl's innocence would be so solid even Juliet couldn't poke holes in it.

'We've got nothing, ma'am,' I admitted.

'I'm going to authorise their release then.' Angela moved to the door, her broad hips swaying under her stiff uniform. 'One of you needs to come down to deal with the paperwork in about half an hour.' She sighed. 'Their solicitors are threatening legal action, so we need to make sure everything is done perfectly.'

'It will be, ma'am,' Juliet promised.

Angela tapped on the doorframe. 'Have you got any strong leads left?'

My cheeks burnt as I avoided looking at David and Juliet. 'Nothing strong, ma'am. Not yet.'

'Start taking steps to wrap it up then.' Angela's tone brokered no space for argument. 'You've had long enough. Anything else comes to light, you can open it back up. Things have been too quiet the last week. Something new is going to come in, and I want you two ready for it.'

'Yes, ma'am,' Juliet said, her voice devoid of emotion.

Angela marched from the room and I slumped into my chair, resting my head in my hands.

'I'm sorry,' I mumbled. 'I shouldn't have brought Dunlow in. This case has been a mess from the start. All I've done is make it worse.'

'Don't talk shit,' Juliet said.

I looked up. 'I've led us in so many wrong directions, lost a key suspect, and we can't pin anything on the killer.'

'None of that is your fault.' Juliet sat down at her computer. 'Some cases don't go the way we want. It's not because we've done anything wrong. You can't beat yourself up over this.'

But I would. I looked at Melanie's smiling selfie. No matter what Juliet said to comfort me, I knew deep down that I'd failed.

Unless we found the plastic gloves. But I had no idea where to look.

'Can I get you both a tea?' David asked.

I spun my chair. David hovered in the doorway, his jumper pulled down over his hands. I'd assumed he'd scuttled off after Angela.

'What?'

He mimed drinking, his pinkie finger held aloft. 'Tea. The beverage. Do you want one?'

'We prefer coffee.' Juliet recovered from the surprise of David acting like a normal human quicker than me. 'Black for me, milk with two sugars for Gabe.'

'Give us your mugs.'

I passed them over and he strode out of our office.

'He helped with the case and he's making us coffee.' I wrinkled my nose. 'David might not be a complete arsehole?'

Juliet shook her head. 'I don't have the capacity to cope with such a monumental paradigm shift.'

I stared at the space my mug had occupied. It was easier to focus on David's uncharacteristic actions than this clusterfuck of a case. The first I'd taken the lead on, and I'd made a mess of it.

'You going to be okay, Gabe?'

I mustered up a smile. 'I'll be fine. I appreciate you asking.'

Juliet pursed her lips. 'You didn't do anything wrong. It doesn't work out every time.'

She turned to her computer, her attempt at consoling me over. I couldn't help but read into her words; she'd given up. We would go see Karl's dad, but that was only to tie up our final loose end. We had no more leads, no other avenues to rush down. Juliet didn't want to beg Angela for more time.

My eyes caught on the crumpled photo of Dunlow. Karl said that whoever killed Melanie was either stupid or didn't know the body was going to be found. There was a third option. Melanie's murderer could be so arrogant, so sure he wouldn't be brought to justice, that he didn't care if her body was discovered.

Call connected at 10:50.

'999, which service do you require?'

'Ambulance. Someone's been beaten up.'

'Can you tell me where you are?'

'Near that big hotel on the sea front. I don't know what it's called.'

'Hold on one moment. The Harbour Hotel?'

'Yes. That's it. We're at the far edge of the car park.'

'Who is it that's been beaten?'

'I don't know. I came around the corner and some maniac was kicking him in the stomach. He's breathing, but he's not conscious. There's some blood.'

'Okay. An ambulance is on its way. You're not in danger?'

'No, they ran off when I shouted at them. And there's other people here now. Someone who knows first aid. They're helping him.'

'That's great. Could you please pass the phone over to the person administering first aid?'

Recording started: 10.56.

Police Constable Alice To: All units in position, sir.

Detective Inspector Paul Willis: Let's go ahead.

Strategic Firearms Officer Ruby Douglas: We have AFOs at all entrances to the warehouse. Officers are to proceed with caution. Suspects are believed armed and dangerous, and the building is condemned. Bravo, you have the go-ahead to approach.

Authorised Firearms Officer Dev Afzal: Armed police! Stand away from the door.

SFO Ruby Douglas: Armed police! Down on the ground!

AFO Dev Afzal: One suspect is cooperative.

SFO Ruby Douglas: Someone's running.

AFO Dev Afzal: I'm in pursuit. Armed Police! Down on the ground!

[Two shots fired]

DI Paul Willis: What's going on?

AFO Dev Afzal: Second suspect is down, two shots to the left leg. I have removed a handgun from the suspect. Emergency first aid required.

PC Alice To: They're on the way.

DI Paul Willis: Is it them? Justin and Sonia?

SFO Ruby Douglas: We've got them, sir.

Gabe

My eyes flicked around the assorted notes, photos and newspaper clippings on the wall. After Juliet left to release the Dunlows, I'd barely moved. The coffee David made cooled on my desk.

'I don't use the word hate lightly,' Juliet said as she strode into our office, 'but I really do hate Timothy Dunlow.'

I didn't stop my staring contest with the wall. 'How was he?'

'Smug as a pig in shit. Less so when I left the duty officer to finish off. I have far more important things to do than watch him gloat.'

An involuntary smile tugged at my lips. 'I'm sure he'd appreciate the comparison.'

'Come on then.' Juliet stood next to me. 'Talk it through one last time.'

Juliet wasn't the most emotionally intelligent person or, if she was, she disregarded the information in favour of getting the job done, but she knew I needed this. If we were going to lay this case to one side, there couldn't be any avenues left unchecked, any threads unfollowed.

I wasn't ready to clear the wall. I'd leave the evidence up until ordered to take it down. Even then, the case file would sit on my desk rather than slotting neatly into the cabinets behind Juliet's desk.

I flicked through the photos of Melanie, from her smiling selfie to the clinical shots of her marred face.

'Melanie travelled by bus to the Dunlow Estate on the evening of the 9th October.' I tapped her bus ticket. 'She was met by Leo, with whom she had been carrying out a secret relationship. He snuck her onto the estate and into the den above the garage, where they had sex.' I pointed at the DNA results from her body. 'Afterwards, Melanie and Leo argued and she left.'

'Enter Dunlow,' Juliet said.

'The things we know; he saw Leo and Melanie from the house, he came over to tell Leo off, then he headed back in the direction of the house.'

Juliet stuck her tongue out at Dunlow's austere portrait. 'He says he went to the house. He slept like a baby while Melanie was shot and mauled. The first thing he knew about the murder was when Karl called him in the morning.'

'Alternative theory; Dunlow killed her.' I looked at the annotated map of the estate. 'He grabbed a gun and went to the barn for a dog to help him find Melanie. While he was there, he saw Karl's leather gloves and the plastic ones, and he hatched a plan to pin the blame on Karl. He followed Melanie out into the forest and shot her three times. After, he shot the dog and hid all the incriminating evidence.'

'Another theory is that Karl killed Melanie. The latex residue is there because he put the gloves on to diddle with some poor dog's anal glands.' Juliet grimaced. 'This is why I could never have a pet. There's far too much close contact with faeces.'

Karl's section of the wall was sparse. A copy of his note and the article about his mother's murder were pinned either side of his picture. 'Do you honestly see him as a suspect?'

'I have to. You do too,' Juliet said. 'He's got a history of violence in the family and he ran off in the middle of the investigation. Most damning, his DNA is on the gloves most likely worn to kill Melanie. We can't discount him because he seemed like a nice guy.'

'But why would he have reported the bodies if he was guilty?' I asked, rolling the corner of David's latest forensic report between my finger and thumb.

'That is one thing in his favour. He would have to be a colossal moron to report them if he was the killer, and he didn't seem dim to me.'

That was wild praise coming from Juliet, but it didn't mean she wouldn't pursue Karl if any sighting of him was ever reported. Hopefully he could keep himself hidden until I found something Dunlow couldn't talk his way out of.

'Leo is another suspect with no real alibi.' I flicked his tragic love poems. 'He lied several times about the nature of his relationship with Melanie, denied knowing her, and then denied meeting her. We only got the truth once the DNA results came through.'

'He's in the running, but only just.' Juliet wrinkled her nose. 'My Lion is a terrible nickname.'

'Agreed.' I shook my head at his school photo. 'Leo, as much as he tried to lie, is transparent. It was obvious he was keeping something from us, we just had to throw enough evidence at him to force the truth out.'

'His DNA probably got on the scarf when he and Melanie were canoodling.'

I grinned as my eyes flicked over Leo's differing statements. 'Canoodling?'

'Exactly.' Juliet lifted her chin. 'Plus, Leo is reportedly a terrible shot and would have gotten mauled himself if he'd tried to use Lucy to find Melanie.'

I glanced at the picture of the dog's partially buried body. 'It had to be someone who was familiar with the dogs, or particularly gifted at getting them to obey, who hunted Melanie down.'

'Which puts Jordan in the running,' Juliet said, her nose wrinkling as she looked at his section of the wall.

'He was Melanie's boyfriend and he was abusing her physically. He seemed genuinely shocked when we told him she'd died, but he doesn't have a good alibi,' I rattled off the facts. 'We don't know if he knew Melanie had sex with Leo, but he would have been incredibly angry if he did.'

'The abuse doesn't look good for him.'

I tapped his text transcripts. 'Even though he didn't start the fire, he displayed a high level of comfort roving around the grounds. Whoever killed Melanie knew their way across the estate.'

'Which brings us to Terence,' Juliet said.

'He has an uncorroborated alibi.' Benedict Hogan was still AWOL. 'Karl running off doesn't look good for him. At the moment, we only have his word that he didn't come back to the estate to silence Melanie himself or get someone else to do it for him to keep his secret safe.'

Juliet tipped her head to one side. 'Don't get me wrong, I'm not convinced Dunlow is the killer, but no matter how you look at this, the whole case revolves around him.'

'What do you mean?'

'At the very least, Melanie was killed on his property,' Juliet said. 'But he instils such fear into his sons that they follow his commands blindly and hide their relationships from him. He employed Karl, he owned the dog, he most likely owned the gun used to kill Melanie.' She narrowed her eyes. 'No matter what the outcome is, I'd be shocked if he's not involved in some way.'

'Involved is one way to put it.'

'I've got a couple of things to sort before we head over to the prison.' Juliet left me standing in front of the wall, her fingers clattering against her keyboard before her weight had settled in her chair.

I nodded absently. I tried to look at all the evidence we'd collected, but my gaze snagged on Dunlow's photo.

Juliet was right; he was smug. He'd killed a young woman and he was going to walk out of here freely. Yet another man who'd gotten away with something terrible. There were too many of them in the world, too many in my life.

I grabbed my coat and swung it over my shoulders. 'See you in a minute.'

Juliet shot me a penetrating look as I hurried out of our office, but she didn't try to stop me. Odds were, she knew what I was going to do.

I half walked, half jogged across our floor and past the lift. This was a bad idea, but that didn't mean it was wrong. Something was bubbling up inside of me, something only contained by my mad dash downstairs. I needed to let Dunlow know he might have gotten away for now, but that he hadn't fooled me.

I met him and Alice as they crossed the wide expanse of reception, the huge front facing windows flooding the space with crisp rays of light. Taking a deep breath, I plastered an empty smile on my face.

'I'll take him from here.'

Alice's neat eyebrows quirked upwards. 'Right you are, ma'am.'

She turned on her heel. I gestured towards the front doors, encouraging Dunlow to keep moving, rather than glaring down at me like a stray dog that had dared get too close.

The door swung shut behind us. Bright sunlight bounced off car windscreens but there was a chill to the air. I refused to shiver.

'I know you did it.'

A flicker of something crossed Dunlow's face before a mask of distain settled into place.

'You know nothing.' He turned away, tracking sleek cars up and down the road. 'That's why you're releasing me. It's why you shouldn't have arrested me, and why you're not going to bother me or my boys again.'

'I won't stop searching for the gun, or anything that will prove me right.'

To an onlooker, Dunlow's smile might have seemed like that of a kind uncle. Only up close could you see the sharp edges.

'You know, you should be careful. I haven't decided whether to bring a complaint against your department, but being harassed as I left the station; that would be a great place to start.'

I balled my hands into fists, pressing my blunt nails into the skin of my palms. Dunlow was a bully, through and through. 'No one would believe a woman like me could intimidate a man like you.'

I didn't often play this card. I strove to help those I worked with forget my small stature and slight frame. But that was all a man like Dunlow would ever see.

He straightened. I fought the urge to step back, but it was like he could sense the instinct.

'They'd be right,' Dunlow sneered. 'You couldn't.'

The station door swung open. 'Dad?'

Dunlow stepped away, his gaze softening as he turned to Leo. 'Let's go.'

Leo nodded, his mussed hair falling over his glasses. 'Bye, Detective Martin.'

His voice was husky, like some of the time in his cell had been used to shed tears that had no place in the Dunlow men's home. His reddened eyes danced over my face before he was steered away by his father.

I watched them walk down the road, finally buttoning my coat. I couldn't tell if I'd made my point, but I was surer than ever that Dunlow had killed Melanie Pirt in the grounds of his ancestral home.

I wouldn't rest until I proved it.

The station door swung open again, just as the Dunlows disappeared. Juliet's heels clacked on the mottled concrete.

'Terence Dunlow has been attacked.'

'What?' My face pulled into lines of disbelief. 'Who by?'

Juliet shook her head as we rushed towards the station car park. 'All I've got is a copy of the intake form that Maddy got from Southampton General.'

I struggled to wind my head around this new information. 'Too many people involved in this case are getting hurt.'

I wasn't pleased that Terence had been beaten, but chatting with him was another pitstop before I had to let this case go. If there were enough delays, something might eventually come to light that we could use against Dunlow.

From: Juliet Stern **juliet.stern@mit.gov.uk**
To: Madison Campbell
madison.campbell@mitadmin.gov.uk
CC: Gabriella Martin **gabriella.martin@mit.gov.uk**
Date: **17 October, 11:50**
Subject: **Operation Chalice – Press release**

Maddy,

Please put out the following urgent appeal for more information. We're moving towards shelving this case, but one more plea for information won't hurt.

Juliet

Detectives are appealing again for more witnesses and information about the murder of a young woman on the Dunlow Estate in the New Forest.

The victim, Melanie Pirt, was shot dead on the Dunlow Estate on the night of 9 October.

Police have recovered the body of a dog involved in the attack and other key pieces of evidence. However, the murder weapon has not been recovered. It is believed to be a hunting rifle.

Two men were arrested in conjunction with this enquiry but have been released without charge.

Detectives are appealing for anyone with any information to come forward.

Detective Inspector Juliet Stern said: 'We are anxious to trace any potential witnesses as soon as possible so they can help us to piece together what happened. If you know anything, please contact us.'

AN ACCIDENT AND EMERGENCY TRIAGE FORM

DATE: 17 October
TIME: 12:15
NAME: Terence Dunlow
AGE: 24

PRESENTING COMPLAINT: Assault – torso and head pain, leg and hand laceration

HISTORY OF PRESENTING COMPLAINT: Patient reports he was assaulted by a masked person in the Southampton Harbour Hotel car park at around 10:50 on 17 October. He was kicked and punched until he fell to the ground. He was then kicked in the head and chest until he lost consciousness. Patient was unconscious when paramedics arrived but was treated at the scene. He was self-mobile and able to walk to the ambulance. There did not seem to be any significant head injuries. There is a laceration on the patient's left thigh and left palm.

ON EXAMINATION: The patient can stand aided but is unstable when unaided due to leg laceration. There is blood on their hand from a cut of about one inch and blood on their thigh from a cut of about three inches. The patient is alert and has multiple contusions across their face, chest, arms, legs and back.

PAST MEDICAL HISTORY: None.

MEDICATION: None.

SOCIAL AND FAMILY HISTORY: None.

REPORT COMPLIED BY: Senior Staff Nurse Consuelo Day

Gabe

We were shown into a side room. I didn't know whether Terence's private health insurance had secured him such luxury, or whether he'd gotten lucky. This beating notwithstanding, Terence was the kind of man who always landed on his feet.

He lay on top of the hospital sheets, the back raised so he was reclining. His green top was stained with blood, his face bruised. A white bandage stood out against his olive skin on his left hand and there was another on his thigh, peeking under the hem of his running shorts.

'Ah, you,' he said, as we entered the room.

'Hello, Terence.' I sat on a chair beside the bed and balanced my notepad on my knee. 'We were sorry to hear that you were attacked earlier today. Can you tell us what happened?'

Juliet maintained her position at the end of the bed. Terence's face turned a blotchy red between dark bruising.

'I went out for a run. As I was coming back to the hotel, someone grabbed me. I tried to shout but they punched me in the stomach. I fell over and they kicked me until I fell unconscious.'

'Did you see your attacker?' I internally winced at the violence Terence had endured but I didn't think he would react well to overt sympathy.

'They were wearing a balaclava, and jeans and a dark jumper. They were tall, strong enough to grab me. After they punched me in the stomach, they hit me on the head. I covered my face with my hands when I was on the floor. I didn't see anything after that.'

The person driving the van that hit Leo was also wearing a balaclava. That didn't necessarily mean the two incidents were linked, but it was something to pull together the seemingly random violence being meted out to those connected to this case.

'Did they say anything?' I asked. 'Do you think they were male or female?'

'They didn't speak but I'd say male, maybe? Their jumper was bulky. Too much of their face was hidden to be sure.'

'Have you had any indication someone was interested in hurting you?' Juliet asked.

Terence huffed out a laugh, which he swapped for a wince. 'I was outed by an online rag this morning.'

My stomach swooped. 'I'm sorry.'

Terence accessed me, then sniffed. 'It's fine.'

'Would anyone other than your father have a problem with your sexuality?' Juliet asked.

I held a cringe inside as Terence laughed again. Only a straight person would assume random strangers wouldn't turn against Terence.

'Of course they do,' he sneered. 'But I don't think anyone but my father matters.' He glared between me and Juliet. 'I think Dad ordered the attack.'

My pencil hovered over my notepad. 'What makes you think that?'

'Because he hates me now,' Terence growled. 'He's always gone on about how homosexuals are a perversion from what's normal, and now he's got a gay son. He's obviously going to disown me, but apparently that isn't enough. He needed to put me in my place. He wouldn't get his own hands dirty, so he got someone else to assault me.'

Terence's chest expanded with each of his laboured breaths. In this side room, the noises of the rest of the ward were muted. Bleeping monitors and scuffing footsteps were quiet in Terence's sanctuary.

'We'll look into the possibility that your father orchestrated this attack,' I reassured Terence. I'd do it, if only because it was tenuously connected with Melanie's case. I didn't think it likely, since Dunlow was at the station when the news broke, but he could have found out another way. Us arresting him could have been incredibly convenient. 'Can you think of anyone who has any specific ill-will towards you?'

Terence leant back. 'Not really.'

'Were the photos the same ones that Karl blackmailed you with?' Juliet asked.

Terence's head snapped up. 'Karl did not blackmail me, and of course they're not the same photos. Those were taken weeks ago and I made sure he deleted them. The ones in the article are from last night.'

'They couldn't have been taken by him?' Juliet pressed, undeterred by Terence's ire.

'How would I know?' He threw up his injured hand, the bandage bright under the fluorescent lights. 'I haven't studied his unique photography style, for Christ's sake.'

Without access to the original photos, which Terence had ensured were long gone, there was no way to compare the two.

'Karl wouldn't have sent pictures anywhere,' Terence grumbled. 'He didn't want to publicly expose me, he just wanted me to talk to my dad.' He shrugged, his petulant energy fading. 'Maybe if I'd talked to him he would have disowned me, rather than setting some lacky on me.'

I glanced over at Juliet, then stood. 'Thank you for talking to us. If you remember anything else, please give us a call.'

'I won't be staying at the hotel anymore,' Terence said. 'If you need me, I'll be at Benny's house. I assume he hasn't contacted you yet?'

'No,' I said. 'You've not heard from him either?'

Terence shook his head. 'I've got a key for his place. If I find anything that explains where he might be, I'll let you know.'

'Thank you.'

As we walked from the room, Terence's face pulled tight with misery and pain. If he was to be believed, he'd had a bad run of luck recently.

Juliet and I walked through the ward and down busy corridors, the normal thrum of the hospital washing over us. I couldn't see how this attack connected with Melanie's murder, but I desperately wanted it to be related. At least it was linked enough that I could hold onto this case for a little longer.

'We need to find out where Jordan was during the attack,' I said, as we reached the hospital entrance.

Juliet fumbled with an anti-bacterial dispenser. 'You think he could be involved?'

'Someone tall attacked a member of the Dunlow family. Jordan's a young man with a history of violence. He's already beaten up Leo. We have to consider that his grudge might extend to the wider family.'

'Could it have been Karl?' Juliet moved aside to let me pump the stinging gel.

I nodded begrudgingly. Just because Karl couldn't defend himself, I didn't want to pin every unexplainable thing on him.

We stepped out into the chill air, rubbing our hands. I searched my coat pocket for my car keys. All my fingers encountered was my notepad and the blunt end of my pencil.

'Mr Dunlow?' Juliet said.

I jerked my head up. Timothy Dunlow rose from a bench beside the hospital entrance. Alongside the habitual frown lines, his mouth was downturned and his eyes reddened. He didn't look like the same man who'd stood and goaded me outside the station.

'He won't let me in,' Dunlow croaked. He ran a hand over his face. 'Terence doesn't want me near him.'

'I'm sorry.' The apology was automatic. No matter what I thought of this man, his son turning against him was clearly causing him pain.

Dunlow looked at the bustling hospital, something in his expression hardening. His spine straightened as he took a deep breath.

'Could I follow you to the station? There are some things I should tell you.'

My heart skipped, but Juliet answered. 'No. We have an important interview to get to.'

I struggled to understand what she meant for a second before it clicked; Matthew Biss. We couldn't miss this chance to investigate Karl's past, no matter how important Dunlow's new information might be.

'We'll be back late this afternoon,' I said. 'Could you come into the station?'

Dunlow nodded, before spinning on his heel and marching to his car.

'What do you think he's got to say?' Juliet asked as we walked across the car park.

'No clue.'

I shot her a half smile, trying not to let my frustration bleed through. This visit to Karl's father was a formality that would likely be of no use. What would be far more helpful was a signed confession from Dunlow. We had to delay talking to him, and what if he changed his mind about whatever he had to share?

'Chin up.' Juliet's elbow brushed my upper arm, a barely there touch. 'There's nothing a visit to a convicted murderer in a high security prison can't fix.'

Leo. Sent 14:14.

Ted – I hope you're okay? Dad told me you've been beaten up? I saw the article as well. I don't care about it. It doesn't change anything. Dad says you won't talk to him. I hope you'll talk to me x

Gabe

My bum was already numb on the hard plastic seat I'd had to awkwardly scoot into since it was bolted to the floor, and my hands frozen. When we entered the prison, we surrendered our coats and all electronic devices. The only things I'd brought into the closed visit room were my notepad and pencil, which I tried not to tap against the table while we waited for Karl's father.

'He's got a busy schedule,' Juliet muttered as heavy footsteps finally rung out along the corridor. 'A hectic morning of beating fellow inmates and staring at grey walls.'

This was an accurate representation of how Matthew Biss had spent his time since he'd been sentenced to life imprisonment for beating his wife to death and attempting the same with his son. His sentence had been gradually increased, the sheer amount of violent altercations he got into ensuring he would never be a free man again.

The door on the other side of the room slid open and I suppressed a shiver as Matthew entered, flanked by two prison officers. Juliet was unaffected by the fridge-like conditions. She watched, impassive and still, as our interviewee settled on the other side of the table, separated from us by a thick plastic screen.

Matthew's greying hair was shorn close to his scalp and his body was broad and meaty. His freckled skin was further marked with overlapping tattoos, the words and symbols indecipherable. He sneered at the guards as they left, an expression I couldn't imagine crossing Karl's face.

Matthew's upper lip curling, a scar down the left side of his face stretched as he examined us through the scratched plastic. Perhaps there was something of Karl in the dark brown of his eyes and what was once the long line of his nose but was now a misshapen lump.

'Thank you for meeting with us, Mr Biss,' I began, my back pressed firmly into the unyielding plastic seat. Even with the screen between us, I wanted distance from this man. 'I'm Detective Sergeant Gabe Martin and this is Detective Inspector Juliet Stern.'

Matthew's bristly eyebrows rose. 'What's a couple of detectives doing, coming to chat with me?'

Here was a resemblance to Karl; he and his father's voices rose and fell with the gentle cadence of Yorkshire. On Karl, the accent was soft and spoke of his placid nature. On his father, there was a harsh edge.

'We have some questions about Karl,' Juliet said, leaning forward to speak through the holes at the bottom of the screen.

While I wouldn't have said Matthew was friendly before, he was at least open and curious. One mention of his son, and he closed down. He sat rigid, dark eyes narrowed.

'What about him?' His voice had hardened, the words clipped.

I tapped my pencil on my notepad. 'We're wondering what you can tell us, Mr Biss.'

He cringed. 'You can stop with that formal shit. Call me Matt.' He swallowed, grinding his stubbled jaw. 'What do you want to know?'

Juliet leant forward, her elbows resting on the table. It wasn't hard to figure out what had captured her interest. All reports had described Matthew Biss as an unrepentant monster. He'd killed his wife and tried to kill his son, and he'd refused to accept the blame. He'd then continued his streak of violence in this prison.

All of that didn't fit with the reaction he'd had to his son's name. He'd come into the room swaggering and cocky, but that thin armour had been knocked off.

'Can you tell us about Karl's childhood?' Juliet asked.

I stopped tapping my pencil, preparing to take notes. We hadn't planned a deep dive into Karl's past, but I understood why Juliet had started there. I wanted to unpick why this hardened criminal had such an undeniable reaction to one of his victims.

Matthew's eyes searched Juliet's face. He found nothing threatening behind her encouraging smile. 'He was a runty little thing. No good at sports, no help around the house. All he wanted to do was read. Wasn't even interested in TV.'

'Were you close?' Juliet asked. We knew the answer, but this was one of the ways she lulled men like Matthew into revealing their darkest secrets. Play it dumb, let them talk, and then they'd slip up when she struck out. This was why she was taking the lead here, something I was happy to relinquish after my failure in every other aspect of this case.

Matthew shook his head. 'Na. He was a strange lad. Course, his mam encouraged him.'

Absently, he rubbed his fingers over his knuckles. There was a thick tattoo across the back of his hand. I tilted my head to make a note, hiding my shock that Matthew had the name of the wife he'd murdered inked into his skin.

'Were they close?' Juliet asked.

'Peas in a pod.' There was a soft edge to his voice. 'I never knew what she saw in me. I wasn't smart like her. Or like him.'

'What happened on the night you killed her?'

Matthew flinched. Juliet widened her eyes at me while he stared down at his hand, fingers rasping over the letters printed across his knuckles.

'Matt, are you alright?' I asked.

His hand stopped moving and he pinned me with his gaze. 'Do you want to talk about it properly? Because no one else did. No one else gave me a chance.'

'What do you mean?'

Matthew ground his teeth together. I tried not to shrink away, kept my expression neutral as my hand tightened around my pencil.

'As soon as that little shit woke up and started shouting his mouth off, no one listened to me,' he spat out.

I eased my grip. 'We want to hear your version of events.'

His eyes grew round. 'You do?'

I pressed the tip of my pencil into my notepad. 'Please. In your own time.'

Matthew tipped his head towards the ceiling, his broad chest expanding as he breathed deeply. His eyes slammed to mine as he sat forward.

'Like I said, he was a strange child.' His words rushed over one another in his eagerness to tell a story he'd been refused a listening ear for. 'I tried not to let what I knew cloud how I treated him, but he was a weird one.'

'What did you know?' Juliet interjected.

Matthew's eyes darted to her but landed on my pencil and notepad. 'He wasn't mine.'

There was a triumphant sheen to his whole being as I noted that down. 'Not yours?' I clarified, my heart thrumming.

'Jenny was up the duff when I met her,' Matthew rushed on. 'Didn't bother me. She was a beauty, the most wonderful woman I'd ever met. Didn't matter to me that she was having some other bloke's kid. I was happy to help her raise it.' His expression soured. 'It mattered to him, though.'

'Karl?' Juliet checked.

Matthew nodded, apparently unwilling to say the name. 'We didn't tell him, even put me on the birth certificate.'

That was remarkably accepting. I tried to reconcile a man who would willingly parent another's child with the one sat before me.

'How did Karl find out?' I tried to keep the jumpy energy filling me from my voice. If this was true, it had to mean something.

'No idea.' Matthew rubbed his knuckles again. 'I came home after work and he was screaming at Jenny. Said he hated her, had always hated me. He went on and on about how we'd lied and how he could have had a better life. In the end, he ran out of steam and scarpered to his room.'

Shadows shifted across Matthew's face as he looked towards the bar covered window. 'At least, that's where I assumed he went. I made sure Jen was okay, she always hated it when Karl shouted, and then I went for a shower.' He turned from the window, a pleading edge entering his voice. 'I worked at a garage, always came home covered in muck.'

'Where had Karl gone?' Juliet urged. It wouldn't be obvious to Matthew, but I could hear the echo of my own eagerness in her question. In a case full of lies and confusion, we hadn't expected even more here. Potentially, we'd uncovered a secret we hadn't known to search for.

'He went to the garden shed,' Matthew said in a low monotone. 'He found an old set of golf clubs one of my mates gave me. I'd never used them, had half-forgotten they were there.'

He tailed off, his fingers rubbing harshly over his knuckles.

We'd read the official report of what happened next. Matthew beat his wife to death, then tried to kill Karl. Police arrived in time to stop him causing fatal injury to two members of his family. It was the story that made me liken Karl to myself.

'He brought the club in, and he killed her.' Matthew paused, working his jaw. 'I was getting dressed when I heard the screams. Then they stopped. He was still beating her when I ran into the kitchen.'

317

I swallowed hard as my hand flew across my notepad. This was not the story fed to the jury, was not what the world believed happened on the day Jennifer Biss was killed.

'What did you do then?' Juliet asked.

'I tried to stop him.' Matthew's hands shook as his fingers moved compulsively over the tattoo. 'I didn't know Jenny was gone, thought I could save her. I pushed him away, but the little shit kept coming back. He attacked me, and I threw him off. Grabbed the club from his hands.'

'You hit him with it?' Juliet prompted.

I examined Matthew's face as he formulated an answer, the first time he'd fumbled in his account of what happened that night. I suppressed a shiver as his eyes darted between us.

'I did,' he admitted. 'He wouldn't stop coming at me. Once I had the club, I made him stay down. I needed him to stop so that I could help Jenny. But the police arrived before I could get to her.'

'You only hit Karl to subdue him?' Juliet checked.

Matthew glared at her, taking longer than needed to answer. 'Yes.'

I hadn't been sure about his story, but now I knew I was looking at a liar.

'Karl's injuries were so severe that he didn't regain consciousness until he'd been in hospital for several hours,' I said. 'He was beaten so badly that he had to have physiotherapy for weeks to regain full use of his hands. He had to relearn how to walk, how to eat and talk. All while you barely sustained a scratch.'

'He wouldn't stop coming at me,' Matthew repeated, his hands clenching into fists. 'I only hit him to stop him.'

We'd read the medical reports. Matthew beat Karl with that club far beyond the point of simply stopping him. He'd wanted to kill Karl, just like he'd killed his wife.

Juliet took a deep breath, rolling her shoulders. 'Let me get this straight. You were happy to raise another man's son, even if he was odd. Then Karl found out about this monumental lie, and he murdered his own mother?'

Matthew's eyes narrowed. 'That's what happened.'

I doubted that. We'd look into Matthew's claims that he and Karl weren't related, but this visit had been a monumental waste of time.

'Why didn't you say any of this before?' Juliet asked, her face pinched. 'You pleaded not guilty, but you didn't put forward an alternative timeline.'

'I was grieving.' Matthew's eyes settled on me. 'I couldn't believe what had happened. Before I knew it, I was on trial and everyone was telling me I'd killed Jenny. My solicitor told me to plead guilty, but I couldn't do it. I knew no one would listen, that little shit had everyone too far wrapped up in his pathetic lies.'

'And the years since?' Juliet tipped her head to the side. 'You never tried to tell the truth?'

Matthew didn't look at her, continued drilling me with his gaze. He might have sensed the waves of disbelief crashing off Juliet even through the screen. He couldn't know I'd seen through his lies too.

'I know who I am.' He spread his hands wide, the palms free of blurred ink. 'I know how it looks. I was an angry man before I came in here, and it's only gotten worse. You've got a kid saying the big, bad bastard killed his mam, and then you've got me, trying to pin the blame on some innocent flower. How's that going to go?'

Exactly the way it went. 'Do you have any idea who Karl's biological father is?' I asked.

Matthew clasped his hands together. 'No idea. Jenny said she didn't know.'

Having met both Karl and Matthew, I knew who I was more inclined to believe. Matthew's story had gaping holes he couldn't fill. I had no doubt he'd found out about Karl's parentage the same day Jennifer died. It made no sense that this man wouldn't speak up when falsely accused, and his violent record spoke for itself. He hadn't had darkness thrust on him, he'd gathered it into himself.

'Karl is a suspect in a murder case,' Juliet stated. 'He's absconded. Any idea where he could be hiding?'

Matthew sighed. 'Done it again, has he?'

I bit the inside of my cheek. Matthew really wanted us to believe Karl was a killer. His lies made little sense. He wouldn't get out of here even if he was acquitted of Jennifer's murder. He was throwing muck at Karl out of pure spite.

'No idea,' he said. 'We didn't have much money, so we didn't go on holidays or nothing. Me and Jen were only children, our parents are dead.' Matthew shrugged. 'He's got no one he could run to.'

I flicked my notepad shut rather than rubbing at the dull ache his words elicited in my chest.

'That everything?' Juliet checked with me, before pressing a button to summon the prison officers. 'Thank you for your time,' she said to Matthew, standing gracefully.

I engaged in an awkward dismount, not unmissed by Matthew if the sneer on his face was anything to go by. Juliet swept out of the room when the officers appeared, stalking towards the locked reception.

'Do you believe a word of it?' she asked, while an officer in the room beyond fiddled with the controls to free us.

'No.' I followed her into the reception area and over to a bank of lockers. 'But we have to investigate it. He could have been lying about who killed Jennifer but be telling the truth about not being Karl's biological father.'

Juliet shrugged on her coat. 'Would Karl's parentage make a difference if he didn't kill his mother? It wouldn't be proof of a violent past, just messy family history.'

I huddled into my coat. Juliet was already absorbed in her phone as I signed us out. As we walked across the vast car park, I turned over the interview in my head. There were too many holes in Matthew's story. He wasn't the kind of man anyone would think was innocent, and for good reason, but I couldn't see why he would lie about Karl's parentage. It was too easy to prove.

I unlocked the car and set up the satnav to take us back to the station, dread sinking into my barely warmed limbs. I hadn't held out much hope that Karl's dad would throw a curveball at us that would sustain this case, but part of me had been clinging to the possibility. Instead, all he'd done was point the finger at a man we couldn't question even if we'd wanted to. I'd investigate his claims about Karl's parentage, but the likelihood it would have anything to do with Melanie's death was wafer thin.

We'd talk to Dunlow, but he wasn't about to hand us a signed confession. This case was finished. I'd failed not only to lead well but, more importantly, to find justice for Melanie.

You have one new voicemail. Voicemail left today at 3:10 p.m.

'Benny, I hope you're okay. With everything else that's been going on, I'm beginning to wonder if something's happened to you. I don't know if you saw my message, but I've been outed. Dad knows I'm gay. He wants to talk about it, but I don't want to be told how disgusting I am. I'm going to go stay at your place. I hope you don't mind. I'll clear out if you want me to, but I need a few days to get myself sorted. I'll feel better, being there. If I can't be with you, staying in your house is the next best thing. I've always felt safe there. Sorry. I'm rambling. A nurse just gave me some pain meds. I miss you. Please call me.'

Gabe

I pressed the button on top of the recorder. 'This is a voluntary interview commencing at 3:45 p.m. on 17th October. The interviewee is Timothy Dunlow. He has declined legal representation. Interview conducted by myself, Detective Sergeant Gabriella Martin, and Detective Inspector Juliet Stern. Mr Dunlow, you are not under arrest and are free to leave at any time.'

Nothing from Dunlow except his continued docility. He was waiting when we got back to the station and had sat quietly in the interview room while we prepared. He'd thanked us for the offer of water and a solicitor, but he needed neither.

Terence's rejection had clearly had a profound effect, but I couldn't believe it had changed Dunlow's essential nature. Before we'd met him outside of the hospital, I'd have said Dunlow was arrogant and selfish, fully capable of killing Melanie because she wasn't who he believed his son should be with. Now, he looked broken, the veneer of untouchable entitlement I'd assumed went bone-deep stripped away.

'Thank you for granting me this interview,' Dunlow said. 'First of all, I would like to apologise for my behaviour, particularly this morning, but in truth for the duration of our acquaintance. I've been unpleasant on a number of occasions, and for that I'm sorry.'

'What was the reason for your unpleasantness?' Juliet asked, not as shellshocked as me by Dunlow apologising.

'In the business I'm in, being liked is of no importance. I need to get the best deal for everyone involved.' He cleared his throat. 'That attitude carries into my interactions with others, especially when I feel threatened.'

'Why did you feel threatened?' Juliet asked.

An expression flitted over Dunlow's face that was reminiscent of the bulldog of a man we'd met before. I couldn't blame him for being annoyed by Juliet's question. Anyone's hackles would rise if they thought their children were suspected of something they truly believed they could never be involved in.

'A young woman was killed on my grounds.' Dunlow maintained the desolate calm that had fallen over him since his eldest son pushed him away. 'You questioned Leo.' He paused, squaring his jaw. 'My sons are all I have. I won't let anyone harm them.'

Before Juliet could jump in to ask the exact lengths he would go to when he'd decided one of his sons was endangered, I said, 'Thank you for the apology, Mr Dunlow. As you can imagine, our time is incredibly valuable, especially during an active murder investigation. What was it you wanted to share with us?'

Dunlow's light blue eyes flitted over my face. I'd been speared by his gaze before, observed under the sharp edges of his abundant disapproval. There was something different in his expression, in his whole demeanour. He no longer wanted to keep us far away but needed us to come close and listen.

'Someone is targeting my family.'

Juliet's eyebrows crept towards her hairline. My heart thumped discordantly. Only hours ago, I'd said that people connected to this case kept getting hurt. The protective instincts of a father turned that into a calculated attack against his loved ones, but I wasn't sure I disagreed. It wasn't people associated with this case who had been hurt since Melanie died, it was the Dunlows.

'What makes you think someone is targeting you and your sons?' I asked.

That caused another flicker of disdain across Dunlow's face. 'Numerous things. No matter what you might believe, neither me nor my sons killed Melanie Pirt. Someone came onto my land and shot her, which caused distress and disturbance for my family. Then my youngest son was attacked by that thug and hit by a car. Our family home was set on fire. Then, my oldest son was attacked. This can't all be coincidence. Someone wants to harm us.'

I took a deep breath and tried to think through what Dunlow had said without bias. It was difficult after he'd insinuated someone had killed Melanie to harm his family. He would never see her as anything other than a tool to be used against him.

'If you didn't shoot Melanie, then it does seem a pattern is emerging,' Juliet conceded, lending emphasis to the first word.

'There's more.' The expensive fabric of Dunlow's suit whispered as he took a deep breath. 'I lied about where I found the scarf and gloves.'

'You lied?' Juliet laughed harshly. 'How original.'

'Your family has a nasty habit of lying to us.' I flicked my notepad open and picked up my pencil.

A blotchy blush as pronounced as his sons' rose across Dunlow's face. 'I apologise if it seems my sons and I haven't always been truthful. Every half-truth was only ever told to protect my family.'

'How did lying about where you found the scarf and gloves protect your family?' I asked.

Dunlow rested his hands on the table. 'I didn't know what finding them meant. I didn't know if they would, wrongly I must add, incriminate either of my sons or myself, or if they were left to toy with us. Either way, I didn't want to play anyone's game.'

Murderers were usually motivated by a primitive desire for violence, or something selfish like power, money or jealousy. But there were some, like Dunlow, who had such a strong need to protect those they loved that they forgot their victims were someone's granddaughter.

'Please explain to us, truthfully, how you found the gloves and scarf,' Juliet said.

'It was the morning of the fire.' A heavy mixture of sadness and frustration sat more comfortably on Dunlow's face than a smile ever would. 'We'd been allowed into the house to gather our things. I discovered the scarf and gloves when I put my suitcase in the boot of my car.'

'Someone planted them after the fire?' I asked.

'They could have been put there any time after I arrived home from work the previous day. Whoever set the fire would have had ample time to plant the scarf and gloves.'

I rested the point of my pencil against my notepad. 'You think the same person did both?'

'Of course.'

'Do you have any evidence?' Juliet asked. Her tone was flat, but an edge of irritation had crept in. She didn't like Dunlow and she hated being lied to. This man was skating on the thinnest of ice.

'Evidence?' Dunlow broke into a familiar frown. 'What more do you need? I've told you everything that's happened to my family. There has to be someone behind it all.'

I pressed my lips together. Dunlow was happy to chalk Melanie's killing up as a random act of violence until it fit into a pattern of abuse towards those he loved.

'The scarf and gloves definitely weren't in your car before the fire?' I asked.

'My car had been valeted earlier in the day,' Dunlow explained. 'If they'd found anything unusual, they would have told me.'

Sweet wrappers and crumpled tissues littered my car. Dunlow's was evidently a different beast, where something misplaced or planted would be noticed with haste.

'Why would we believe anyone put the scarf and gloves in your car?' Juliet asked. 'Maybe you stashed them there, and it was only bad luck that someone saw you get rid of the evidence.'

The lines across Dunlow's forehead deepened. 'Why would I tell you the truth about where I found them if I'd had anything to do with them? I'm only telling you now because their appearance is one of the many ways someone is trying to harm my family.'

'Can I clarify; you didn't know someone was watching when you binned the scarf and gloves?' I asked. 'You weren't aware some of your staff went to the car park during their breaks?'

Dunlow raised his shoulders in a controlled shrug. 'I know it won't make me more likeable to you people, but the movements of my staff are of little consequence to me. I've not set foot in the staff room in years.'

Juliet's theory that Dunlow was aware of his underlings held water, but his assertion he was disinterested in their comings and goings was airtight. This was a man for whom a murder on his land was only of interest when it impacted him and his sons. The movements of his staff members were so far beneath him, they became invisible.

'Why did you get rid of the scarf and gloves?' I asked. 'Why not tell us as soon as you found them?'

'I didn't want to play their game,' Dunlow ground out. 'I didn't know what you would find on those gloves, but I wasn't going to hand over something that would incriminate my son.'

'Or yourself?' Juliet added.

Dunlow started. 'Me?'

A slight smile bloomed on her face. 'It might interest you to know that a large amount of your DNA was found on the gloves.'

Dunlow's face paled. 'That must be from when I found them. Or when I lost them.'

'Perhaps.' Juliet's mouth tightened. 'Or maybe you thought you were clever, taking latex gloves from the barn and putting them on inside the leather gloves. You thought you could pin Melanie's murder on someone else.'

Finally, Dunlow looked rattled. 'Latex gloves?'

'There's a box of them in the barn,' I said. 'Did you take them, plus a pair of gloves you knew would incriminate someone else, then shoot Melanie?'

Both Juliet and I avoided saying who else's DNA was on those gloves. Dunlow had cast blame on Karl before. He didn't need any fuel added to that fire.

Dunlow swallowed, visibly controlling himself. 'None of that is true. I don't know what latex gloves you're talking about.'

'They were in your barn,' Juliet stated, broadcasting her disbelief.

'A place where I spent very little time until recently,' Dunlow retorted. 'Groundskeepers have maintained the land and looked after the dogs since long before I was born. There has rarely been any reason for me to go to the barn. I had no idea there were latex gloves in there. I don't know why there would be.'

I resisted the urge to tell him why Karl kept plastic gloves in the barn, instead turning over the idea that Dunlow hadn't known they were there. It fit with his disinterest in anyone who worked under him, but not with my theory that he'd taken both pairs of gloves to frame Karl for Melanie's murder.

Dunlow had been a drastically different man at the start of this interview, but his true nature had resurfaced. What if his disdain for everyone but the ones he loved proved his innocence?

'Mr Dunlow, did you have any relationships prior to your marriage to Mrs Dunlow?' I asked.

Dunlow flinched. Juliet shifted, affected by the conversational whiplash I'd subjected them to.

'How is that relevant?' Dunlow asked.

'It's another line of enquiry we're pursuing.'

Juliet shifted again. I'd used *we* loosely.

'My wife and I met when we were young.'

'There was no one else?' I pushed. 'No one-night stand? No affair?'

Blotchy blush spread across Dunlow's face. 'No,' he snarled.

'You were a virgin when you slept with Mrs Dunlow for the first time?' Juliet pressed. I suppressed the urge to smile at her. She might not know where I was going with this, but she had my back.

Dunlow glared at her, but slowly the puce patches receded from his cheeks. 'There was nothing significant. No one I remember.'

'No one ever got in contact with you afterwards?' I asked.

'No,' Dunlow stated, his monosyllabic answer a slamming door against any further enquires.

Juliet glanced at me. 'That's all we need for now. Thank you for popping in, Mr Dunlow. We'll keep you updated.'

'Wait,' Dunlow cried out as I reached for the recorder. He clenched his fists on the table. 'I need to know what you're going to do.'

'What are we going to do?' Juliet asked, her voice hardening. 'The first thing we'll do is sort out a transcript of this interview to replace the lies you fed us with the truth. Then we'll go over the evidence which, along with your continued lies, gives us good reason to suspect you were involved in the murder of Melanie Pirt. Then, if we haven't found something to pin you down, we'll look into your theory that someone wishes harm upon your family.'

Dunlow wasn't cowed, more able than others who incurred Juliet's wrath to maintain eye contact during her tirade. He didn't protest when I lifted my hand again to stop the recording, nor did he say another word until Juliet had swept from the room. I paused at the door when he spoke.

'Do you believe me?'

The same man we'd met outside the hospital sat before me; broken and contrite. But I knew how quickly Dunlow could switch to what I suspected was his natural persona.

'Did you know that Terence thinks you had something to do with the attack?' I asked.

Dunlow visibly crumpled. His hands fell limply onto his lap, his sharp eyes dimming. It was all the answer I needed. I had to pick through everything he'd said before I would consider exonerating him for Melanie's murder, but there was no way the broken man before me would have done anything to harm either of his sons.

'I'll send someone to sign you out of the station,' I said, as I walked out of the room.

Now, to go upstairs and do exactly what Juliet had said we would. Solving Melanie's murder was our priority, at least for the moment.

Dunlow's theory that someone had it in for him and his sons was secondary.

His final question nagged at me. Prior to this interview, I wouldn't have had to think before saying no. I'd been convinced Dunlow killed Melanie.

I took the stairs to give me more time before I had to talk this through with Juliet. Doubt wound through me.

I'd avoided Dunlow's question for a reason.

Gabe. Sent 16:05.

Things are kicking off here. I'm not going to get away until late. But I'd still like to see you x

Ollie. Sent 16:06.

I've had a mad one too – as much as prancing around in tiny underwear compares to chasing bad guys. Let's meet tomorrow night instead xx

Gabe. Sent 16:06.

You're sure you're not up for tonight? x

Ollie. Sent 16:06.

Do we need to have a refresher about booty calls? xx

Gabe. Sent 16:07.

No. I don't want to see you to have sex. I just want to
see you x

Ollie. Sent 16:08.

How romantic. But you need to put your money
where your mouth is. Wine and dine me, and then I'll
consider putting out again xx

Gabe. Sent 16:09.

I've never looked forward to a meal so much x

'Juliet?'

'Hi, Keith.'

'I wasn't expecting to hear from you today. Found your murderer yet?'

'No.'

'Why are you calling then?'

'I want to make plans for this weekend. I'd like to take the girls out, alone.'

'I don't think so. I'm not getting them all excited, only for you to let them down again.'

'Don't tell them about it then. It can be a surprise.'

'How about we plan something we can all do together? Then, if you back out, they will still have a fun day with their dad.'

'I'm allowed to see the girls on my own.'

'Of course. I'd never try to stop you.'

'Then let me do it this weekend.'

'Let's see how it goes. A lot can change before the weekend. Murders could occur that would be so much more important to you than our girls.'

'I'm coming home this weekend, and I'm going to take the girls out on my own.'

'If you say so.'

'I'll see you Friday night.'

'Sure.'

Gabe

Juliet slammed her mobile onto her desk as I walked into our office.

'What do you make of the latest version of the truth?' She gestured at the wall of evidence. 'Has Dunlow told us what actually happened this time, or are we going to be adding another layer of notes in a couple of days when he decides it's advantageous for him to come forward again?'

I leant against my desk to look at the notes and photos crisscrossed with lime green twine. Juliet's agitation didn't create the ideal setting for sharing the conclusions I'd come to on the long climb up to our floor.

'I believe him.'

Juliet sidestepped to get a good look at me. 'You're joking?'

I bit the inside of my cheek. 'Afraid not.'

Juliet squinted at the ceiling. 'Explain.'

'I still think it could be Dunlow. I want it to be him.'

He'd put on a show of remorse and sadness downstairs, but he was an arse and a bully. His sons were terrified of him and he exuded the belief that he was above everyone else. He was the kind of man who believed he could commit crimes because laws weren't made for people like him.

Dunlow's dismissive words and attitudes were beginning to turn my mind away from him, which was wrong. Being horrible should result in punishment, not absolution.

'Tell me what you're thinking,' Juliet urged.

I paced towards the evidence wall. 'Dunlow thinks someone is targeting his family. If he and his sons are telling the truth, then a series of events has happened to and around them that are hard to assign to coincidence.'

'I don't like blaming chance for incidents that are unlikely to be accidental.' Juliet's voice had lost its harsh edge. Her eyes roved over the wall as she leant on her desk.

'Everything kicked off with Melanie's murder.' As much as I didn't want her death to be a strike against the Dunlows, it could be. 'Then we have Leo's hit and run, the fire, the gloves and scarf being planted in Dunlow's car, and finally Terence's beating.' I rested against my desk. 'It could all be random. Dunlow and his sons could be having a run of bad luck. Melanie could have been killed for unrelated reasons; the van could have been cruising too close to the pavement. The fire could have been accidental and Terence could have been beaten by someone with a homophobic grudge.'

'But you don't think that's what's happening?' Juliet asked.

'No.' My heart felt heavy as I uttered the single syllable. 'Again and again, we've encountered liars in this case. Dunlow. Leo. Terence. Jordan. But who have we never suspected of lying?'

Juliet's eyes snapped over to the right section of wall. 'Karl?'

I nodded, my nose wrinkling. Right from the start, I'd felt an instinctive protectiveness towards the groundskeeper. I'd not wanted him to come under real scrutiny, and I didn't relish pushing him into the spotlight.

'What if Karl lied to us right from the beginning?' I forced myself on despite the guilt churning in my guts. 'He had the means and opportunity to kill Melanie, and he definitely knew about the latex gloves. He could have followed Leo to the memorial and hired the van that hit him. He knew his way around the grounds, so could have easily avoided Jordan and started the fire. We know a pair of keys is missing for the BMW; what if Karl stole them and planted the scarf and gloves? And he could have beaten Terence. The attacker was tall.'

Juliet took a deep breath. 'I didn't think you saw Karl as a real suspect?'

'I didn't. I don't.' I clenched my hands a couple of times to dispel the restless energy demanding I stop this and get back on the correct path. It was my job to find Melanie's killer, even if that meant searching avenues I'd rather leave undisturbed. 'If Dunlow is telling the truth, then Karl could easily be the link between everything that's happened.'

'Or you could be stretching,' Juliet mused. 'Karl could link these events, or he could be an easy scapegoat Dunlow wants us to pursue. What if Dunlow killed Melanie and planned to blame Karl all along? The hit and run could have been random chance, as could Terence's beating. Dunlow could have set the fire himself to destroy evidence. He could have changed his mind about where he found the scarf and gloves because he decided someone else planting them tossed the blame even further away.'

I pushed my weight into the desk as I scrubbed my fingers through my hair. 'I can't believe I'm considering Karl while you're fighting for Dunlow.'

'Do you think he could be Karl's father?' Juliet had figured out why I'd asked Dunlow about his past relationships.

'I don't see any similarities between them and Matthew could be lying, but we have to consider it.'

I lowered my hands. Juliet stared at Karl's photo. I couldn't do the same.

'There's also Jordan.' I didn't feel good throwing the younger man under the bus, but if I wanted to be a good detective, I couldn't let softness towards suspects get in the way of finding the truth. 'He could have killed Melanie, pushed Leo into the van, started the fire, and attacked Terence.'

'Terence,' Juliet huffed. 'Who we still have no bloody alibi for. We can't discount him yet.'

'I called Jordan as I walked up here,' I carried on, unwilling to be derailed by a rant about how Benedict Hogan was uncontactable. 'There was no answer on his mobile or at home. We don't know where he was when Terence was beaten.'

'We're no closer to pinning this on any of them,' Juliet said slowly. 'And we have a major problem. We need to talk to Karl, but he's in hiding.'

I pushed away from my desk and grabbed my coat from my chair. 'I have an idea. It'll either lure Karl out of hiding, or force whoever is lying to show themselves. For it to work, we need to visit Leo.'

From: Gabriella Martin **gabriella.martin@mit.gov.uk**
To: David Rees **david.rees@forensics.gov.uk**
CC: Juliet Stern **juliet.stern@mit.gov.uk**
Date: **17 October, 17:17**
Subject: **Operation Chalice – Paternity test needed**

David,

Please could you use the DNA samples already collected to do a
paternity test for Timothy Dunlow and Karl Biss?

Gabe

Gabe

Leo's expression transformed from mild curiosity to stark panic as he opened the door to his hotel suite.

'Is Teddy okay? Has something else happened?' he said in a jumbled rush.

I held up my hand. 'Terence is fine. He was released from hospital this afternoon and, as far as we know, he went straight to a friend's house.'

'That's where he is then.' Dunlow pulled the door from his younger son's grasp.

'He didn't inform you of his new arrangements?' Juliet asked in mock innocence.

Dunlow's eyes narrowed. 'He did not.'

'Might we come in?' I asked, keen to avoid a scene in a hotel corridor. 'We have a request to make of Leo.'

'Me?' Leo stepped back, allowing us inside. His father led us through to the adjoining sitting room, confirming my suspicion that Leo's temporary accommodation was at least twice the size of my maisonette.

'Following on from new evidence, we have reason to believe someone could be targeting your family. Perhaps the same person who killed Melanie.'

I didn't look directly at Dunlow as I spoke, busying myself with extracting my notepad as we sat down on sofas designed with expense rather than comfort in mind. I didn't know if he would be smug or alarmed. I had no resource to deal with either.

'Who is it?' Leo perched on the edge of his seat, his bandaged hands plucking at the fraying knees of his jeans.

'We can't say.' Wouldn't say. If Karl or Jordan turned out to be innocent, I didn't want to have acquired a new enemy for either of them.

Leo looked between me and Juliet. 'How can I help?'

I'd come into contact with a lot of different families while on the force, meeting them at times of great pressure. It revealed their true nature. Often, families moved like starlings in a dark wave; grief, anger and frustration displayed in patterns that became familiar during each case.

Terence, despite his differences, was an echo of his father. He was unhelpful and self-serving, had the makings of an entitled bully. Leo was different. He'd lied, but only because he was told to. His eagerness to help shone through his unwavering gaze.

'We'd like to use your social media to lure someone out,' I said. Juliet and I had planned how to explain this to the Dunlows. We didn't want them gaining any inkling of who we thought might respond. We weren't sure how they would react, especially if they discovered Terence was in the running, and there was still a cloud of suspicion hanging over Dunlow.

'Here.' Leo pulled his phone out of his hoodie and tapped rapidly to unlock it. 'What do you need?'

One glance at Dunlow confirmed he wasn't as trusting as his son, but since we were taking his allegations seriously, there wasn't much he could do.

'What do you use the most?' I asked, scooting forward to look at the small screen. The background was the shot of Melanie that tipped us off to Leo's connection with her; she smiled shyly while his blazer clad arm reached into the frame. 'Where would you post about something you were going to do?'

'I don't use any of them much.' Leo's eyes flicked to his father. Apparently social media was another item to add to the list of things Dunlow disapproved of, alongside homosexuality and telling the truth to the police. 'The easiest one for someone to find would be my Instagram.'

Leo tapped on the app and navigated to his profile. The screen filled with pictures of landscapes, a mixture of exotic and the woods near his home.

'This is brilliant.' I pulled my phone out of my pocket and showed him the photo I'd found during a quick Google search. It was the same aesthetic as the rest of his posts. I airdropped it over to Leo's phone, where he cropped it and added a dusky filter.

He tipped his head to the side, his auburn hair falling over his forehead. 'I recognise this. Isn't it the old burial place near the house?'

'Do you go there sometimes?' I asked.

Leo nodded, and I had to fight to contain a broad smile. This was perfect. If Leo recognised it, chances were our suspects would too.

'That's the place.' I put away my phone and showed Leo a page of my notepad. 'These are the details we need in the post, but it would be best to put it into your own words.'

Leo bit his tongue between his teeth as he tapped at his phone screen. Dunlow lounged in his seat, gazing out of the window. The early evening darkness was broken by the lights of boats in the harbour.

'Done.' Leo tilted his phone towards me and Juliet. 'Is that okay?'

'That's great.' Juliet wiggled her fingers. 'Can you send it out to all of your subscribers?'

Leo bit his lip to hide a smile. 'Sure.'

'Please don't tell anyone about this,' I warned. 'It can't leave this room.'

Frowns graced the men's faces, unnatural on Leo and far too familiar on his father.

'Stay here tomorrow morning.' I waited for Dunlow to turn from the window and acknowledge my request with a single dip of his head. 'We'll update you on whether or not we've been successful.'

Juliet and I stood. Dunlow stayed sitting, leaving Leo to show us out of the suite.

'I hope you catch them,' he said, before easing the door shut behind us.

I struggled to identify my churning rush of emotions as I followed Juliet over to the lift. I was pleased my plan had worked so far, that Leo had been cooperative and Dunlow hadn't been actively unhelpful. But under that swirled a sickening mixture of regret and dread.

Juliet wasn't the one pushing this forward; it was me. If no one turned up tomorrow, I would have wasted time and precious resources for nothing. But if someone did turn up, that was on me too. I couldn't decide who I would be more gutted to catch on that ancient hill: Karl, Jordan or Terence. Yet, if none of them appeared, we would be no closer to finding Melanie's killer. The moment when we would have to close this case was ticking closer. This was our last shot.

'We should pick up something to eat on the way back to the station,' Juliet said, as we walked into the lift. 'I fancy chips.'

'Whatever you want.'

One sharp look from Juliet confirmed that my dull tone and uncharacteristic disinterest in food had been noted, but she didn't push me to talk. I was glad. There wasn't a thing I wanted to say, not about this case or the events of my past that may have caused me to make a mess of it.

leoisroaring

Stagbury Hill, New Forest

You think you know someone, then you find out something that proves you wrong.

I've suffered a lot of rubbish in my life, sometimes it feels like the sadness might overwhelm me.

When that happens, when I have a big decision to make, I come here.

I've been spending a lot of time here recently, watching the sun rise each morning.

I hope that tomorrow it will bring me comfort and I'll know what to do.

#sunrise #hopeful #toughdecision

FORM 91A – FORMAL REQUEST FOR ARMED ASSIST-
ANCE

REQUESTING OFFICERS:

Detective Inspector Juliet Stern and Detective Sergeant Gabriella
Martin

CASE NUMBER:

10098755

CASE DESCRIPTION:

Murder of Melanie Pirt on the grounds of the Dunlow Estate in the
New Forest on 9 October.

REQUESTED ARMED RESPONSE TIME AND PLACE:

18 October – early morning, before sunrise. Stagbury Hill in the New
Forest

REASON FOR WARRANT REQUEST:

Karl Biss, a prime suspect in this case, has gone into hiding. Evidence
suggests he could be targeting other members of the enquiry. Jordan
Haines, another prime suspect, has beaten at least one member of the
Dunlow family and has motive for Melanie Pirt's murder. Terence
Dunlow, our third main suspect, has no alibi and may have been
directly or indirectly involved in Melanie's Pirt's murder. We have
placed a fake post on Leonard Dunlow's Instagram in an attempt to
lure one of these men out of hiding. They will expect Leonard to be
at Stagbury Hill at sunrise tomorrow (Stagbury Hill is adjacent to the
Dunlow Estate on the east side). Armed assistance is necessary as the
gun used to shoot Melanie Pirt has not yet been recovered.

Call connected at 19:18.

'Hello, how can I help you?'

'Hello, this is Detective Gabe Martin. Is that Terrie?'

'Oh, yes. Hello, detective.'

'Gabe is fine. We've been trying to get in contact with Jordan since this morning. His college said he didn't go in today.'

'Um, no. He wasn't feeling well. He was home today. I guess he didn't hear the phone.'

'Right. Is he there now?'

'He's just left.'

'Do you know if he's taken his mobile? I tried calling that, but it went straight to voicemail.'

'Yes, that, uh, makes sense. He was watching TV with me and fiddling on his phone until about half an hour ago, when he suddenly got cross. He wouldn't tell me what was going on, and he threw his mobile at the wall. It's broken.'

'Jordan saw something on his phone that upset him, then he left the house?'

'I assume it was something on his phone. He wouldn't let me look.'

'Did he say where he was going?'

'He barely said a thing. Just grabbed his hoodie and ran out.'

'Okay, Terrie. Please ask Jordan to give me a call when he gets home. He can leave a message if there's no one here.'

'I'll tell him. Can I, I mean. Is he in trouble?'

'I hope not.'

Gabe

'That's it.' Juliet tapped her mouse and pushed away from her desk. 'Armed assistance is confirmed.'

We'd wolfed down chips while staring at our computer screens, wading through the reams of virtual paperwork necessary for a last minute and potentially volatile operation. I'd spent the last ten minutes clicking through transcripts of Dunlow's interviews, hopeful I'd find something to conclusively prove his guilt so I could stop all of this.

If one of our suspects didn't arrive tomorrow, this case would be over. Angela would order us to shelve it, placing it at the same priority level as other cold cases while we moved onto solving fresh crimes. My first time leading would be a failure.

If any of them did arrive, then my instincts would be proven wrong. My past, as much as I tried to forget it, would have intruded. My softer side would have won over hard logic.

I would rather catch Melanie's killer than be vindicated. If someone did appear tomorrow morning on that Bronze Age burial mound, then I'd push down all my fears and doubts. This wasn't about me. I would deal with my own inadequacies once we'd brought Melanie's killer to justice. It didn't matter if her murderer was a groundskeeper I pitied, an arrogant yet scared older son, or a young man who had let his jealousy overcome him.

Jordan may have already taken the bait. I didn't know if he was desperate to stop Leo from blabbing, or if he'd spotted a good chance to terrorise him.

Juliet and I shrugged our coats on. I jumped at my name being called as we walked out of our office.

Paul leant against his doorframe. 'Do you have a minute?'

'What do you need her for?' Juliet snapped.

'Are you Gabe's keeper?'

Juliet glared across the open plan floor. 'I hope you've not been working his case as well,' she hissed at me.

343

'What?' I resisted the urge to elbow her. 'When would I have had time for that?'

Juliet's expression didn't soften. 'Don't let him keep you too long.'

She stalked off towards the lifts, leaving me to walk between abandoned desks to the other side of the floor. Paul's office was a mirror of mine and Juliet's, but the similarities stopped at the worn carpet and beige walls. Whereas ours was crammed with two desks and long lines of filing cabinets, Paul's office was spacious and light. His desk faced the door and a window looked out over the main floor space. I didn't know if mine and Juliet's office originally had a window, but that wall was covered by a huge corkboard. A filing cabinet stood in one corner of Paul's office, the top crowded with flourishing plants. Opposite his desk, comfy seats made any visitor welcome.

'Sit, sit,' Paul urged distractedly while he rifled through his desk drawers.

I took the seat nearest the door, trying to work out why he'd called me in. Juliet would roll her eyes if it was to show me the latest exploits of his sons. They both wanted to be police officers like their dad, so had been uncontrollably delighted when I'd let them play with my handcuffs the last time Paul had me over for dinner.

'There it is.' He straightened, holding a Twix. He unwrapped it and took out one bar, holding the other over the desk.

I took it automatically. 'Thank you?'

'Clink, clink.' He shook his section of the chocolate bar at me.

I raised mine to tap his, familiar with his post-case ritual. 'Paul, I have no idea what's going on.'

He took a healthy bite from his half of the Twix. 'I'm sensing that.'

I frowned at him before nibbling off a section of chocolate-covered biscuit. It would be rude to refuse.

Paul shoved the rest of the chocolate bar into his mouth and hummed happily. 'We caught the Barretts.'

I covered my flinch by taking another bite of caramel and biscuit. Habit had numbed me to the sight of Krystal's face as I walked across the main floor. I should have realised that the only case Paul would be celebrating closing was hers.

I swallowed. 'Congratulations. Where did you find them?'

'Where do you think?' Paul nodded at the chocolate bar melting over my fingers. 'Why else would I invite you to share the Twix of Glory?'

I racked my brain and came back empty. 'I'm not following.'

'Your tip about warehouses,' Paul crowed. 'Even when we're not working together, we're a dream team.'

I was unendingly glad Juliet had left without me. If she'd heard Paul's claim that we'd been working together unofficially, I would have been on her shit list for weeks.

I popped the last bite of Twix into my mouth and licked the melted chocolate off my fingers. 'That was not a tip, more like a throwaway comment.'

'Throwaway or no, it was a good shout.'

I tried to smile at him, but even the chocolate crowding my belly couldn't raise my spirits. Paul tipped his head to one side. 'I hear you haven't closed your case?'

'Yeah.' I tucked my hands under my legs. 'We thought we had the guy who did it, but there isn't enough to charge him. And new evidence has thrown other suspects back in the ring.'

'Those cases are the worst.' Paul pulled his face into an exaggerated frown. He'd done the same when his youngest son complained of the epic unfairness of his brother staying up for an extra half hour while he had to go to bed. It was hard not to let my lips curve into a small smile.

'I followed my gut, and it didn't get us anywhere. In fact, it probably led us in the wrong direction.'

Paul stood and limped around his desk, taking a seat in the chair beside me. He gripped my shoulder. 'Hey.' He waited for me to look at him before he dropped his hand to a knee that would be twinging after he'd neglected to use his stick for even such a short distance. 'You're still getting used to this, I forget that sometimes. You have to remember; we're all working with the information we have. Some of that is facts from the case and some of that is the experiences we've had that inform how we feel about the things and people we encounter. Your gut was invaluable on my case, and it might have slowed things down on yours. That's okay. It's not something that will go away, but you'll learn to refine it with time.'

He wrinkled his nose. 'It doesn't help that you're working with the automaton over there. She'd make anyone feel inadequate for being so human as to feel things and make mistakes.'

I looked down at my lap. It wasn't Juliet's fault I'd messed up, but Paul wouldn't appreciate any attempt to defend her. I wasn't sure everyone else was as affected by their past as me, but I'd take all the comfort I could get. I wouldn't let it get in my way again.

'A good night's sleep, and you'll feel better.'

I stood, recognising a dismissal when I heard one. 'Thank you for letting me know about the Barretts.' I paused at the door. 'Have you told anyone where the tip came from?'

Paul was back behind his desk. He might have shared his post-case Twix with me, but his job was far from over. To make sure the Barretts faced justice, he would be filling in forms and fielding emails for a while to come.

'Not yet.'

'Could you not?' I leant against the door frame. 'Only, Juliet will get pissy with me for working any other case but ours.'

Paul saluted. 'Got to keep the evil overlord happy.'

'Thanks.'

I walked across the quiet floor to the lift. Paul might think my intuition was to be trusted, but I knew better. I'd gotten lucky with the Barretts. Someone not so inclined to think well of me would be able to see that. It would be all too easy to link my incompetence in Melanie's case to random chance with Krystal's. They would only have to take a quick look at my file to discover why I was so preoccupied by warehouses and people with tragic pasts.

I pressed the lift button and took a deep breath. At least part of this would be over tomorrow. Someone would turn up in the woods, or we would be left waiting. I had to hope for the former, even if it sent the chips and chocolate in my stomach churning.

Leo. Sent 22:35.

Teddy – I hope you're okay. And I hope you know I
love you. I know we don't say stuff like that much,
but everything that's come out today doesn't change
that you're my brother and I'd do anything for you.
Maybe, if you can, stay in tomorrow morning?
There's some stuff going on, and I want you to be
safe x

Day 9

Wednesday, 18 October

KRYSTAL'S KILLERS FOUND – POLICE STUMBLED ACROSS
CHILD MURDERERS HIDING IN A CONDEMNED
WAREHOUSE…

Scroll.

BETTER LATE THAN NEVER – POLICE DIDN'T ACT QUICKLY
ENOUGH TO STOP HER MURDER, BUT AT LEAST THEY'VE
DISCOVERED KRYSTAL'S KILLERS…

Scroll.

WHO ELSE IS HIDING? – THE BARRETTS MIGHT HAVE BEEN
FOUND, BUT THERE ARE COUNTLESS MURDERERS WHO
HAVE NEVER BEEN BROUGHT TO JUSTICE…

Scroll.

Gabe

Our breath misted through the thin torch beams where we stood at the base of an uneven hill, Juliet's voice ringing in the still morning air as she talked through the details of the operation.

'You'll be by the cars?' Ruby Douglas confirmed. The leader of the firearms team was a tall woman, her slim figure bulked out with heavy bulletproof clothing.

Juliet nodded, her hair falling neatly across her shoulders. I hadn't had time for more than a quick brush of my teeth and a splash of water over my sleep crusted eyes before I'd rushed to the station this morning. At least my hair was stashed under a beanie.

'Don't come over to the active site for any reason,' Ruby warned, pulling on her helmet. 'If you're concerned, call us on the walkies.'

'Keep talk to a minimum,' I interjected through chattering teeth. 'All of the suspects are skittish. One hint they're going to meet anyone other than Leo Dunlow, and they'll scarper.'

'No worries.' Dev Afzal grinned from under his helmet. 'We'll activate stealth mode.'

Even in the torchlight, Ruby's eye roll at her second in command was evident.

'Good luck,' I said, as the team departed.

Their black-clad figures were swallowed in the shadows cast by swaying trees. This place was as creepy as the Dunlow forest over the road. Only Stagbury Hill itself was devoid of tall greenery, the pocked grass hazardous in such low light.

The team was headed over to the opposite side of the hill, taking up positions in pockets of pre-dawn darkness. A distinctive rock jutted from the hillside over there, which had featured in Leo's Instagram post.

I'd alternated, during a largely sleepless night, between imagining three different men appearing and the hillside remaining empty. I couldn't decide which option would leave me less crushed.

If Karl came, my past would have intruded on the present in an undeniable way. We hadn't heard from Jordan since he stormed out of his parents' house. If he arrived, then another young man in a world far too full of them would be too prone to violence. If Terence appeared, then at least Dunlow wouldn't have kept his nose spotlessly clean but Melanie would have been sacrificed for a secret that had been revealed.

Juliet and I shuffled from side to side by my car, the armed response team's van parked behind on the short lane off the main road. We were completely hidden, a safe distance from where the action would take place.

My eyes hadn't adjusted to the inky blackness enough that I could tell what expression Juliet wore while we waited. She'd been quiet this morning. I couldn't tell if that was due to the early hour or if she was pissed because Paul had called me into his office.

The walkie clipped to my coat pocket bleeped. Static crackled, then it bleeped again.

Baring my hands to the cold air, I pulled it free. 'What was that? Over.'

A few seconds of nothing, then another bleep followed by more static.

Juliet heaved a sigh. 'Maybe the hill is interfering with them?'

'It shouldn't be.' These walkies were designed for use in packed city centres. A measly hill should have been nothing to them.

'Let's leave it for now.' Juliet shuddered, the cold seeping through her coat as well. 'Once the sun's up, we'll find out everything anyway.'

I reattached the walkie to my coat, less comfortable than Juliet with having no way to communicate with the armed team. In truth, we shouldn't need to talk to them during the operation. Their directions were clear. They were only to fire if someone posed a clear and present threat. Most likely, one of our suspects would appear unarmed and be arrested. It was galling to be excluded from the action, but we'd learn the outcome soon enough.

As minutes passed with nothing but awakening birds for company, the lack of information from the team gnawed at me. They hadn't been trying to tell us someone had already arrived, since frigid minutes passed and no one appeared with a suspect handcuffed in tow. They probably wanted to let us know they were in position and waiting.

Despite the freezer-like temperature, sweat gathered on the back of my neck. My hands were clammy inside my pockets, my heart skipping each time another bird joined the morning chorus.

The waiting went on forever. Gradually, the sky above the tops of the trees lightened from star studded black to a deep navy. The bird song increased, shrill cries surrounding us. Nearer the ground, no sounds gave any indication there was anyone but me and Juliet left in the world.

I pressed my teeth into the insides of my cheeks. Every minute that passed was another closer to someone appearing. Or not.

And what if someone else appeared? I'd pinned Melanie's murder down to either Karl, Terence or Jordan. If I'd been wrong about them, then who knew if I'd correctly judged everyone else.

From: Laura Peters **peters@dunlowconsultants.co.uk**
To: Timothy Dunlow **dunlow@dunlowconsultants.co.uk**
Date: **18 October, 6:02**
Subject: **Morning cleared**

Mr Dunlow,

I have cleared all the appointments from your diary for this morning and will make sure you're not disturbed.

Laura

Benny – I don't know if you've gotten any of my messages, but I'm staying here for a bit. If you appear while I'm out – please don't leave again. I'll be back soon and I'll explain everything, but there's something I need to deal with this morning. Love, Teddy x

Gabe

The sky was shot through with deep reds and pinks near where the sun would appear soon, when the walkie bleeped again. There was long period of static before it cut off and we were left with only the riot of awakening birds.

A crease formed between Juliet's brows as she looked at the device clipped to my coat pocket. 'I hate technology.'

Stuck in an endless round of wondering whether someone would appear or not, I nodded. 'I'm going to go check on the team.'

'What?' Juliet straightened out of the hunch she'd adopted to retain as much body heat as possible. 'We need to stay here.'

'We need to know what the team is trying to communicate. It might be important.' I couldn't stand here, doing nothing, for another second. 'I'll circle in from the back. I won't get in the way if someone appears.'

Juliet bit her lip. 'You're wearing your vest?'

I patted my padded chest. 'Of course.'

'Find the first team member you can, then head straight back.'

I plunged into the undergrowth beside our car before she could think better of my plan. I'd examined the aerial map of this area so many times that I knew it like the back of my hand. A short walk would bring me to the road. I'd follow that around to the other side of the hill, where I'd find a member of the team and ask what was going on.

Despite the close-packed trees, the lightening sky made my way clear. I picked over fallen branches and skirted patches of nettles, careful not to make too much noise. The last thing I wanted to do was distract the team by blundering through the forest.

I broke from the tree cover earlier than expected, nervous adrenaline making me swift. Edging back from the road, I squinted at a car parked on the other side.

It was a black BMW. That made no sense. The gate onto the estate was further down the road. Dunlow had no reason to park here.

A chill that had nothing to do with the cool morning air crept across my skin. We'd told Dunlow to stay at the hotel this morning. Why would he disobey that direction, especially if he thought someone wished harm on his family?

Unless he didn't think that. He'd seemed genuine when stringing together the bad luck his family had endured recently, but we had no idea how good an actor Dunlow was. What if he was here because he knew no one was going to hurt him, that no one would be lured out by our trap?

I needed to warn Juliet and the team there was someone potentially dangerous in the mix. Dunlow's presence was negligent at the least, but more likely an indication of his guilt. He didn't know we had an armed unit here. Perhaps he expected to find me and Juliet alone. Maybe he was hoping to get rid of us, since we were getting closer to the truth.

I hurried back the way I'd come. Juliet had to be warned of Dunlow's presence first. The rest of the team had guns, whereas Juliet was unarmed and alone. She was wearing a vest, but Dunlow was too arrogant to be anything other than a perfect shot. If he'd come here to cause harm, he could easily take aim somewhere unprotected by bulletproof panels.

'What are you doing here?' Juliet's voice pierced through the densely packed trees.

I stopped walking, straining to hear more. The wisest course of action was to stay hidden and assess the situation.

'I'm sorry. You said not to come, but I had to know who it was.'

Holding onto the tree in front of me for balance, I leant to one side. The low light highlighted the auburn burnish of Leo's hair.

'I came with Dad,' Leo rushed to fill Juliet's disapproving silence. 'He's gone to look after the dogs. I said I needed to get something from the den.'

Juliet shook her head. 'You've made a bad decision. Come on, get in the car. You'll be safe in there.'

Leo's head dipped as he walked over to her. He had no reason to lie about why his father was here, but I didn't think Dunlow would feel any compunction about lying to his son if it saved his own skin.

He wouldn't consider himself a danger to Leo, only to us. I needed to talk to the team.

A crack of breaking wood lanced through the forest. I froze. Footsteps shuffled through fallen leaves to my left.

'Is someone out there?' Juliet called.

Keeping my feet planted in place, I leant to the other side. I could see nothing but thick trunks of trees.

Juliet assumed it was someone, but it could be something. I'd researched after she made another joke about horses in the New Forest. They did wander wild around here.

Juliet stood in front of Leo, scanning the trees. The young man peered over her shoulder. Their heads twitched in the same direction at another sharp snap.

Leo's mouth fell open, while Juliet's pressed into a thin line. It was impossible to tell if she was resigned or angry. My heart pounded wildly as I squinted into the trees, searching for the source of the noise.

'It's you,' Juliet said.

Jordan,

Where the fuck have you been all night? Call me as soon as you see this.

Your mum says the police are trying to find you. If you've gotten messed up in anything serious, you can pack your stuff and clear out.

Think hard on how you want to play this, son. You're getting on my last nerve.

Dad

Gabe

My fingers ached as I dug deeper into the tree bark, desperately straining to see who Juliet had spoken to. My heart thundered in my ears, but not so loud I couldn't hear snapping twigs and rustling leaves as someone moved closer to the clearing.

'What are you doing here?' Leo had swapped shock for horrified outrage. 'Did you kill Melanie?'

Leo's reaction didn't give me much to go on. He would have said the same to any of our suspects.

Leaning far out to the left, keeping my feet planted to avoid making a sound, I could discern the silhouette of whoever we'd lured into the forest. They were tall, which ruled out Dunlow. The shape of their body was bulked out by a heavy coat. The half-light of the rising sun leeched all colour from their hair and clothes.

'Get behind me, Leo,' Juliet ordered. 'And you. Stay there.'

They stopped moving. I controlled my breathing, willing away the clouds of vapour released with each exhalation. Leo looked mutinous, but he allowed Juliet to place herself between him and the newcomer.

'Where's the other one?'

My heart shoved other organs out of the way in an attempt to sink several inches. I knew that voice. The Yorkshire lilt was unmistakable. The green of his worn coat became clear, the hair sticking out under a bobble hat tangled and mane-like.

'The other what?' Juliet asked.

'The other detective,' Karl said, as calmly as every other time we'd talked to him. Like he hadn't come to this hillside to finish what he'd started the night he killed Melanie.

Jordan hadn't killed his girlfriend in a jealous fury. Terence hadn't murdered Melanie to silence her. Dunlow hadn't shot a girl he deemed inappropriate for his son. Leo hadn't killed Melanie in a spurned rage.

Karl Biss shot Melanie Pirt. His appearance here couldn't mean anything else.

'She's unwell.'

I exhaled slowly. I wasn't sure why Juliet had lied, but it gave me options. Karl didn't look like a threat, but that could easily change.

I'd gotten everything wrong about him. He'd never been a victim, he wasn't anything like me. He was no bystander, but the villain.

'Sorry to hear that.' Karl shuffled, the fluffy ball on top of his hat bobbing. 'I didn't expect to see you here.'

'Why are you here?' Juliet matched Karl's gentle tone.

'To talk to Leo. I saw his Instagram post last night.'

The flash of triumph that my plan had worked was drowned by a rising flood of self-flagellation. We'd caught Karl, but it was a close thing. If I'd trusted my gut, a murderer would have gotten away.

'I've been hanging around, waiting for Leo.' Karl's head swivelled, but not far enough to see me. 'I saw you arrive. You didn't hear me call your name, so I followed you up here.'

'What do you want to talk to me about?' Leo said over Juliet's shoulder, his voice nasal. I'd been so fixated on Karl that I'd not noticed Leo breaking into tears behind Juliet.

'I wanted to warn you,' Karl said, taking a step closer. He was largely hidden in the shadows of trees, the yellow wool of his hat brightening as the sun rose.

'What did you want to warn him about?' Juliet asked.

'Someone's trying to hurt him, and the other Dunlows.'

My heart, which had taken up residence beneath my stomach, leapt back to its rightful place. Maybe Karl appearing here was like when he'd stumbled on the bodies. He was in the wrong place at the wrong time. Karl couldn't have known Leo's post was designed to lure out a killer; he thought he would be able to catch Leo on his own to impart a warning.

Maybe I hadn't read him all wrong. He was like me; someone who couldn't help their past. He couldn't help how others would judge him because of it.

But that meant Melanie's killer could be on their way. I listened to the sounds of the forest.

Nothing. Yet.

'How do you know that?' Juliet asked. Behind her, Leo wiped his streaming eyes on the cuffs of his coat.

'Because I saw them.' Karl took another step forward. 'I didn't go far when I left, stayed on the estate. There's someone lurking in the forest. They've been putting out traps and stuff. They must know the Dunlows will be back to look after the dogs.'

Karl had seen someone who intended to hurt the Dunlows. That cleared his name, but it meant these woods weren't safe. We needed to re-establish contact with the armed response team. I needed to tell them Dunlow was roaming around nearby. They needed to know that one suspect was out of the picture, but whoever might appear on this hillside next was vindictive and highly dangerous.

I pulled myself towards the tree, fingers cramping when I released them from the craggy bark. Karl was as innocent as I'd thought. My judgement wasn't skewed by my past, but we were no closer to finding Melanie's killer. Hopefully, they had been lured out of hiding as well. This morning would see us freeing an innocent man from blame and bringing a guilty one to justice.

Just visible around the tree I'd clung to, Karl took another step forward. The movement brought him out of the forest's shadow. Light from the new day's sun revealed what had been impossible to make out while he was drenched in darkness.

His shape wasn't hard to discern because of his coat. He held himself awkwardly, one arm behind his back. From that hidden hand, hung a long hunting rifle.

I slapped a palm over my mouth to stifle a gasp. Wrong. I'd gotten it wrong. Again.

'You didn't shoot Melanie?' Leo asked.

Karl shook his head, the bobble on his hat swaying drunkenly. 'Of course not. I don't have it in me.'

His voice didn't change. I was sure if I could see his face, that wouldn't have betrayed a drop of guilt either. We thought the other suspects in this case were liars, but this man had them all trumped.

'Stay there,' Juliet snapped, when Karl took another step forward. How he was holding his arm must have looked odd. Juliet couldn't tell what he was hiding, but she knew there was something.

There wouldn't be much of a gap between Karl revealing the gun and using it. I needed to make a move before he got bored of pretending to be innocent. Juliet had a vest on, but a gun shot at close range would kill her. And there was Leo, mopping tears from his face.

'I didn't think it was you,' he said wetly. 'Dad was adamant, but I told him you were a good guy.'

It was galling that Dunlow had seen through Karl's act, while I was duped along with his son. Too eager to believe Karl had darkness thrust onto him, I'd not seen his true nature.

Placing my feet carefully, I edged out from behind the tree. My clothes were close fitting to keep out the morning chill, so didn't rustle as I crept over the forest floor. My enemies were brittle twigs and brown leaves.

'Thank you, Leo.' Karl took another step forward despite Juliet's warning. I used his movement to mask my own. 'You need to get away from here. Can I take you somewhere safe?'

My nostrils flared with the effort of keeping silent. I didn't like to think what Karl would do to Leo if he got him somewhere alone. Karl didn't seem particularly poetic, but he might like the symmetry of Leo and his lover being shot in the same woods.

'The safest place for Leo is here with me,' Juliet stated baldly.

Her eyes widened infinitesimally when she spotted me. I froze, sure Karl would notice her looking over his shoulder, but the moment was over in a split second. I clenched my teeth against the breath that threatened to whoosh out and took another measured step forward.

'But maybe he should go with you,' Juliet said, a line forming between her brows as she pretended to consider Karl's offer. 'Where would you take him?'

'My car is just down the road.' Karl gestured with his free hand in the direction we'd sent the team. A leaf crunched under my heel, masked by a bird's shrill call. 'I could take him to the station?'

'That might work,' Juliet mused, eyes trained on Karl. 'Or maybe his hotel? Do you know where the Dunlows are staying?'

I was coming to the edge of the trees. Soon I'd be exposed, with no hope of hiding if Karl turned his head. Taking another step, I assessed his tall form. He was bigger than me, probably stronger, but all I had to do was disarm him. Then Juliet could spring into action.

She had a different plan.

'Now,' she commanded, running at Karl.

'No,' I cried out breathlessly. I slipped on a patch of leaves. Catching myself on my hands, I pushed back to standing.

Karl had swung the gun up, straight at a frozen Juliet.

I didn't give him a chance to notice me. Or shoot.

Running full pelt, I closed the short distance between us. I shoved one hand into the side of his head, using the other to swing the gun out to the side.

The kickback as it went off knocked my hand away. Crying out, I smacked at Karl's head again and shoved into him with my whole weight.

Maybe he was overbalanced by the force of the gun going off. Maybe it was the shock factor. I shouldn't have been able to push over a man so much bigger and stronger than myself, but we both tumbled to the ground.

We landed in an uncomfortable heap. Despite my aching arm, I wrestled Karl's hand away from the gun. He struggled beneath me, hat over his eyes. His teeth flashed in a snarl.

Acting on instinct honed by a lifetime of being the slightest person in any confrontation, I balled my hand into a fist and jabbed hard into his groin.

Karl's snarl disappeared under a winded moan. His whole body cradled in on itself. I rolled off to the side.

'Gabe?' Juliet's voice was almost unrecognisable. No coolness, no calm command, only a high note of panic. 'Are you okay?'

'I'm fine.' I sat up. My heartbeat ratcheted as my gaze caught on the gun. 'Are you two alright?'

'The gun didn't go off anywhere near us.' Juliet eyed me as I stood.

I took a deep breath, Karl moaning on the ground. My arm hurt from where the gun had crashed into it, but not too badly. I'd have some scrapes and bruises, but nothing too severe to contend with.

'You got some cuffs?' Juliet asked.

I looked over at Leo after I'd passed them to her. 'You alright?'

The young man didn't take his eyes off Karl, who sat gingerly while Juliet clipped the cuffs around his wrists.

'Did he try to kill us?' Leo asked.

I licked my lips. It was a question I didn't have an immediate answer to. With the adrenaline of the last few minutes fading, nothing seemed as clear cut as it had in those breathless moments.

Karl coming here with a gun was highly suspect, but he hadn't seemed inclined to use it until Juliet startled him. He said he was here to warn Leo. What if he was so scared of whoever was out to get the Dunlows that he'd brought a weapon to protect himself?

Or was I making excuses for him again? As Juliet recited his rights, I examined Karl's face. When his eyes met mine, there was no tinge of guilt. He was unchanged from when we'd met him on that first day.

'What the fuck's going on?' Dev burst out of the forest, gun held ready. He lowered it once he clocked Karl, cuffed and subdued. He cocked an eyebrow under his helmet. 'Having a party without us?'

'Leo?' A hoarse shout had Dev raising his gun again, but even a barrel pointed at him didn't stop Dunlow from running over to his son. He dragged him into his arms.

'Why were you both here?' Juliet snapped the tender moment. 'We told you to stay away.'

Dunlow pulled away from his son. 'Someone had to look after the dogs.' His eyes swept across the clearing. 'What's he doing here?'

Karl had stood while the Dunlows embraced, one elbow in Dev's tight grip. He scowled at his former employer. 'Trying to keep your son safe. Unlike you.'

Dunlow flinched, and satisfaction flashed across Karl's face.

'Can you take him to the station?' I asked Dev. He saluted, then marched Karl towards the armed response van.

'We need to find the rest of the team.' Juliet eyed Dunlow like he was a scuttling creature she'd like to stamp under her boot. 'Can you go and ask them to search for Karl's car?'

'We need to make sure no one else has turned up as well.'

Juliet gave me a sharp look, but I turned and walked into the forest. She clearly wasn't inclined to explain away Karl's appearance. The gun was going to be hard to justify, even if he'd only intended to protect himself. But he was holding to his story, even when arrested and faced with the man he could have been trying to hurt.

I came out of the forest and hopped down onto the road. Following the narrow lane, I rubbed my hands over my face. I didn't know which way this was going to go. If Karl talked his way out of this, then we were no closer to finding Melanie's killer. If he didn't, I'd have to face the fact I'd been taken in by him.

I'd take finding Melanie's killer over feeling good about myself, but I wished the two didn't have to sit at opposite ends of the spectrum.

Call connected at 7:20.

'Detective Inspector Juliet Stern.'

'Hello, ma'am. This is Dev. We've found a four-by-four. We've not gone inside, but it opens with the keys we took from Mr Biss.'

'That's great. Anything obviously incriminating that you can see?'

'I'm afraid not, ma'am. It looks pretty tidy in there. Some clothes, but not much else.'

'Fine. Can you arrange to have it brought into the station and seen by the forensics team?'

'Will do, ma'am.'

From: Joanna Byford **joanna.byford@artforall.org.uk**
To: Terence Dunlow **terencedunlow@gmail.com**
Date: **18 October, 7:42**
Subject: **Thank you**

Dear Terence,

Thank you for coming in for an interview this morning. We know such an early start is inconvenient, but it's the only time when punters aren't floating around!

It was great to meet you. We have a couple of other people to see over the next couple of days, but we'll be in touch soon!

Joanna

Jordan,

   I can't wait in for you any longer – I have to get to work. Give me a call as soon as you see this.

   There isn't anything you can't talk to me about, and we'll figure out what to do together.

   Love you,

   Mum xxx

From: David Rees **david.rees@forensics.gov.uk**
To: Juliet Stern **juliet.stern@mit.gov.uk**, Gabriella Martin **gabriella.martin@mit.gov.uk**
Date: **18 October, 8:13**
Subject: **Operation Chalice – Initial report on the hunting rifle**

Stern and Martin,

Before sending the firearm retrieved this morning off to the National Forensics Firearms lab, I had a quick look.

An initial dusting revealed fingerprints matching **KARL BISS**, **TIMOTHY DUNLOW** and **TERENCE DUNLOW** (listed in order from most to least).

There is some white dust around the trigger, which I believe will be a match for the latex residue found in the leather gloves.

Gunshot residue around the nozzle of the gun suggests it was fired recently, although this will be skewed by the discharge this morning.

In my opinion, as the casings are a match, this could be the weapon used to shoot **MELANIE PIRT**.

Please bear in mind that these are initial thoughts, and you'll need to wait for a full report for anything more conclusive.

Rees

Gabe

I opted to take the stairs up to our floor rather than ride in the lift with Juliet. Karl was being processed. Before we questioned him, I needed to work off the adrenaline that had flooded my system in the forest.

Our office was empty when I arrived. I scribbled on a post-it note and stuck it above the tangled jumble of evidence on the wall.

Who is the mystery man?

Juliet clocked it as she walked in, a coffee in each hand. 'You believe there is one?'

I thumped heavily in my chair and shoved my fingers into my hat-flattened hair. 'You don't think there is?'

Juliet sat opposite, wiggling her mouse to awaken her computer. 'We've faced one liar after another with this case. Until I see evidence to back up what Karl's said, I'm taking it all with a ladleful of salt.'

Her voice was the same as always, her movements sure as she jabbed at her keyboard. That didn't mean what happened this morning hadn't affected her.

'Are you alright?' I asked.

Juliet frowned at her screen. 'I'm fine.'

Apparently, being held at gun point hadn't cracked her implacable calm.

'I'm frustrated,' I said. 'We might have brought Karl in, but without more evidence or a full confession, we're going to find it hard to charge him with Melanie's murder.'

'Maybe this will help?' Maddy hovered in the doorway, her arms laden with evidence bags. 'David called me down once they'd gone through the car,' she explained, walking over and dumping the contents of her arms over our desks. 'He's taken all he needs from this lot. He thought you would want to take a look as well.'

Juliet turned in her chair. 'That man is being strangely helpful.'

'Don't question it,' Maddy warned, backing towards the door. 'Who knows how long it will last? Capitalise on it while you can.'

'Wise woman.' I smiled tightly at Maddy before she disappeared, then grabbed a pair of plastic gloves from my bottom drawer.

Sifting through Karl's possessions gave me something to do while we waited to interview him. Tugging clothes out of evidence bags made my arm ache, but useless energy coursed through me. There had been far too many moments when it seemed this case was about to make sense. Everything aligned, but then the light changed and all the pieces were revealed to be in complete disarray.

Our office filled with the stench of stale smoke as we tugged various items of clothing out of bags. Karl must have been on the estate during the fire. Had he started it?

Despite knowing the forensic team would have gone over them, we checked pockets and looked for distinctive stains. I finished with the clothes that had slid over to my side of the desk and started on a pile of papers retrieved from the four-by-four's glove box. They were as boring as the stack of MOT reports and service information stashed in mine.

Juliet piled the plastic-covered clothes beside our door. The only thing left on her desk was an evidence bag containing Karl's wallet. The outside was duct taped together.

'Shit,' Juliet swore, as coins bounced across her desk. She tipped the wallet to the side, releasing more pennies. 'Zip's broken.'

Happy to pause my perusal of the car's last oil change, I set the papers down and helped Juliet gather the coins. My eyes caught on something blue as she swept them towards her.

Juliet flinched when I grabbed her wrist.

'Stop.'

'What?' she asked, loosening her arm from my grip.

I poked the top coins out of the pile, my heart hammering a punishing rhythm. Under green tinged pennies and shiny five pence pieces, was an oval of blue plastic.

Juliet squinted. 'What's that?'

I stared at it, then rushed over to the evidence wall. With clumsy hands, I moved Melanie's selfie and transcripts from her phone out of the way. I'd purposely pinned things to cover photos of her mauled body, but that was exactly what I needed.

It was a miracle I extracted the post-mortem pictures from the wall without dislodging anything else. Frantically, I flicked through.

I placed the bottom photo on top of the pile. 'Here.'

It was a shot of Melanie's arm. Bruising discoloured her skin from her shoulder to her elbow. What interested me was lower than that, almost out of shot.

Juliet whipped the photo out of my hand and laid it beside the shard of plastic on her desk.

It was a perfect match for the fake nails on four of Melanie's fingers. The one from her middle finger was missing.

Juliet's face transformed with triumph. 'This is it.'

Why would Karl have kept her false nail unless he'd killed Melanie?

I nodded but couldn't revel in catching our killer. I'd led us here, but the route was winding. If I'd listened to my gut, the man hoarding a trophy from Melanie's body would have gotten away with killing her.

A sharp tap at the door made us both flinch.

'What?' Juliet snapped.

David scowled from the doorway. 'Sorry to interrupt.' He sauntered in, two evidence bags tucked behind his folded arms. 'I thought you'd want me to come straight away if we found important evidence.'

'You missed some.' Juliet pointed at the broken off nail in its nest of coins.

The sneer on David's face faded. 'Where did you find that?'

'It was in the wallet,' I cut in before Juliet could say something overly scathing and make David revert to being an unhelpful arse.

He tutted. 'I didn't check that, but I'll get on to whoever did.' He held out his evidence bags. 'We found these stashed under the spare wheel.'

The nearest bag contained a set of car keys. The BMW insignia was clear through the crumpled plastic.

Juliet beamed at the bag David held closest to her. 'We've fucking well got him.'

The torn fabric was frayed and stained with mud, but grey birds flew across a navy background.

From: David Rees **david.rees@forensics.gov.uk**
To: Gabriella Martin **gabriella.martin@mit.gov.uk**
CC: Juliet Stern **juliet.stern@mit.gov.uk**
Date: **18 October, 10:11**
Subject: **Operation Chalice: Paternity test results**

Martin,

Attached are the full paternity test results requested for Timothy Dunlow and Karl Biss.

There are enough identical DNA markers to confirm that Karl Biss is a direct descendant of Timothy Dunlow.

Rees

Call connected at 10:26.

'Timothy Dunlow speaking.'

'Hello, Mr Dunlow. This is Detective Sergeant Gabe Martin.'

'Yes. What is it?'

'Following on from evidence gathered this morning, we need to ask if one of your relationships prior to your marriage with Mrs Dunlow was with a woman called Jennifer Clements.'

'Christ almighty. Is it honestly of any importance whom I had liaisons with before getting married?'

'I'm afraid it is.'

'Like I said before, I had two or three brief trysts before I met my wife. They were all inconsequential. I can't remember the names of any of the women.'

'Jennifer Clements doesn't ring any bell?'

'No, it bloody well doesn't.'

From: Timothy Dunlow
dunlow@dunlowconsultants.co.uk
To: Laura Peters **peters@dunlowconsultants.co.uk**
Date: **18 October, 10:31**
Subject: **Search**

Laura,

Do a search for a woman called Jennifer Clements. She may be based in York, or have been there when I went to university.

I want all the information you can find.

Timothy

Gabe

I pressed the button on top of the recorder. 'Interview commencing at 11:40 a.m. on 18th October. The interviewee is Karl Biss. He was offered the chance to seek legal representation but has declined. The interview is being conducted by myself, Detective Sergeant Gabriella Martin, and Detective Inspector Juliet Stern. The interview is regarding the murder of Melanie Pirt and the attempted aggravated assault of Juliet Stern and Leonard Dunlow.'

Karl sat impassively on the other side of the metal table. His coat and beanie were gone, leaving him in a blue-and-yellow-striped jumper and mud-stained jeans. I had to hope my hair fared better than his, which stuck up erratically.

'We'd like to go back to the beginning.' I pushed a map of the Dunlow Estate into the centre of the table. 'Can you please explain your movements on the night of the 9th October?'

Reaching out one long finger to tap the relevant places on the map, Karl told an unchanged story of how he'd walked the dogs in the evening and retired to his cottage. We'd thought this was how it might go: more lies. I tried not to react to the sandpaper scratch his monotonous voice provoked across my skin.

'Did you hear gunshots in the night?' I asked.

Karl shook his head, his wayward hair lazily following the movement.

'Really?' Juliet measured the distance between the shooting and the groundskeeper's cottage with her finger and thumb. 'There's less than a mile between where you were sleeping and where Melanie was shot. If I remember correctly, the windows of the cottage are single glazed.'

Karl drew his hands off the table and focused on the map rather than either of us. 'I have trouble sleeping. I use a white noise machine.'

I knew how hard it was to drop into unconsciousness when past demons came out to play. I frowned at the file sitting on the table between me and Juliet. I felt sympathy for this man, but the evidence in there suggested it was misplaced.

'Can you talk us through the next morning?' I asked.

'I walked a couple of dogs through the forest.' Karl traced his path to the barn, then towards where Melanie was shot. 'They found her. As soon as I saw the body, I called the police. Then I called Mr Dunlow.'

'You didn't recognise Melanie?' Juliet asked.

Karl shook his head, pressing his lips together into non-existence. Uneven stubble coated his cheeks and jaw, the beginning of a scraggly beard. He could be telling the truth. We'd uncovered no connection between him and Melanie.

'Okay.' I flipped open the file and took out the evidence bag containing Karl's note. I placed it beside the map. 'Until you left, you'd been cooperative with our investigation. Can you talk us through your reasons for going into hiding?'

'It's all there. You knew about my parents. You'd try blaming me.' Karl twisted his hand in an encompassing gesture. 'That's why I'm here now.'

'You're here now because you disarmed a gun near a police officer and a member of the public.' The sharpness of Juliet's retort was softened by the gentle smile on her face. 'Please tell us about your parents.'

Karl's jaw clenched. 'Is that necessary?'

'I wouldn't have asked otherwise.'

Karl's eyes flicked to me. I tried to keep my expression neutral while snakes of pure guilt writhed in my stomach. Imagining someone prying into my family dynamics made me want to cringe away, but this was necessary.

'I didn't get on with my dad. He wasn't a kind man, not to me or Mum.' Karl paused, opened his mouth then shut it. 'I don't know what you want me to say.'

'When we visited your father in prison, he had a different account of what happened on the night your mother died,' Juliet said.

I tried to imagine Karl taking a golf club and hitting someone with it so hard and so many times that their skull caved in. His father, with his home-inked tattoos and record that spoke of violence heaped upon violence, was a more likely culprit.

But then, I couldn't imagine Karl shooting a young woman three times and leaving her for dead. The evidence said he was capable of that.

'Your father said you killed her.' Juliet spread her hands wide. 'He said you found out who your real father is, and it drove you to kill your mother.'

Karl's nostrils flared as he shook his head. 'I can't believe he's still saying that.'

'You knew about it?' I interjected. Matthew said he hadn't shared his version of events with anyone before. It seemed he'd lied to us about almost everything, but his lies had led us to view Karl as a viable suspect.

Karl let out a humourless bark of laughter. 'Oh, he made sure I knew. Before I sold the house, he sent me letters. They were full of that bull.' He tightened his hands into fists. 'It doesn't make sense. I loved my mum. Why would I kill her if I found out that scumbag wasn't my dad? I'd be happy to not be related to him but, as far as I know, he's my father.'

I stared at Karl. He had no tells and there were no clear indicators that he was lying. Maybe he didn't know his true parentage, but could coincidence account for him working for the Dunlows?

'Let's talk about after you went into hiding,' I urged, keen to finish the part of the interview where Karl lied to our faces repeatedly. 'You said you didn't go far?'

Karl's shoulders relaxed. 'I stayed on the Dunlow land. That forest is vast, and there were bits only I ever walked through.'

'Why didn't you go further?' Juliet asked.

'I didn't know where else to go, and I didn't want to hide away. I just wanted to avoid something like this. I thought that once you caught the killer, I could reveal myself and make a plan for where to go next.'

Matthew Biss hadn't lied about one thing. Karl had no relatives to flee to, no familiar haunts to hide in. Instead of running far away, he'd stayed near the last place he'd felt safe.

'Did you take anything other than your own belongings when you left?' I asked.

'I don't think so.'

We'd come back to this. For now, we'd see how long he could spin this out for.

'While you were hiding on the estate, you mentioned seeing someone else?' I asked. Someone we suspected was a figment of Karl's imagination.

'Yeah.' His gaze sharpened. 'I never got a good look at them, but I think it was a man. They skulked about, using the broken-down bits of wall to come and go.'

'Did you see them on the night of the fire?' Juliet asked.

Karl grimaced. 'I didn't see anything that night. I was downwind. I woke up and there was smoke everywhere. It took me a couple of days to stop coughing.'

Smoke deepened the earthy smell of someone who hadn't had access to proper bathroom facilities that surrounded Karl.

'You said you came to the hill because you saw Leo's Instagram post.' I flicked open the file and pushed a screen print beside the map and Karl's note. 'Why did you want to see Leo?'

'Because of the person I saw on the grounds.' Karl's face was open and guileless. 'The murder, the fire, Leo and Terence's beatings. That couldn't all be coincidence. I didn't know what the Dunlows had done, but someone had it in for them. I didn't want Leo to get in trouble by posting silly stuff online.'

Karl's theory took a step Dunlow's had not; he thought one of the Dunlows had brought this punishment down on the family. I didn't need three guesses to puzzle out who Karl would blame.

'I follow your thinking with coming to meet Leo,' Juliet said, steepling her fingers on the tabletop. 'What I don't understand is the gun.'

'That's reasonable.' Karl licked his lips. 'I'm not good at being cooped up. While I was hiding, I walked around the grounds. I didn't go near the crime scene. Over on the other side, I found the gun.' Karl pointed at a spot on the map. 'About there, I reckon.'

'Why didn't you call it in?' I asked.

Karl wrinkled his nose. 'I was in your sights because of what my father did. I wasn't about to make myself more of a suspect by handing you the murder weapon with my fingerprints all over it.'

'Why did it have your fingerprints all over it?' Juliet probed.

'I didn't realise what it was at first,' Karl said, his expression pinched. 'As soon as I figured it out, I put it down, but the damage was done. I thought the best thing to do was to keep it away from whoever was wandering around in the forest.'

'Why did you bring the gun to meet Leo?' I asked.

'I didn't know who else might turn up. I didn't know what they might bring. I needed some way to protect us, if things went south.'

'Why did you turn the gun on Leo and myself, particularly if you were so determined to protect him?' The hard edge to Juliet's voice betrayed that having a gun pointed at her this morning had affected her.

'You jumped at me. I reacted without thinking. I didn't mean to point the gun at you, and I didn't realise it would go off. I'm sorry.'

Juliet didn't react to Karl's apology. 'Why didn't you reveal the gun as soon as you arrived?'

'Leo was there. I didn't want to scare him.' Karl swung his gaze over to me. 'That's why I asked where you were. I thought it would be better to hand over the gun when Leo wasn't around.'

I stared into Karl's eyes. They were an unremarkable brown, just like mine. In them, there was no hesitancy or fear.

He didn't look or act like he was guilty, had none of the tells of the countless other people I'd interviewed. No nervous twitching, no desperate over-talking, no tearful appeals. But the fact seemed to be that Karl was guilty of murder of at least one woman. It didn't matter that everything about him calmly protested his innocence. That was a lie. One I wouldn't allow myself to believe any longer.

I opened the file in such a way to block the contents from Karl's view. 'These were found during a search of your car.'

Juliet straightened as I slid a picture of Dunlow's car keys and the second half of Melanie's scarf to the middle of the table. She was like a fox, coiled and ready to strike. She hadn't noticed I was lagging behind. I was pleased we'd found Melanie's killer, but there was no room for me to manoeuvre anymore. My judgement was undeniably faulty.

Karl's eyes tripped between the two pictures. 'I knew how this would look.'

'Please explain to us how it looks,' Juliet requested.

'It looks like I took those things. I assume the scarf is the girl's?'

'It was Melanie's,' I said. 'How did you come to have it? And the keys?'

'You found them under the spare tyre, right?' Karl sighed. 'That's where I found them too.'

'Please elaborate.' Juliet sounded genuinely interested, but her fist clenched under the table.

'I've not been driving around a lot, but I must have gone over a nail or something. I had to put on the spare tyre. That's when I found that stuff.'

The papers from Karl's car were mind-numbingly dull, but the topmost had been a receipt for a new tyre.

'Need I ask why you didn't report them as soon as you found them?' Juliet asked. Her razor-sharp gaze didn't leave Karl for a second.

His mouth twisted. 'I guessed that the scarf was something to do with Melanie, since there wasn't any other woman I'd been around. I wasn't sure what to do with that. I'd planned to sneak the keys into the garage when I got the chance.'

'How do you think those items got into your car?' I asked.

'I don't want to be paranoid, but I assume someone put them there.' Karl bit his lip. 'I said it was the Dunlows someone was trying to hurt, but I'm wondering if I've gotten mixed up in it. Maybe they think I'm closer to the Dunlows than I am.'

I marvelled at Karl's gall. He couldn't know what other evidence we had, but he was determined to spin and deflect until we had him flattened against a wall.

'What do you think of the Dunlows?' Juliet asked, in the same manner someone might ask about the weather before a picnic.

Karl wrinkled his nose. 'I guess I can say now because Dunlow isn't my employer anymore, but I don't like any of them.'

'Not even Leo?' I asked.

'The best of a bad bunch,' Karl conceded. 'Terence's head is so far up his own arse, I'm surprised he can fit anything else up there.'

I hoped I kept the shock off my face. Karl had seemed tolerant before. Perhaps, as we neared the truth and he had to think on his feet, we were getting closer to the bare reality of who he was.

'And Timothy?' Juliet asked.

'Horrible.' Karl's expression soured. 'Stuck up and rude. No time for anyone but his sons, and he barely seemed to like them most of the time.'

'Were you aware of any connection between yourself and the Dunlows before you began working for them?' I asked.

Karl stilled, his eyes narrowing the merest amount. It was the most damning reaction he'd had. Despite his guilt throwing my judgement into question, a thrill ran through me. We were getting somewhere.

After a moment of silence that lasted a beat too long, Karl said, 'There's no connection between us.'

'We've found one.' Juliet flipped the file open, hiding the final piece of paper from Karl. She placed a copy of the full paternity report on the table.

Karl's eyes raced from side to side as he read the jargon filled page. 'What is this?'

'It's proof that Timothy Dunlow is your direct relative,' I said. 'In other words, he's your father.'

If we hadn't received a positive DNA result, the uneven blush rising in blotches across Karl's neck was proof enough he was a Dunlow. I'd seen that distinctive pattern across Leo's skin each time he'd spoken about Melanie, on Terence when we pried into his private life, on Dunlow as we poked him into outrage.

'Does he know?' Karl asked.

Juliet quirked an eyebrow. 'Why would that matter?'

Karl released his hands from their tight grip on one another and rubbed at his nose. 'I just didn't think he knew.'

Juliet snuck a quizzical glance at me while Karl scanned the document again.

'Karl?' I waited for him to look up. 'Why is it important Timothy doesn't know he's your father?'

He clasped his hands again. 'I always held out hope he didn't know. I thought, if he knew, he'd treat me differently.'

Juliet tapped one painted nail on the table. 'You did know of a connection between you and the Dunlows then?'

Karl was shaking his head before she finished the question. 'There's no connection between us. This means nothing.'

'It means enough that you sought Dunlow out,' I said.

Karl shifted his weight. 'I wanted to know what he was like.'

'When did you find out Dunlow's your father?' Juliet asked.

Karl's eyes were flint sharp; a different colour to Dunlow's, but the effect was the same. 'It wasn't the night my mother died, if that's what you're thinking.'

'We're not thinking anything right now,' I lied. 'It would be helpful if you told us the truth about both how you discovered Timothy Dunlow is your father, and the night your mother died.'

Karl took a breath. 'I said before; me and my dad, the man I thought was my dad, we didn't get on. It got worse as I got older. Mum used to comfort me after he'd had a go, and one day she told me he wasn't my biological father.'

'When was this?' I asked.

'I was about fourteen. It gave me hope,' Karl said. 'I didn't have to be like him. I planned to go find my real dad one day. I had childish dreams; that he would know me straight away, that me and my mum would go live with him. But then Dad found out.'

'How?' Juliet asked.

Karl's eyebrows scrunched together. 'I don't know. I was upstairs in my room when I heard him shouting. Everything went quiet so I went downstairs to check Mum was okay. He often stormed off to the pub when he was mad. Mum was the saddest I'd ever seen her, proper crying. I was trying to get her to explain what was going on when he came back in.'

The similarities between this story and the one he'd told in court were enough that it felt believable. Before, he'd left out any reason why Matthew would attack him and his mother. They'd simply gotten caught in the storm of his violent rage.

'He shouted about me not being his son, and he hit me with the golf club.' Karl's voice took on a lifeless quality as he recounted what happened. 'It knocked me out. When I came to, Mum was on the floor. There was so much blood. When he saw I was awake, he hit me again.'

'You didn't kill her,' I stated. Beside me, Juliet's expression tightened.

'I honestly didn't.'

That didn't mean much coming from a man we were reasonably certain had been lying to us from the first moment we'd met him. But, like when Dunlow told us the truth about where he'd found the scarf and gloves, I believed Karl.

I didn't know how much of a fool that made me. If this case had taught me anything, it was that I needed to have cold, hard evidence in front of me before I trusted what my gut said.

'Let's leave that for now,' Juliet said. 'There's a final piece of evidence we found among your possessions.'

Karl watched Juliet flip open the file with dull eyes. It was the same look I sported each time another enquiry asked me to give details about my brother's killer. Those kinds of memories were best left untouched.

Juliet pulled the picture of the fake nail from the file and placed it in the centre of the table. It had been rushed down to the forensics team, where they'd determined there was enough DNA for testing. That result could take days. We were hoping the mere presence of this damning trophy was enough to force Karl into telling the truth.

'Shit,' he said on an exhale. 'I hoped you wouldn't find that.'

There was no panic or guilt, only a slight edge of remorse. Things hadn't worked out the way he'd wanted.

We'd planned to let the silence stretch. Karl had to know this was when the net closed around him, but we would let him flounder until he told the truth.

Maddeningly, he gazed at the enlarged picture of the blue nail. His breathing was even and his skin untouched by the blotchy Dunlow blush.

Karl wasn't the floundering type.

'Karl?' I licked my lips, ignoring Juliet stiffening beside me. 'You need to tell us the truth now. We're going to get DNA from this nail, but we already know it's Melanie's. There's no good reason for you to have this, other than if you killed her.' I pressed my heels hard into the floor. 'If you cooperate, that will be taken into consideration when you're sentenced.'

During my plea, Karl's face was immovable. His dark eyes tracked mine. A trickle of doubt wound down my spine. I'd been sure about Dunlow, evidence seemed to point towards him, but I'd been wrong. My head and heart and guts were all leaning in different directions. I didn't know which to trust.

Karl could have a good explanation for why he had Melanie's fake nail. He could be a man with a tragic past who had gotten caught up in something awful. As unbelievable as it seemed, he could have told the truth about the scarf and keys being planted in his car. He could have stumbled across the gun and genuinely only thought to use it for protection.

Or, like every one of his blood relatives, he could be a liar. A good one. Better, maybe, than his biological father.

'We know you did this,' I said into the silence Karl and Juliet seemed happy to let stretch to breaking point. 'We won't let you get away.'

I injected belief that was strong and unwavering into my words, despite the riot of uncertainty I was contending with.

Karl inhaled, held his breath for tense seconds, then exhaled. 'Okay.'

'Okay?' Juliet repeated.

Karl unwound his fingers from their tight hold on one another, then he spread his hands flat on the table. 'I'll tell you everything.'

My stomach skipped. Karl hadn't confirmed his guilt yet, had only said he was going to reveal the truth. What twisted version would it be this time?

'Everything I've told you about my mum and the man who raised me was true,' Karl began. 'Mum told me about my father and made the mistake of telling Matthew a few years later. The one difference is, she told me my dad's name.'

'Timothy Dunlow?' I checked.

'Yes. Mum made me promise not to contact him. After she died, I didn't see why I shouldn't.' Karl's gaze dropped to the table top. 'Recovery was long, but the thought of finding my real father sustained me.'

'When did you first make contact with him?' Juliet asked.

'As soon as I left hospital.' Karl's voice had taken on the same deadened tone as when he'd spoken about his mother's death. 'I travelled south and found his office. I arrived as he was stepping outside.'

'What happened?' I asked, already dreading the answer. There was no happy ending here.

Karl swallowed. 'He didn't know me. When I tried to talk to him, he told me to piss off. He said he didn't give to charity and had no time for filth who lived on the streets.'

Despite where this story was headed, I couldn't help but feel sympathy for Karl. He'd had his family torn away and when he'd reached out to the only family he had left, he'd been cruelly rebuffed.

'I didn't try again,' Karl went on. 'He didn't want to know me, and I told myself I had better things to do with my life than fight for the attention of someone who thought they were above me.' His fingers moved restlessly over one another. 'I finished school, went to uni. It was only when I was feeling lonely that I looked Dunlow up online. The night before my final year exams, I found my brothers.'

'You didn't know about Leo and Terence?' I asked.

Karl shook his head. 'There was nothing about them online. It was only when I went deeper, looked for any Dunlows and searched the parish records, that I found them.'

The resounding impression Karl gave was of a man quietly broken down, but the moment of finding his brothers held power. His father might have rejected him, but he was no longer Karl's only hope at having a family.

'I wanted to know them, but I didn't want to be rejected again,' Karl explained. 'It was random chance that the groundskeeper job came up. I'd been flitting around after uni, not sure what I wanted to do. But I wanted this. Even if Dunlow was a dead end, I thought one of my brothers would be more promising.'

'How did it go?' Juliet asked. I wondered if she was moved by this story. She was as closed off about her childhood as with every other aspect of her life. I didn't know if she'd experienced loneliness as a youngster, whether she understood the desperate lengths that could drive someone to.

'Not well,' Karl said, his hands stilling. 'Dunlow was as rude as before. He didn't bother to interview me, had his secretary do it. The first time we spoke was after I'd moved into the cottage. I'd gone to the barn to meet the dogs. He came in to shout at me about where I'd parked my car, then barked a load of orders.'

Karl's voice had lost the deadened quality. He wasn't a man prone to outrage, but heat burned behind his words. 'For a while, I didn't meet Ted or Leo. Ted was away a lot and Leo was busy with school.'

'When did you meet them?' I asked.

'A few weeks after I started working there, Ted came to the barn. I'd seen him passing in his car, and I guess he'd noticed me too.' Karl pushed his dirt encrusted thumb nails together. 'He asked if I had any weed he could buy.'

That must have been a crushing blow. Karl's father let him down, and one of his brothers had done the same.

'And Leo?' I asked.

'Like I said, he was the best of a bad bunch.' Karl shrugged. 'He came to the barn during one of his holidays to spend time with the dogs. He was shy, didn't talk much at first. When he did, it was only about himself or the dogs. He didn't see me as a real person. I was one of the help.'

'When did you form the plan to kill Melanie?' Juliet asked.

Her question was as shocking as a pail of freezing water to the face. We'd been treading the way softly. Juliet had unearthed a machete to hack her own path through Karl's reminiscence.

He blinked. 'I didn't plan to kill her.'

'Go back to the start,' I urged, shucking off the aftershocks of Juliet's intervention. 'When did you make the first move towards killing her?'

Karl looked off to one side, and the last vestiges of doubt I'd clung to faded away. An innocent person protested, no matter how unflappable and emotionless they seemed to be. Someone making a full confession took their time to think about how to answer.

Karl had killed Melanie.

I baulked at the surge of emotion threatening to overwhelm me. We'd found Melanie's murderer; her family could have closure. I would be able to set this case aside without loose ends.

I'd have to move on, find a way to make peace with all the wrong turns I'd taken.

'The longer I worked for Dunlow, the angrier I became.' Karl didn't seem angry, not the hot flash of emotion we often encountered between these four walls. His rage was different. Burning, like embers at the bottom of a fire. Almost hidden, but still deadly.

'I didn't make plans, but I began gathering things,' Karl said. 'I took the car keys to piss Dunlow off. He told me to take the gun for cleaning, which I did, but then I kept that as well. Told him it was still being worked on. I found a pair of his fancy gloves in one of the outbuildings and took them. It was all quite petty, but it made me feel better.'

'How did you know Melanie was on the grounds that night?' I asked, eager to move Karl's story on before Juliet could charge in again.

'The dogs.' A hint of a smile graced Karl's face. He looked younger, less careworn. 'They were a comfort to me during those lonely months. I was out walking a couple when one of them got obsessed with following a trail.'

'Lucy?' Juliet asked.

'Yeah.' Karl ran his fingers over his knuckles. 'She was a brilliant tracker, but Dunlow didn't like taking her on the hunt. She was as likely to rip a fox to shreds as she was to find it.'

I swallowed against the lump in my throat as the mess Lucy made of Melanie's face rose to mind. I'd not managed breakfast when I woke before dawn, which I didn't regret. There was nothing in my stomach to turn over.

Karl had been lying to us right from the start. He told us Lucy was Dunlow's favourite dog. Such a small misdirection, but enough to keep our eyes firmly away from the groundskeeper.

'I followed Lucy through the forest, right to the garage,' Karl continued. 'She wanted to go inside, but I dragged her away. I could see Leo had a girl up there.'

'What did you do then?' Juliet asked.

Karl tapped his fingers together. He'd not admitted anything damning yet. He could pretend he'd misunderstood where this was heading. If he protested his innocence, he might walk. For now. There was no way, since the blindfold had been ripped from my eyes, that I was going to let him get away with this for long.

'I went back to the barn,' Karl said, holding Juliet's gaze. 'I put the other dog, Artemis maybe, into its stall. I took a pair of latex gloves and put Dunlow's old gloves on over the top. The pair I'd taken. And I went and got the gun.'

I breathed out shakily. Karl wasn't pretending anymore.

'What did you do then?' Juliet asked.

'I walked to the garage.' Karl tipped his head to the side. 'I was hoping to scare Leo, maybe shoot the gun nearby to freak him out, but then the girl came charging outside. Before I could stop her, Lucy gave chase.'

What a horrifying moment for Melanie. She'd been jilted by a young man she thought she could trust and, when she stepped outside, found herself pursued. That forest, with its close packed trees and creaking silence, was creepy enough when we'd walked around it together. In the dark, panting breaths behind; it was the stuff of nightmares.

'I ran after her,' Karl went on. 'She didn't listen to my commands. I'm not sure she could hear me. By the time I caught up with them, the girl was in a tree and Lucy was going mad on the ground below.'

Maybe Melanie had thought she was safe. She'd died with her mobile in her pocket. Given the chance, she could have called for help.

'What did you do then?' I asked.

Juliet looked at me, but I didn't turn from Karl. I'd felt sympathy for him, I'd thought he was like me. We were nothing alike. I could never, no matter how angry or unjustly snubbed I believed myself to be, turn a weapon on another person.

Some of my brittle anger must have bled into my tone. Curdled blush rose across Karl's cheeks.

'You have to understand; I had to make Dunlow suffer, like he'd hurt me. All the other stuff I'd done barely affected him. This, here, was a chance to cut him to the bone. At the least, Dunlow would have to answer for what happened on his land. Leo's perfect life would be interrupted. Even Ted wouldn't float above it all.'

It was the most animated Karl had ever been. His mind, placid on the surface, was a wild tangle of illogical hurts. Dunlow had treated Karl poorly and his sons had made bad decisions, but it was an insurmountable leap to conclude they deserved the kind of trouble Karl had rained down on them. It was unspeakably callous to decide killing a stranger was the right way to punish his neglectful family.

'You were standing in the forest while Melanie was in the tree,' Juliet said, stern as a teacher when a class got out of hand. 'Then you shot her?'

Karl breathed heavily. 'I could see her up in the tree. She would climb down after Lucy lost interest. My chance to force Dunlow to confront how fragile his seat at the top of the pile is would be gone.' He pointed one finger. 'I shot three times; once for each of them. Leo. Ted. Dunlow.'

Silence rang as Karl coiled his finger back into place.

'What happened next?' Juliet asked.

'She fell.' There was no drag of remorse to his words. 'It took a while to get Lucy to leave her alone.'

'Did you go over to Melanie?' I lowered my hands under the table and pressed my nails into my palms in an attempt to contain the roiling energy inside of me.

Karl shook his head. 'She was dead.'

'What did you do next?' Juliet asked, her voice mild.

'I took Lucy further into the forest and shot her,' he stated. 'She was going mad, and I couldn't chance her biting me as well.'

'And then?' Juliet prompted.

'I walked back through the forest. I knew all the lesser used ways. I hid the gun and both sets of gloves. After that, I followed the way the girl ran to check there was nothing to link me to what had happened. I found the scarf torn between two trees, so I hid that too.'

Even though his plan was to frame Dunlow, the cold way Karl recounted his actions after he'd murdered Melanie made my skin crawl. Her death was a means to an end, one that affected him no more than tipping over a glass of water.

'And the nail?' Juliet asked.

Karl let out a puff of air. It took me a couple of seconds to realise it was a short laugh. The muscles in my neck spasmed with the effort of not lurching away. 'I found that the next day, after the police arrived. There were only the two officers to begin with, the old guy and the Asian woman. I showed them over to the body. While they were setting up a cordon, I spotted the nail embedded in a tree.'

I'd catch Juliet before she laid into Alice and James. They couldn't have watched Karl every second from when they walked into that forest, but that wouldn't stop Juliet from taking her frustration out on them.

'Why did you keep it?' I asked. He didn't know Melanie, had no connection to her. Without the nail, our case against Karl wouldn't have been half as robust. He'd been calculated all along. It felt like a misstep.

Karl considered my question. 'It felt right.'

I swallowed the outraged sound rising up my throat. Melanie's death meant nothing to Karl, other than how it impacted him, how it fitted with his plan to ruin Dunlow's comfortable life. Karl kept the nail not to remember his victim, but because Melanie had been the catalyst for everything he'd wanted.

Juliet tapped on the table, and it was like someone opening a window in a stifling room. It snapped me back to myself. We needed to clarify other things before we left this interview. I couldn't be overcome by disgusted outrage. Not yet.

'What did you do in the days following the shooting?' I asked.

Karl looked to the side, like he was consulting an imaginary calendar. How remarkable, that the events after shooting a young woman wouldn't be stark in his memory.

'I tried to stay out of your way. I thought the bare facts would make you suspicious of Leo and Dunlow, and I was ready to step in with new evidence if it seemed you were backing off.'

'Were we not making enough progress?' Juliet asked. 'Is that why you hired the van and hit Leo?'

Narrowed eyes, another beat of silence. Karl might not have many tells, but he wasn't quick enough when unexpectedly confronted with the truth.

'Do you have any evidence that was me?' His words were drenched in studied calm.

'Not yet,' I said. 'The fire; were you involved in that too?'

Karl's dark eyes switched to me. 'Like I told you, I was in the forest when the fire started.'

'You didn't cause the fire?' Juliet asked.

Karl shrugged. 'A happy coincidence.'

I clenched my fist tighter under the table. Was that how he thought of Melanie's death too?

'Did you send the pictures of Terence into the magazine?' Juliet asked.

'There's no way you can prove that.'

'How about his beating, was that you?' I snapped. I schooled my face as soon as the words rushed out, but Karl caught the difference in my tone.

'There's no way you can pin that on me.'

No flat denials, no protestations of innocence. Karl wasn't concerned with proving he hadn't done these things, only that there was no way for us to definitively blame him. He'd denied the fire. His skirting around the hit and run and the beating made me even more certain he was the only person targeting the Dunlow family.

'To clarify, there was no mystery man lurking on the Dunlow land?' I asked.

Karl shook his head. No one else wished so much ill on the Dunlows.

'You'll admit to using the stolen keys to plant evidence in Dunlow's car?' Juliet asked.

Karl lifted his shoulders. 'That was me. Dunlow was too unaffected by what was happening. You weren't looking at him closely enough. It was a risk, putting them in his car rather than somewhere you would find them, but it was worth it. The look on his face when he found them was everything I wanted.'

The idea of Karl watching Dunlow sent shudders across my chest. People like Matthew Biss were overtly sinister. Karl's brutality was hidden under layers of cultivated civility.

'And the gun?' I forced out. 'Why did you bring it to meet Leo?'

Karl considered me for a long moment. 'I didn't have a plan, but I thought it might be useful.'

We had stark evidence of what happened when Karl followed chance. Leo had been unbelievably lucky Karl had been caught in our trap rather than finding the youngest Dunlow alone.

'That's everything we need.' I gathered the papers into the file. 'We have more than enough to charge you with. You'll be transported to a more permanent facility to await trial.'

'Are you going to tell him I'm his son?' Karl asked.

He was still obsessed with Dunlow. I bit my tongue, rather than shout that Melanie Pirt was dead because of him. Nothing had worked out how he'd planned, but her life was forfeit regardless.

'It doesn't matter.' Juliet stood, towering over the two of us. 'In the sense that you're a fucking monster. You don't seem to feel an ounce of remorse over killing a young woman just because your daddy wouldn't give you the attention you craved.'

I jammed my finger down to stop the recording. I couldn't erase Juliet's reply, but I could make sure no more outbursts were recorded. We needed the case against Karl to be unquestionable, and passing one insult off as a moment of heightened emotion was plausible. The judge and jury wouldn't know Juliet wasn't overcome by anger, but simply wanted Karl to know exactly what she thought of him.

They regarded each other coolly, Karl no less ruffled than before.

I stood, holding the file to my chest. Despite how ill-timed Juliet's proclamation was, I was in total agreement. Karl Biss was a monster.

'Goodbye, Karl.'

His brown eyes were unreadable. 'Goodbye, Gabe.'

Call connected at 13:13.

'Hello, this is Detective Sergeant Gabe Martin.'

'Yes, hello. This is Benedict Hogan. I hear you've been trying to reach me.'

'We have, Mr Hogan, for several days. Can I ask why you didn't get back to us sooner?'

'I'd gone on an impromptu ski trip with my family and broke my phone the first day out there. Took it as a chance to have a tech detox. Had no idea anyone would need me.'

'I see. Can I ask where you were on the night of the 9th October?'

'I was with Teddy. Terence Dunlow, that is. I own a place in Cornwall. We meet there several times a year.'

'What were you doing there?'

'We, ah. Well. We're in a relationship, of sorts. We were connecting, after a while without seeing each other.'

'Over the night of the 9th or during the day, was there any point when Terence talked on his phone, or were there any periods when you can't account for his whereabouts?'

'We don't see each other a great deal, so we make the most of the time we have. We spent a couple of minutes apart, here and there. He didn't seem overly interested in his phone until his father summoned him home. We argued then, and it's the reason I went off skiing. Didn't want to mope around without him.'

'Do you know anyone called Karl Biss?'

'Doesn't ring any bells.'

'Terence didn't talk to you about the estate groundskeeper at all?'

'We don't tend to talk about Teddy's homelife.'

'Thank you, Mr Hogan.'

'I really am dreadfully sorry that it's taken me so long to get back to you.'

'It's fine. It's all worked out in the end.'

Gabe

Nothing helped.

I threw myself into the mountain of paperwork that came with charging a suspect. I went for a walk and considered buying a Twix to share with Juliet, but thought better of it.

My last-ditch attempt to calm my frothing thoughts was splashing water over my face. It helped after my initial reaction to dead bodies. Apparently, it was no use after finding out someone I would have bet wasn't a killer turned out to be a cold-hearted murderer.

I scrubbed a paper towel over my face and abandoned any attempt to make my hair look like it hadn't started the day by being stuffed under a beanie. Pressing my hands to my cheeks, I stared into my bloodshot eyes in the mirror bolted above the sink.

'Get it together.'

There was work I needed to put my head down and do. I had to be helpful, especially as my bad judgement led us away from the killer. It wasn't Karl's plans that led me astray. My inability to separate my past from the present was the real problem.

I made my way back to the office, only to stumble to a halt in the doorway. 'What are you doing?'

Juliet spun around, lime green wool tangled in her hands. 'Taking down the wall.'

I pressed my face into my palms to block out her quizzical look. 'Can I have a moment?'

Juliet bundled the wool around one hand and chucked the misshapen ball into the basket with the others. I took her place in front of the wall. I stepped so close that Melanie's smiling selfie filled my vision.

'He didn't know her.'

This was the other, much louder, thing I couldn't get out of my head. Most killers felt guilt and remorse about their victims, no matter how selfish or shallow they were. Karl hadn't betrayed any such feeling. He was only interested in Melanie's death so far as it benefitted his plan. He'd confessed because he couldn't cause any more disruption to Dunlow's life, knew revealing the truth was the most damaging thing he could do. He didn't care about his victim, felt nothing about cutting her life short.

Melanie's smile was wide in the selfie, her eyes shining with joy. The investigation to find my brother used a similar beaming picture. Not for the first time, I wondered how Barnabas's killer felt about my brother's death. It was likely he didn't care at all. He'd needed a victim, and either of us would do. He'd gone on to kill since, so he hadn't felt life-changing remorse about what he'd done.

I couldn't remember the bad man's eyes. I didn't know if I ever fully looked him in the face or if fractured memory had cloaked his features in shadow. I thought they might look like Karl's. Cold. Unfeeling.

I started when a hand brushed between my shoulder blades. I hadn't noticed Juliet's approach.

'Try not to let him affect you,' she said, her voice uncharacteristically gentle. 'We got him.'

I backed away from the wall and slumped into my chair. 'No thanks to me.'

'This again?' Juliet rolled her eyes as she turned to the wall. 'I'm only going to tell you one more time; you did great work on this case.'

I raised my eyebrows at the back of her head. 'I did? I feel like I flailed about in the dark most of the time.'

'You did that too.' Juliet unpinned various pictures of Melanie from the corkboard and placed them in a folder on her desk. 'That was more to do with the case itself. You conducted yourself well despite trying circumstances. You coaxed witnesses into talking and pursued all lines of enquiry vigorously.' She started unpinning Leo's section. 'You're coming into your own.'

A plume of warmth opened inside my chest. 'Thanks, Juliet. That means a lot.' My eyes caught on Karl's graduation photo, and the heat dimmed. 'I didn't want it to be him.'

'I know.' Juliet placed Leo's information in the file.

'I'm gutted it was,' I went on, wanting to purge this with someone I was certain would have read my file as soon as we started working together. 'I thought Karl was like me, that he had a sad history. I didn't think that made him a murderer.' I bit my lip. 'I let my past get in the way of seeing him clearly.'

'He hid his true self pretty damn well.' Juliet unpinned the mass of evidence around Dunlow. 'It's hard not to be informed by our experiences.'

'You're not,' I retorted.

Juliet paused, her back to me. 'I didn't want it to be Jordan.'

'What?' I'd noticed Juliet was affected by Jordan's home situation but didn't think much of it.

Juliet continued staring at the wall. 'I was reluctant to pursue Jordan as a suspect.'

She heaved with a sigh before she turned around. Juliet was saying this because she didn't want me to be too down on myself. She didn't want me to blame myself for letting my history intrude. She was being kind.

I didn't want to repay that kindness by prying, but she'd not wanted to chase down Jordan because of how his experiences echoed her own.

'Juliet, if there's ever anything you want to talk about—'

'There isn't.'

She spun to face the wall. Her hands were steady as she took down Terence's section. Benedict Hogan's belated call had finally exonerated him.

'Afternoon.'

I swung around in my chair. Angela stood in the doorway, her eyes roving between Juliet and the half-dismantled wall.

'Afternoon, ma'am,' I said, temporarily banishing my curiosity about Juliet's home life. It was like one of the post-its I'd stuck to the wall. I didn't have the answers yet, but I'd search for them.

'I looked over the paperwork for this case,' Angela said, while Juliet continued unpinning evidence. 'It looks robust. Good work.'

The ember Juliet had ignited with her praise glowed. 'Thank you, ma'am.'

'A call came through earlier.' Angela tucked her thumbs into her belt loops. 'A possible human-trafficking ring has been uncovered. The scene is a mess, so no need to rush down there. Forensics aren't going to let you into the building, and all the women are being processed and assigned translators. Paul is overseeing it for now, but he'll need help. Tidy this up, take the rest of the day to tie up loose ends, and I want you on the new case in the morning.'

Juliet deposited Jordan's information into the file. I nodded at our superintendent. 'We're on it, ma'am.'

Angela eyed Juliet before turning on her heel and marching out of our office. I jostled my mouse, my screen flashing blearily to life.

'It's never ending, is it?' This job allowed no time to dwell on my failings. I'd take what I'd learnt on this case and apply it to the next. Other people needed my help, and I couldn't give it to them if I was punishing myself for past mistakes.

If Juliet said I'd done a good job, then maybe I had. She wouldn't lie.

Juliet hadn't moved when I looked up after typing in my password. Her blonde hair formed screens either side of her face.

'It never is, is it?' she murmured.

My forehead crinkled. Normally, Juliet relished a new case coming in, especially on the heels of a closed one.

She grabbed her phone from her desk. 'I need to make a call.'

I didn't have time to do more than open my mouth uselessly before she was gone.

Abandoning my awakened computer, I stood and took down the last of the evidence. Juliet had rushed out before unpinning Karl's section. I couldn't work with him watching me.

The wall cleared, I flipped the file shut and placed my hand on the rough card. I'd use today to tie up loose ends, both physical and mental, and I'd launch into the new case tomorrow. I'd leave my history behind and trust the evidence more than whatever my gut tried to tell me.

I glanced out of the door before heading back to my seat. Juliet was nowhere to be seen.

'Hello, darling. To what do I owe this pleasure?'

'Keith, please don't start.'

'Start what?'

'I'm not playing this game. Another case has come in.'

'Has it now?'

'Don't make this difficult. I'm not going to be able to come out this weekend, but I want you to bring the girls here.'

'I'm not sure that's a good idea.'

'Please, Keith.'

'Say we come in but you have an interview to conduct or some bad guy to chase down. Are you really going to put that on hold to see us?'

'I can take more time at the weekends. I just can't come out to see them.'

'I don't know if it's worth the heartbreak. I'm the one comforting them when you let them down again. They're already going to be distraught you're not coming home, do you really want me to drag them into the city only for you to spend odd minutes with them when you can?'

'I won't let them down. I can't help when a case comes in.'

'You always prioritise your work over us.'

'You know why I have to work so much, Keith.'

'That's my fault as well, is it?'

'I'm not doing this. Make a decision about whether you're bringing the girls in and let me know.'

'Not going to fight for them then?'

'Goodbye, Keith.'

Gabe. Sent 15:36.

I should be out of here at about 6.30 p.m. x

Ollie. Sent 15:37.

Does this mean you've caught your baddie? xxx

Gabe. Sent 15:39.

Yes. We charged him earlier today. Which means I
need help celebrating x

Ollie. Sent 15:39.

Always happy to oblige xxx

Call connected at 16:22.

'Hello, how can I help you?'

'Mum?'

'Jordan, love. Where are you?'

'I just got home. I saw your note. Sorry I worried you.'

'That doesn't matter. Where have you been?'

'I went over to a mate's house. Dad put something online, some bullshit about family being the most important thing. I couldn't be around him.'

'That's okay, love. I'm going to come home as soon as I can.'

'Why? What's he done?'

'No. It's not about your dad. It's about Mel. The police are going to come over to explain some things.'

'What things? Please don't make me wait until you get home. Tell me whatever you know now.'

'Okay, love. They've found her killer. It was the groundskeeper on the estate.'

'What?'

'They've charged him with murder.'

'But how did he know Mel? Was it anything to do with the other guys that lived there?'

'The police only mentioned arresting him. I guess they'll be able to tell us more when they come over.'

'God, Mum. I've made such a huge mess of everything. Since Mel died, I've not been thinking right.'

'It's okay, love. I'll be home soon. We can have a cuddle. Things won't always feel this bad.'

'You promise?'

'Promise.'

Gabe

Juliet returned to the office surrounded by an invisible yet tangible wall. To my surprise, she insisted on accompanying me as I explained the case's conclusion to Ida and Evie, then Jordan and his mum. Juliet was a quiet spectator as Ida absorbed the news in sad silence, her friend gripping her hand. Jordan had sobbed brokenly from his mum's arms.

The end of a case was hard for friends and relatives to navigate. Their relief it was over swamped by guilt as their last tenuous link to someone they loved was severed.

The lift doors opened. Where we'd been greeted on our last visit to this hotel by expensive silence, now muffled shouting filtered into the hallway. I followed it to suite four. It stopped abruptly when I knocked.

Juliet finally seemed interested in proceedings as a breathless Terence opened the door. 'What?' He caught himself, realising we weren't hotel staff. 'Oh. How can I help you?'

'Can we come in?' I asked. 'We know you're all anxious to hear what happened to Melanie.'

Terence stood aside to let us into the suite. Leo's eyes were rimmed with pink behind his thick glasses. He sat on the bed, his school blazer and tie discarded beside him. His father stood straight backed and imposing in a spotless grey suit. Terence gravitated to a bulging suitcase beside the desk, the wooden top swept bare.

Juliet and I stood just inside the door. There was a collective stillness in the already tense room, like the intake of breath before a diver jumped off the board.

'Melanie was killed by Karl Biss,' I announced. 'He confessed and was charged with her murder this afternoon.'

Leo bunched a fist to his mouth, desperately holding back tears. Terence's eyes widened while his father's narrowed.

'Karl didn't know Melanie,' I went on. 'He had no plan to kill her, but instead took the opportunity when it presented itself. As she left the estate, he followed her into the forest and shot her.'

'Why did he kill her?' Leo asked, his voice wavering.

Dunlow's rough words cut across the room. 'He wanted to hurt me.'

Juliet straightened. 'What makes you say that?'

Dunlow's blue eyes fixed on her. 'Because he's my son.'

Leo and Terence turned to their father, faces slack.

'It's true,' I said, drawing all eyes. 'Jennifer Clements, Karl's mother, became pregnant after a brief relationship with your father. I believe you didn't know about this?'

Dunlow shook his head. 'She didn't tell me. He didn't either. I discovered it today.'

'Jennifer told Karl about his true parentage, but he only searched for you after he'd lost his mother,' I said. 'He began working at the Dunlow Estate to get to know you all.'

'Why didn't he say anything?' Terence's face was marred with uneven pockets of pink.

'He thought you would treat him differently,' I stated.

If the mixture of guilt and shock on the Dunlows' faces was any indication, then Karl was right. He might not have been welcomed with open arms by his biological family, but more would have been offered than casual dismissal and rudeness.

'But why did he kill Mel?' Leo asked again, hands bunching on his lap. 'If Karl wanted to hurt Dad, why didn't he kill me or Teddy?'

His older brother blanched, not as willing to offer himself up in Melanie's place.

'We believe, despite how he felt snubbed by your family, he retained a connection to you,' I explained. 'He was looking for an opportunity to hurt you, and killing Melanie had a huge impact on all of your lives. He didn't plan to do it but grabbed the chance. Very sadly, Melanie was in the wrong place at the wrong time.'

Too often, women were the fatalities when men butted heads. They were discarded like pawns, not seen as people with their own lives.

Leo shook his head violently. 'I should never have let her leave on her own.'

Dunlow gripped his younger son's shoulder. 'No. This was my fault. I should have done more background checks before employing him.'

'Enough.' Juliet's crisp command broke through their self-admonishment. 'There's no one to blame for what happened to Melanie other than Karl. He pulled the trigger.'

'There's no way you could have predicted what would happen that night,' I added. Juliet's brand of comfort needed softening. 'You can't blame yourself for what you did or didn't do. That's no way to live.'

I spoke from experience. I'd spent enough sleepless nights wondering if Barnabas would be alive now if I'd hidden for longer, if I'd turned right instead of left when I searched the warehouse for food, if I'd screamed louder when the bad man pulled me across the floor.

Nothing brought my brother back. Just like regrets wouldn't bring Melanie back either.

'Right then.' Terence grabbed the handle of the suitcase. 'I've had enough of this.'

Dunlow's face instantly blotted with patches of bright red. 'Terence. Do not leave.'

'I'm done.' Terence charged towards the door. 'I don't want to be part of your mess.'

Juliet and I sidestepped out of his way, but Terence paused with his hand on the door.

'Leo, that doesn't apply to you,' he said briskly. 'Dad, do you want to know why that woman didn't tell you she'd had your son? It's because no one would ever choose you as a father, if they could help it.'

Terence stormed from the room, allowing the door to whisper shut behind him.

There had always been an edge of hardness to Dunlow, a solid certainty of his place in the world. That had been stripped away. His eyes darted, fingers fidgeting with his cufflinks as his Adam's apple bobbed.

I wasn't sure how to comfort this man I both pitied and reviled. His family was broken. I understood how isolating and confusing that could be.

'You couldn't have known what Karl was going to do,' I offered.

Neither Leo nor Dunlow should blame themselves for what happened. I hoped it would bring them closer. Maybe Dunlow would see the people around him as worthy of kindness and respect. Consideration, at least.

If the way he looked down his nose at me was any indication, he wasn't a changed man yet. 'Come, Leo. We need to see to the dogs before it gets too dark.'

'You're looking for homes for them, right?'

Leo smiled as he stood from the bed. 'Would you want one?' Even his father looked interested at the prospect of offloading one of their dogs.

'Maybe. I'll give you a call.'

As Dunlow led Leo through one of the suite's inner doors, Juliet and I walked out into the hallway. I rubbed my face as we rode down in the lift, my brain heavy like a waterlogged sponge.

There was no hint that what had transpired had affected Juliet at all. Our conversations with the various people surrounding Melanie glanced off her.

Maybe that was why we partnered so well together. Juliet was reserved and controlled, kept her distance, while I absorbed what needed to be felt. We shared the emotional and intellectual labour.

'You worked well on this case too,' I said, as we crossed the hotel reception.

Juliet blinked at me. 'Of course I bloody did.'

I grinned as we walked outside. Back to the station now, to dive into the miles of paperwork involved in catching a criminal.

Keith. Sent 18:12.

Hello, love. Sorry but I can't bring the girls to see you this weekend. They're struggling with the upheaval of you living there anyway, and I don't want to add to that. Let me know if you're able to make it home next weekend and we can do something extra special as a family to make up for lost time. Love you x

Gabe

I walked out of the lift with Juliet and Maddy, then held one of the glass front doors open. Once outside, cold air coasted over our faces. I'd been glad of the fresh breeze skimming inland over the summer but was settling into months of being a little too cold at all times.

'You sure we can't convince you to come out for a drink?' I asked Juliet.

She looked across the road at the pub most often frequented by our co-workers. 'Not this time.'

'Did you see that, Gabe?' Maddy linked her arm through mine. 'She very almost might have hesitated for a second.'

'Progress.' I nodded at Juliet. 'See you tomorrow.'

'Bright and early,' she said.

I looked over my shoulder as Maddy dragged me towards the pub. Juliet's head was bowed, her face lit by her phone. One day, she might agree to come for a drink, to becoming more than a friendly colleague. No matter what my plans were, I'd drop everything to have a personal conversation with her. I suspected Juliet had a lot she needed to talk about.

Heat blasted us as we walked into the pub, along with a roar of noise. I squinted into the dim interior, flinching when arms wrapped around my neck.

'We did it,' Alice squealed, clinging on while other officers patted my back and echoed her congratulations. She untangled herself and stood beaming, her glee fuelled by the victory she was celebrating and a couple of glasses of wine.

'What did we do?' I asked, after the crowd of well-wishers moved away.

'Don't be modest. We know the warehouse tip was from you.'

I huffed out a breath. 'You do?'

'We are the dream team,' Alice half shouted. 'Do you want to come sit with us?'

'You go.' A quick scan of the pub revealed Paul on one of the high stools by the bar. 'I'm not going to be here for long, and I need to talk to someone.'

Maddy squeezed my hand before she and Alice bounced off to join their friends. I fought through the crowd and hopped onto the stool beside Paul.

'Evening.'

He straightened. 'You may have caught me before I fell asleep there.'

'Happy to oblige.' I nodded when a bartender held up a pint glass. 'Do you want another?'

'I shouldn't.'

I grinned and held up two fingers. Paul downed the rest of his beer and was ready for the next when it was placed in front of him.

'Jodie's going to be disgusted when I rock up in an Uber instead of driving.'

Paul's wife was the most patient woman I'd ever encountered. 'She won't mind.' I took a sip of my beer. 'I can't decide whether to be annoyed at you or not.'

Paul studied me. 'I'd go with not.'

I side-eyed him. 'Why'd you tell everyone about the tip?'

'Because it was a good one,' Paul said without a hint of shame. 'You deserve the credit.'

I watched the long streams of bubbles racing towards the top of my drink. 'I got lucky. On both cases.'

'Luck or judgement; we caught them.' Paul lifted his glass and clinked it against mine. 'You have to be incredibly lucky and intelligent to get away with killing someone. We weren't dealing with anyone like that.'

'True.' Karl had been manipulative and misleading, but he wasn't clever enough to frame Dunlow. I had to accept there was a mixture of chance and hard work that went into catching a killer. I'd do everything I could on the next case to make sure I didn't get in the way.

'I hear we're all working together from tomorrow,' I said, willing to drop Paul's breach of trust.

'Like a big, happy family.' He took a long gulp. 'Honestly, we could do with the ice queen's help. It's a tough one, from the snippets that have come through so far.'

I sipped the frothy head off my beer. I hated these moments. I'd known Paul for a long time, he'd always been my superior, and he was technically giving Juliet a compliment. But I'd have preferred he didn't call her names behind her back.

He saved me the effort of finding an appropriate response. 'The press had gotten bored. Then this comes in.'

'You can make us do the press conferences if you like.'

Paul choked. 'And let Juliet loose on them? She's worse than me.'

Beer sloshed over my hand as a warm body slammed into my side, jolting my sore arm. I shook droplets off my fingers but Maddy and Alice continued crowding in.

'You mustn't look.' Maddy reached over the bar to grab a napkin and dabbed at my sleeve. 'The most beautiful man in existence has just walked in.'

'Man?' I asked.

Maddy rolled her eyes. 'He's objectively hotter than the sun.'

I twisted in my seat, while Alice hissed, 'She told you not to look.'

Ollie waved, lifting a thumb at the door. His hair fell in messy waves, his jumper sleeves rolled up to reveal several mismatched tattoos.

'That's Ollie.'

Maddy gripped my arm. Over her shoulder, Paul chuckled into his pint.

'Who's Ollie?' Alice asked.

'He's my boyfriend.' I slid off the stool. 'We're going for dinner.'

Alice and Maddy gaped between me and Ollie, but Paul saluted as he commandeered the rest of my beer. 'Have a good evening.'

'I will.' I mimed closing my mouth at Maddy and Alice, then walked over to Ollie.

'Let's get out of here,' I whispered in his ear.

His smile was eager as he ushered me outside. 'I've booked us a table at an actual restaurant.'

My hand tingled as our fingers entwined. 'Sounds perfect.'

While we understand you may wish for your name to be kept confidential, we do have to respect the fire regulations of the buildings we
hold meetings in. The Refuge will keep this register only when necessary, and it will be destroyed permanently when no longer needed.
Please ask one of our trained members of staff for more information
if you're unsure.

Write only your first name and initial below:

Alex A
Christine J
Stephanie L
Mandy L
Juliet S
Martin P
Kate S
Nadine B
Jordan H

The Refuge – providing healing services for those affected by physical
and emotional abuse.

Six months later

Unknown. Sent 16:20.

I'm in position.

Unknown. Sent 16:21.

Get it done.

From: Recruitment Services **recruitment@hampshireconstabulary.gov.uk**
To: Leo Dunlow **leodunlow@gmail.com**
Date: **24 April, 16:53**
Subject: **Next intake**

Dear Leo,

Thank you for expressing an interest in joining the policing team when you have finished your A Levels. Our next recruitment day is on the 5th July. I've attached the details to this email.

If your results reflect those already achieved in your mocks and your physical fitness is at the expected level, then I can see no reason why your application would not be successful.

Best wishes,

Sarah-Jane Trot

Recruitment Services – Hampshire Constabulary

Gabe

I led our group out of the courthouse. The demands of running an ongoing investigation into the human-trafficking ring on top of a slew of other cases hadn't allowed Juliet and I to sit in on the whole trial, but it felt important to be present when Karl was sentenced. He hadn't protested his innocence. Standing beside the judge, his expression hadn't wavered when the jury pronounced him guilty on all counts.

I pulled my collar up as we walked down the stairs. The weather had begun to warm, but it was as likely to rain or shine within a five-minute window.

Juliet was already absorbed in her phone, her brows lowered as she jabbed at the screen. Alice and Maddy chattered with their arms linked. James smiled shyly, standing awkwardly in a suit that complimented his bulky frame.

Juliet had been bemused when they sat around us this morning. I wasn't sure she recalled the uniformed officers from Melanie's case. She'd shaken her head fondly when Maddy called us a team.

I'd nudged Juliet when Jordan and Leo walked into the court room, sitting side by side. I didn't know what had changed between the two young men in the last few months. They were friendly enough that when tears coursed down Jordan's face, Leo had a tissue ready. They'd sat behind Ida and Evie, the older women leaning into one another as the charges were read.

'Pub?' Maddy suggested.

'Not for me.' I held up my hands to staunch her protests. 'I'm meeting Ollie.'

'Ollie,' Alice sighed. She whipped her head around. 'Is he here?'

I looked across the street. Recently, I'd noticed an unswerving ability to pick my boyfriend out of a crowd. His hair had been cut at his most recent shoot, the sides of his head covered in bristle while waves flopped over his forehead. He raised one arm to wave, the other restraining an overexcited Alsatian. Ollie grinned at me, then concentrated on finding a break in the heavy traffic.

'The only thing that makes him hotter is when he's walking your dog,' Alice said.

Before I could ask her to stop objectifying Ollie again, a car backfired. I flinched, my hand flying to my sternum.

I'd had a few moments like this recently. The main content of my nightmares remained unchanged, but the crack of a gun had intruded. Loud noises startled me, my heart taking a while to slow.

I laughed at myself, shaking out my hand. Now Karl had been convicted, this nervous reaction should ease off.

Juliet's phone clattered to the ground. A joke about how I hadn't thought it possible to unglue it from her palm was halfway to my lips when I noticed the red stain growing on her white blouse.

'Juliet?' I pulled her coat to one side.

Blood. Scarlet red. Pulsing from a bullet wound in her chest.

Juliet looked down at it, then up at me. 'Fuck,' she breathed, before collapsing.

'Gabe, what happened?' Maddy grabbed my arm as James and Alice sprang into action. The older man repositioned Juliet on the ground, his jacket held firm over where her blouse was soaked. Alice had her phone to her ear, shouting details to an operator.

Shouting, because people screamed all around. I blinked at their horrified faces as they ran, the tears of those who crouched behind a bus stop. Leo's auburn hair stood out. He and Jordan bracketed Ida and Evie, hurrying the elderly women away.

I blinked at Maddy, feeling as though I was walking in a dream.

Another crack, and pain crashed through my shoulder. The force of it made me stumble. My heel caught, and Maddy's scrabbling hands weren't enough to stop me falling.

Breath punched out of me as my back met concrete. My shoulder screamed, the skin around pulsing with warmth. Above me, Maddy's mouth moved. Half words reached my ears, incomprehensible under the beat of blood and shrill screams.

I turned my head. Juliet lay beside me. Her hair fanned across the ground, her arms flung wide. A stranger had taken over pressing on her wound. James was occupied with pumping her chest.

Her eyes were half closed, her mouth sagging.

I turned the other way, catching another glimpse of Maddy's horrified face. It was much closer. Hands pulled at my front. Chill air danced over me as someone tugged open my coat.

The traffic had stopped. Alice stood shouting, arms pointing. Most members of the public followed her instructions, their movements clumsy as they fled.

One person refused to move. The dog at his side barked, teeth flashing.

I stared at Ollie's stricken face. I wanted to tell him not to cry, to touch his cheek and reassure him that it wasn't so bad. It wasn't even painful anymore. I didn't feel like I'd been shot, more like I was floating along a cool river.

I blinked. Reopening my eyes was an effort. Ollie's mouth was open, moving around a single sound. The kaleidoscope of screams faded.

I closed my eyes and drifted into the dark.

Acknowledgements

First and foremost and always, thank you to my readers. You holding this book in your hands is my dream come true. I've written for many years and only recently has it felt like anyone out there would be interested in my stories. I am so grateful that you picked up *Shot in the Dark* and spent some time with my imaginary friends.

My wonderful agent, Saskia Leach, championed me and *Shot in the Dark* at a point when I was beginning to lose faith in whether Gabe and Juliet would ever find their way out into the world. From our first meeting, she has been kind and professional, everything I could wish for in an agent. She's also a brilliant human being and has a great cat vomit story. You should ask her about it.

Thank you to the wider team at Kate Nash Literary Agency, and the other authors represented by this glorious bunch. They made me feel welcome straight away, like I had joined a very bookish family.

When Siân Heap told me that she'd read *Shot in the Dark* in sneaky moments while she brewed tea and waited for the train, I knew I wanted to work with her. She is a wonderful editor – passionate and knowledgeable and always willing to answer my millions of questions. Thank you, Siân, and the larger team at Canelo, for taking a chance on my story. You've been a dream to work with and have made my first stumbling steps into being an author (!) as comfortable and exciting as they can be.

A small army of people read *Shot in the Dark* to reassure me that it was a story people would actually want to read and not the ramblings of a mad person. Huge thank you to: Simon Benham (and Catrina, you sneaky reader), Nat Jones, Emma Maher, Chris Reddecliff, Chloe Ford, Emma Bradley, and Amanda Golding. That you would spend your time reading my book and chatting with me about it is such an act of kindness.

In addition to generally patting my head and telling me my words made sense, some lovely people used their life experiences to enhance my story. Anything that's remotely accurate can be attributed to them. Thank you to my Uncle Mark, who worked for many years as a police officer and gave me extensive notes on all things procedural. Thank you to Mike Wigley, who gave me advice on the medical aspects. Thank you to my dad, who read through my scene in a prison and made it much better. Thank you to April Newton, who answered my questions about solicitors.

Thank you to the counsellors who have helped me to understand my brain better. Particularly Gabi – I found you when I was falling apart. You helped me to gently put myself back together.

Thank you to my family of writers – Marisa Noelle, Sally Doherty and Emma Bradley. You have cheered with me through the MANY ups and downs of getting a book published. Thank you for enduring a surely inhumane amount of SHOUTING.

Some people like to bang on about the evils of social media, but for me it's been a blessing. Twitter and Instagram have connected me with such a lovely group of people who have supported me and cheered me on. There are, literally, too many of you to list. If you're reading this and wondering if it applies to you because you once sent me a nice message or laughed at something stupid I said – yes, it does. Thank you for walking with me – I love walking with you. (Special thanks to the people who message me about my deep and enduring love for pain au chocolat – you have good priorities.)

Thank you to John. You were the best father-in-law I could have hoped for. I wish I'd had more time to know you. Your death taught me that if there was something I really wanted to do, I needed to hecking well get on and do it. We cannot assume that we have forever to achieve our dreams.

Thank you to my mum. You have read this book twice (maybe three times!) by now and have been my unending cheerleader. I love chatting about my books with you and (even though I pretend it's embarrassing) I love it when you tell everyone that your daughter is an author. It means so much to me that you and Dad are proud of me. Dad – you have to message me when you get here and tell me you've read it. Thank you to my wider family for your kind support.

The biggest thank you ever to my lovely husband. Ben, you are the kindest human being I know. You're my best friend, and I will always feel grateful that you want to hang out with me. Thank you for holding me when things get rough and for celebrating with me when things are brilliant. You've read this book more times than anyone else and always give me the best advice. Thank you for being on my team.

And finally, thank you to Odie. You have no idea why I stare at a weird screen for many hours a day, but you've slept in the same room with me while I've typed away. You've helped me unwind on long walks and have endured many cuddles. You are a very good dog.

Do you love crime fiction and are always on the lookout for brilliant authors?

Canelo Crime is home to some of the most exciting novels around. Thousands of readers are already enjoying our compulsive stories. Are you ready to find your new favourite writer?

Find out more and sign up to our newsletter at canelocrime.com